$20.00

GREATER LOND⌐   ⌐¬V AND HERITAGE HANDBOOK

GREATER LONDON

HISTORY AND HERITAGE

HANDBOOK

The Millennium guide to historical, heritage and

environmental networks, and publications

Compiled by Peter Marcan

London: Peter Marcan Publications, 1999

© Peter Marcan, 1999

Published by:
Peter Marcan Publications,
PO Box 3158, London SE1 4RA, England, United Kingdom. *Tel*: (020) 7357 0368.

ISBN: 1 871811 15 5

Published previously under the title 'Greater London Local History Directory':
1st edition, covering publications 1983-1987, published 1988; ISBN: 0 9510289 8 7.
2nd edition, covering publications 1988-1992, published 1993; ISBN: 1 871811 08 2

Both editions should be retained, they contain much information not included in the new edition.

In addition to the two previous editions, an earlier catalogue *London's Local History*, 1983,
ISBN: 0 9504211 6 2, should be noted. It is a descriptive, borough by borough catalogue of 'non-commercial' publications
from the 1960's through to the early 1980's.
All three publications are still in print.

Frontispiece: 'Crystal Palace skyline', black/white ink drawing by Audrey Hammond, 1998.

Printed and bound by SRP Ltd, Exeter.

CONTENTS

Note: The numbers in brackets are entry numbers, not page numbers.

INTRODUCTION

Greater London History and Heritage Handbook is a development and continuation of the two directories published in 1988 and 1993 under the title 'Greater London Local History Directory'. It continues the format adopted in those previous editions, but listings have now been considerably expanded: 348 numbered entries in the second edition, 867 in the new edition. There are now more entries for museums and visitor attractions, reflecting the growth of the 'heritage industry'; more entries for tourism units and information centres, and guides associations; there are more entries for environmental associations, especially 'friends' groups - for parks, woods, nature reserves, cemeteries. Recently formed amenity and historical societies also appear.

As previously, new and recent publications are highlighted, but publications still in print are also listed (normally in a sequence arranged alphabetically by title).

There is a new section for each borough listing other council contacts, including reference libraries and information services. Contacts for built and natural environments are included; for conservation areas and listed buildings; for Agenda 21, for nature conservation, and ecology centres. It should be pointed out that some council departments are often in a state of 'permanent reorganisation' nowadays; the contact names were probably correct in the early months of 1999, but may change in the course of time. Press officers can often help with contacts within councils and many councils produce A-Z listings.

The 'non-council contacts' sections list bodies such as arts councils, chambers of commerce and councils of voluntary organisations. The later two types of organisation often produce membership directories. At a time when 'partnership' is a political 'buzz word', it seems valid to list such council and non-council contacts within each borough, even if not always totally comprehensive.

Each London borough section commences with an entry for the local studies library/collections run by the local councils with listings of publications - their own and those from outside sources currently sold. Most libraries are engaged in more bookselling activity than hitherto and such sales points are useful for discovering the publications of small presses and author publishers. Most libraries produce sales lists, some better organised and produced than others. The drastic cut in the opening hours of some libraries should be viewed with alarm; the libraries are important, unique collections, run by dedicated and often very knowledgeable staff; they are important resources for their communities and for researchers from farther afield and all need more recognition and expansion.

Inevitably staff retire, many may feel the end of the century is the right time to bow out. Some well-known figures have departed from their libraries: Andrea Cameron (Hounslow); Ralph Hyde (Guildhall); Anthony Shaw (Wandsworth); David Webb (Bishopsgate Institute).

Sections that follow cover tourism, museums and visitor attractions, historical and archaeological, amenity and environmental societies. The exact arrangement may vary from borough to borough. Family history societies are listed in entries 709-721. The listings of hon. officials were correct over the compilation period (winter 1998/9), but they can change; nonetheless some individuals hold the same honorary post for many years, and generally most listed will be able to help if contacted.

As we approach the end of the century, this survey/handbook would suggest an undiminished interest in researching and recording diverse aspects of London's past and topography. Countless subjects are investigated and written up in articles, booklets and books. The monumental, academic series continue: the Buildings of England series, the History of Parliament Trust, the Survey of London, for example; commercial publishers such as Phillimore, Historical Publications, Sutton and Tempus continue their colossal output with undiminished energy, whilst libraries, societies and individuals continue with more modest productions (funds permitting).

Although normally free, one should not overlook the very many folding leaflets offering guided walks and trails. Nature trail leaflets are often extremely attractive and are put together with much loving care; much valuable information is often condensed in architectural and historical walks.

In addition, and equally important, the handbook indicates a flourishing amenity and environmental scene with much active interest in the present-day landscape and community; whilst regeneration schemes endeavour to create a flourishing and positive future.

Greater London may well be an absurdly chaotic and over-complex metropolitan region, but with all these forces at work, it will surely continue as always to be a region of immense diversity and interest, energy and excitement.

Peter Marcan, Bermondsey, May 1999

OBSERVATORY ON THE CROSS OF ST. PAUL'S CATHEDRAL.

Orange Street Chapel

CENTRAL LONDON BOROUGHS:

Camden, City of London, Islington, Kensington and Chelsea, Westminster

BROMPTON
ASSOCIATION

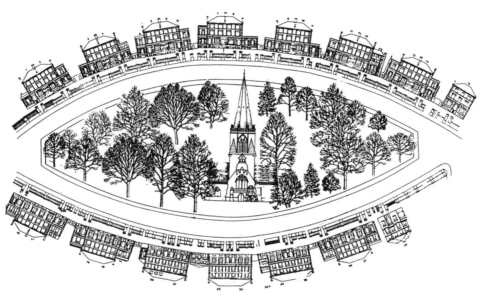

Hampstead High Street

CAMDEN

* LONDON BOROUGH OF CAMDEN *

[1] **CAMDEN LOCAL STUDIES AND ARCHIVES CENTRE.** Holborn Library, 32-38 Theobalds Rd (Gray's Inn Road end), London WC1X 8PA, *Tel*: (020) 7413 6342; *Fax*: (020) 7413 6284. *Senior staff*: Richard Knight; Malcolm J. Holmes (books include: *Somers Town: a record of change*, captioned photographs, 1985 (reprinted 1989); *Hampstead to Primrose Hill*, from Sutton Publishing; and to be published in 1999 a study on the St Pancras Housing Association). *Hours*: Mon 10-7; Tues 10-6; Wed closed; Thurs 10-7; Fri 10-1; Sat 10-1, 2-5. There are two library guides: *Camden Local Studies and Archives Centre: a brief guide*, 1994; and *Camden now and then: a student's guide*, 1989. A series of free information sheets cover: parish registers, census returns, ratebooks and valuation lists, list of researchers, newspapers, local books, directories, maps, record offices and libraries in London, monumental inscriptions, tracing the history of a building, electoral registers, family history and genealogy, publications order form.

Publications 1993-1997:
1992: HOLMES, Malcolm J. *Beating the bounds of Camden*: a long distance walk. 22pp.
1993: CARPENTER, Bob. *The village on the island*: a heritage trail around Primrose Hill and Chalk Farm. 10pp.
1993: MARSHALL, Lesley. *Kentish Town: its past in pictures.* 82 captioned illustrations, including non-photographic material.
Part of a series which also includes *Camden Town 1791-1991, a pictorial record*, published in 1991, and *Somers Town, a record of change*, 1985.
1996: *Camden celebrates Cinema 100*: an exhibition of film stills featuring film locations across Camden. 16pp, illus. Published by L.B. of Camden Arts Department. A gazeteer section lists 102 films with Camden locations, and map.
1997: ASTON, Mark. *The cinemas of Camden: a survey and history of the cinema buildings of Camden, past and present.* 79pp, illus. Covers 51 establishments with map. Author is on staff of the centre.

In addition to its own publications, those of the Camden History Society, and those from Historical Publications, the library also sells some specialist titles, including recent books such as:
A child's eye view of West Hampstead, edited by Caroline Woollett, (31 Broomsleigh St, London NW6), 1995. 63pp, illus. Reminiscences of residents.
Enlightened self interest: the Foundling Hospital and Hogarth. Exhibition catalogue from the Thomas Coran Foundation, 1997. (40 Brunswick Square, London WC1 1AZ, *Tel*: (020) 7278 2424).
The Fitzroy: the autobiography of a London tavern (in Charlotte Street) by Sally Fiber (her family owned the pub). Temple House Books (an imprint of the Book Guild), 1995. 128pp, illus.
Hampstead Heath: the walker's guide, by David McDowall, published by the author, 1998 (31 Cambrian Rd, Richmond TW10 6JQ). 176pp, maps, illus.
The Kenwood Ladies Bathing Pond, by Anne Griswold, published by the Association of Users of Kenwood Ladies Bathing Pond (8 Twisden Rd, London NW5 1DN).
JFS: a history of the Jews' Free School, London, since 1732, by Gerry Black (Tymsder Publishing, PO Box 16039, London NW3 3WL).
St Pancras Chambers, formerly the Midland Grand Hotel. Booklet published by London and Continental Stations and Property Ltd to commemorate the completion of the restoration project.

* MUSEUMS AND HISTORIC PROPERTIES *

[2] **BURGH HOUSE TRUST.** New Road Square, Hampstead, London NW3 1LT. *Tel*: (020) 7431 0144; *Fax*: (020) 7435 8817; buttery reservations: (020) 7431 2516. *Hours*: Wed-Sun. 12-5. *Publicity Officer*: John Stratton. *General Manager*: Helen Wilton. Named after a highly unpopular vicar of St Lawrence Jewry, the Rev. Allatson Burgh (1822-1856), the house was originally built for the Sewells, a Quaker family. From 1858 until 1884 when restored to domestic use, it was taken over by the Royal East Middlesex Militia. It was owned privately until 1937, and was taken over by Hampstead Borough Council in 1946 and later Camden Council who leased the building to the Trust in 1979 to run as a community centre. There is a Friends organisation which can be contacted through the above address, with some 400 members. Concerts, art exhibitions and meetings run throughout the year. A bookstall sells everything about Hampstead. Rooms can be hired.
On the first floor you find the [3]**HAMPSTEAD MUSEUM**, *Curator*: Marilyn Greene, open Wed-Sun, 12-5; it was initiated by Christopher Wade in 1979. There are three special exhibitions a year, often on Hampstead artists, writers and musicians.

Booklet catalogues are issued. A booklet on a 1998 exhibition *A nest of gentle artists* (those living around the Mall Studies areas in Belsize Park) is to be published by the Camden History Society.

[4] **DICKENS HOUSE MUSEUM**. 48 Doughty St, London WC1N 2LF, *Tel*: (020) 7405 2127. *Hours*: Mon-Sat 10-5; Dickens lived here 1837-1839, and wrote Oliver Twist and Nicholas Nickleby.

[5] **ERNO GOLDFINGER HOUSE**. 2 Willow Road, Hampstead, London NW3 1TH. *Tel*: (020) 7435 6166. A National Trust property. *Curator*: Harriet McKay. Guided tours from April to October, Thurs, Fri, Sat. House designed and built by the architect Erno Goldfinger for himself and his wife, the artist Ursula Blackwell in 1939. House includes his art collection and own designed furniture. A guide book by Alan Powers has been issued.

[6] **FENTON HOUSE**. Hampstead Grove, Hampstead, London NW3 5RT. *Tel/Fax*: (020) 7435 3471. A National Trust property. *Curator*: Joy Ashby. *Hours*: March, Sat and Sun only, 2-5; April to October, Sat, Sun, bank holiday Mon, 11-5, Wed, Thurs, Fri. 2-5. A merchant's house built in 1693 with walled garden and wrought iron gates. The panelled rooms contain an outstanding collection of oriental, continental and English china, needlework, furniture and the Benton Fletcher collection of early keyboard instruments. Summer evening concerts.

[7] **FREUD MUSEUM**. 20 Maresfield Gardens, Hampstead, London NW3 5SX. *Tel*: (020) 7435 2002/5167; *Fax*: (020) 7431 5452; *website*: www.freud.org.uk. *Director*: Erica Davies. *Hours*: Wed-Sun, 12-5. Freud's home from 1938 until his death in 1939. Includes much of the original furniture and personal effects of Freud and his daughter Anna, including his study, library and large collection of antiquities. A book *20 Maresfield Gardens* was published by Serpents Tail in 1998. A Friends organisation issues a newsletter and runs special events A substantial bookshop is also maintained.

[8] **HIGHGATE LIBRARY AND SCIENTIFIC INSTITUTION**. 11 South Grove, Highgate, London N6 6BS. *Tel*: (020) 8340 3343; *Fax*: (020) 8340 5632; *Email*: hlsi@demon.co.uk. For more than 150 years the Institution has been the social and educational centre of Highgate and has occupied its premises overlooking Pond Square since 1840. It maintains a large lending and reference library for subscribers, and there is a large London collection: special collections on local poets Coleridge and John Betjemen. From October to April there is a programme on lectures given by speakers of national renown. Adult education classes on art, musical, literary and scientific subjects run throughout the year. Art exhibitions are held in the Victoria Hall. An archives room houses much material on Highgate, environs and residents from the early seventeenth century. *Heart of a London village*: the Highgate Literary and Scientific Institution, written by members of the archives committee was published in 1991. *Newsletter editor*: Vera Crane; *Hon. Secretary*: Anne Riddell; *President*: Laurence Shurman.

[9] **KEATS HOUSE**. Keats Grove, Hampstead, London NW3 2RR. *Tel*: (020) 7435 2062 (answerphone). *Hours*: Mon-Fri, 1-5; Sat 10-1, 2-5; Sun 2-5. Now owned by the Corporation of London. Major building work is planned for 1999. An important centre for Keatsiana and books (some 8,600 volumes). A guide book is issued. A Friends organisation can be contacted through the house.

[10] **KENWOOD HOUSE**. Hampstead Lane, Hampstead, London NW3 7JR. *Tel*: (020) 7348 1286; *Fax*: (020) 793 3891. An English Heritage property. *Curator*: Julia Finlater; *Assistant Curators*: Armina Wright, Cathie Power. *Hours*: April to September, 10-6; October 10-5; November to March 10-4. The Friends organisation can be contacted through the above address. The house and grounds was purchased by the 1st Earl of Iveagh from Lord Mansfield in 1924 who bequeathed it together with his collection of old master paintings to the nation in 1927. The building was remodelled by Robert Adam in 1764 and his library room is a noteworthy interior feature. The second edition of the catalogue and history of the house by Julia Bryant was published in 1998. In 1992 Aidan Ellis published John Carswell's account: *The saving of Kenwod and the Northern Heights*. The estate office and Landscape Visitor Information Centre is based in Mansion Cottage, near the Brew House Restaurant, *Tel*: (020) 7973 3893.

[11] **LAUDERDALE HOUSE**. Waterlow Park, Highgate Hill, London N6 5HG. *Tel*: (020) 8871 8716; (020) 8341 2032; *Fax*: (020) 8341 4892. *Director*: Carolyn Naish; *General Manager*: Katherine Ives. Built in about 1580, the house takes its name from the Earl of Lauderdale, Charles II's minister, who occupied it from 1660 to 1669. In 1889 owner Sidney Waterlow gave the house and park to the London County Council who used it for some 70 years as a tea-room. The Lauderdale House Society was established in 1978 to restore the house and run it as a community arts centre. Concerts, exhibitions and many other social and educational activities are organised. The rooms can be hired. The Lauderdale Restaurant, *Tel*: (020) 8341 4807 is open Tues-Sun 10-dusk. An historical account *Lauderdale Revealed,* by Peter Barber, Oliver Cox and Richard Curwen was published by the society in 1993.

[12] **SALVATION ARMY INTERNATIONAL HERITAGE CENTRE**. 3rd Floor, Salvationist St, Publishing and Supplies Ltd, 117-121 Judd St, London WC1H 9NN. *Tel*: (020) 7387 1656. *Hours*: Mon-Fri 9.30-3.30; Sat 9.30-12.30.

[13] **SIR JOHN SOANE'S MUSEUM**. 13 Lincoln's Inn Fields, London WC2A 3BP. *Tel:* (020) 7430 0175/7405 2107. *Hours*: Tues-Sat 10-5. Built by Sir John Soane, architect of the Bank of England in 1813 as his private residence; many architectural drawings, paintings and antiquities.

* HISTORICAL SOCIETIES *

[14] **CAMDEN HISTORY SOCIETY**. *Secretary*: Mrs J. Ramsay, Garden Flat, 62 Fellows Rd, London NW3 3LJ. *Chairman*: John Richardson (proprietor of Historical Publications) 32 Ellrington St, London N7. *Tel*: (020) 7607 1628. *Publications editor*: Dr F. Peter Woodford (a retired biochemist), 1 Akenside Rd, London NW3 5BS. *Tel*: (020) 7435 2088. The society aims to research and publish on all aspects of the past of the old boroughs of Hampstead, St Pancras and Holborn, and the districts of Highgate, Kentish Town and Camden Town. There is a programme of talks; walks and outings in the summer. There is an illustrated newsletter, issued usually twice a year, and an annual journal the *Camden History Review* (1973-). There are some 400 members. Its active publishing programme has included reprints such as: the *Hampstead and Highgate Directory 1885/6*; *Hampstead at war, 1939-45*; and *Hampstead Wells*, by George Potter, 1904. There have been histories such as Nicholas Bailey's *Fitzrovia*, 1981; and Helen Bentwick's *The Vale of Health on Hampstead Heath, 1777-1977*, published in 1977. Its important ongoing series on streets, their buildings and former residents was initiated in 1972 with Christopher Wade's *The streets of Hampstead* (2nd edition: 1984); and there have also been second editions of *The streets of Belsize*, 1991; *The streets of West Hampstead*, 1992 and *From Primrose Hill to Euston Road*, 1995. The series has continued with *Streets of Bloomsbury and Fitzrovia*, 1997; and *East of Bloomsbury*, 1998. Surveys of other parts of Holborn may follow in due course.

Other recent publications:

1995: DENFORD, Steven L.J. *Agar Town: the life and death of a Victorian slum*. 32pp, illus. map; (Occasional Paper No. 1).

1997: BARBER, Peter, and JACOMELLI, Peter. *Continental taste: Ticinese emigrants and their café restaurants in Britain 1847-1947*. 36pp, illus. (Occasional Paper No. 2).

1998. WADE, Christopher. *For the poor of Hampstead, for ever*. 142pp. illus. An account of the work of the charity the Hampstead Wells and Camden Trust. Christopher Wade is also the author of *Buried in Hampstead* (monuments at St John's), CHS, 1986; and *Hampstead past*: a visual history of Hampstead, from Historical Publications.

1999/2000: A detailed account of Hampstead Cemetery, by Marianne Colums and Dick Weindling is in preparation.

Contents listings for Camden History Review, 1994-8.

No 18, 1994: The Boy's Home Industrial School, Chalk Farm; A Belsize map of 1762; a tale of Hoffmann and Brooke; The Gower Street Bar; Cultural finds in Finchley Road; Edward Walford; Royal Mail coachmakers.

No 19, 1995: The Great Hollow Elm; Rev. Percy Dearmer; The Gees of Fenton House; Forster of Belsize; Hampstead by-pass; Geere of Lauderdale House; Claire Clairmont; Keats; Labour in St. Pancras; The 'Dear Old Bedford'.

No 20, 1996: Isokon flats; Sir Samuel Romilly; Metropolitan Buildings; St. Pancras; Oliver Heaviside; Tobacco pipe makers of Somers Town; West End House and Beckford; Scala Theatre; Hampstead Music Club; Kentish Town butchers' shops; All Hallows, Gospel Oak.

No 21, 1997: Shaw and St Pancras Vestry; Camden Lit & Sci 1835-39; Christ Church, Hampstead; Sir William Job Collins; Orphan working school, Haverstock Hill; London Cabmen's Mission; Repton's Red Book for Kenwood; Old St Pancras church and its fields.

No 22, 1998: The Jews' Free School Camden Town; Camden's mayoral regalia; Bombs on Holborn in World War II; The Forsyths of Finchley Road; Before Camden Town, 1745-97; Advertisements painted on buildings in Camden; The Marylebone and Finchley Road Turnpike, 1820-50.

* AMENITY AND ENVIRONMENTAL ORGANISATIONS *

[15] **CAMDEN CIVIC SOCIETY**. Est. in 1963, it aims to promote discussion and awareness of development and conservation issues, to liaise with officials, to promote high standards of planning and architecture, to preserve features of historic or public interest, and to press for improvements in recreation areas and landscape. A newsletter is issued. *Chairman* (as at 1998): Malcolm Campbell, 98 Agar Grove, London NW1 9TL, *Tel*: (020) 7485 7023.

[16] **CASTLEHAVEN COMMUNITY ASSOCIATION**. 33 Hawley Rd, London NW1 8RU. *Tel*: (020) 7485 3386. *Fax*: (020) 7860 5824.

[17] **FRIENDS OF HAMPSTEAD CEMETERY**. The cemetery opened in 1876, planned by Joseph Fyfe Meston, a leading landscape gardener, with entry lodge and two chapels designed by Charles Bell. The Friends organisation was formed in 1994 and with a substantial lottery grant is doing much repair, conservation and environmental work. A booklet *Hampstead*

Cemetery Tomb Trail was published by the Camden History Society in 1994. *Contact*: Secretary, c/o The Lodge, Hampstead Cemetery, 69 Fortune Green Rd, London NW6 1DR.

[18] **FRIENDS OF HIGHGATE CEMETERY LTD**. Highgate Cemetery, Swain's Lane, London N6 6PJ. *Tel*: (020) 8340 1834. The cemetery opened in 1839 and is one of the greatest Victorian cemeteries. It is now owned by the Highgate Cemetery Charity and managed by Friends of Highgate Cemetery Ltd. Its 1996/97 annual report, illustrated with appealing photographs by John Gay outlines achievements over the last twenty years. John Gay's photographs also appear in *In Highgate Cemetery*, by the chair-person Mrs J.A. Pateman. Over 67,000 persons are buried here in more than 52,000 graves and burials still take place. Entry to the Western Cemetery is by guided tour only. The Eastern Cemetery (in which Marx is buried) is open from 10 (11 at weekends) to 5pm (4pm during winter).

[19] **FRIENDS OF RUSSELL SQUARE**. *Chair* (as at 1998): Maxine Webster, c/o 44-46 Nelson Square, London SE1 0QA. *Tel*: (020) 7803 0530. She is also the chair of [20] **AFFILIATED FRIENDS OF CAMDEN OPEN SPACES**. Other groups include: [21] **FRIENDS OF ST GEORGE'S GARDENS**, Bloomsbury; [22a] **FRIENDS OF ST ANDREWS GARDENS**, Gray's Inn Rd, London WC1; [22b] **FRIENDS OF ST PANCRAS GARDENS**.

[23] **FRIENDS OF WATERLOW PARK**. *Hon. Secretary* (as at 1998): Kate McLay, 72 Highgate Hill, Highgate, London N19 5NQ. *Other contacts*: Richard Taylor, 59 Hornsey Lane, Highgate, London N6 5LE, *Tel*: (020) 8348 1817; Jude Froshaug, *Tel*: (020) 7263 2064. Est. in 1992 by a small group of people concerned about the condition of the park at that time. Since then they have worked with Camden and the community to restore its splendour (£1.1 million lottery funding). Restoration work is still ongoing and events are organised. A newsletter is issued.

[24] **HAMPSTEAD HEATH INFORMATION CENTRE**. Parliament Hill Lido, London NW3. *Tel*: (020) 7482 7073. *Hours*: Wed-Sat 11-4. An information and educational centre run by the City of London Corporation. The Corporation issues an informative *Hampstead Heath Diary*, which includes information on the Hampstead Heath Management Committee, the Consultative Committee, the information centre, local societies listed in this chapter, and the advisory committees for conservation areas - Dartmouth Park, Hampstead, Highgate and Mansfield. Other publications are: *The official guide to Hampstead Heath*, *Hampstead Heath map*, and *Hampstead Heath management plan*.

[25] **HEATH AND HAMPSTEAD SOCIETY**. *Hon. officials* (as at 1998): *President*: Peggy Jay. *Vice-Presidents*: Gerald Isaaman, Margaret Rodgers. *Chairman*: Martin Humphrey, 32 Willoughby Rd, London NW3 1RU. *Tel*: (020) 7435 5386. *Secretary*: Frankie de Freitas, 32 Maresfield Gardens, London NW3 5SX. *Tel*: (020) 7435 0502. *Treasurer*: John Smithard, 23a Buckland Crescent, London NW3 5DH. *Tel*: (020) 7722 9512. Est. in 1897 to safeguard the Heath and to preserve and enhance the old streets and historic buildings of Hampstead. The society is represented on the Corporation of London's Heath Management and consultative Committees and on the Hampstead Conservation Area Advisory Committee. There is a programme of meetings, lectures and nature study walks. A newsletter is issued three times a year. In 1997 the society published *A constant vigil: 100 years of the Heath and Old Hampstead Society*, edited by F. Peter Woodford. The society's walks are arranged by David Watt, *Tel*: (020) 8348 6932.
In 1995 the Parish Church Council of St John-at-Hampstead published: *Hampstead Parish Church*: the story of a building through 250 years, by M.H. Port (available from: the Parish Clerk, Hampstead Church, Church Row, London NW3 6UU). Michael Port is an architectural historian and specialises in the history of London's 'establishment' buildings.

[26] **THE HIGHGATE SOCIETY**. Headquarters at: 10a South Grove, London N6 6BS. *Fax*: (020) 8348 8850. *Patron*: Lord Menuhin; *President*: John Samuel, J.P. Est. in 1966, the society is actively involved in planning and conservation issues, and the organisation of social and cultural events. There is a membership of over 1,000. There is a quarterly magazine *Buzz*.

[27] **NETHERHALL NEIGHBOURHOOD ASSOCIATION**. *Chair*: Dr Mayer Hillman, The Coach House, 7a Netherhall Gardens, London NW3 5RN. *Tel*: (020) 7794 9661. *Secretary*: Margaret Pszenicki, *Tel*: (020) 7794 0874. Est. in 1983, currently with some 180 members, for the Victorian and Edwardian Netherhall residential area (with some 5 schools). Groups are concerned with conservation, greening, tree wardens, neighbourhood watch, etc.

[28] **SOUTH END GREEN ASSOCIATION**. *Contact*: Frances Hetherington, 22 Wentworth Mansions, Keats Grove, London NW3. Represents over 400 residents and businesses in the vicinity of the Green.

[29] **VALE OF HEALTH SOCIETY**. *Chair*: Bobby de Joia, Green Moor, Vale of Health, London NW3 1AZ. *Tel*: (020) 7794 6772. Est. in 1973, currently with some 100 members. Current projects include setting up a volunteer corporation for the Heath, and a recording of some 700 memorial seats on the Heath ('operation benchmark'). *Contact*: Sheila MacLeod, *Tel*: (020) 7435 3631. *Email*: Sheila@sheilaMacLeod.freeserve.co.uk. A newsletter *Vale News* is issued.

* SOME OTHER COUNCIL CONTACTS *

Head of Arts and Tourism: Wendy Neville. The Camden Festival has ceased; currently two festivals are organised: the Camden Mix Music Festival, and the Women in Focus Festival. The small section has produced a number of leaflets recently: *Hidden histories* - a guide to blue plaques commemorating Camden women; *The Camden collection* (museums and historic houses), and *Stay in Camden* (accommodation). They can be obtained from: Camden Information Point, Town Hall Extension, Argyle St, London WC1H 8NL. *Tel*: (020) 7860 5974.

Building Conservation: Robin Harper, Principal conservation and design officer; Landscape officer: Martin Bolhard. There are also four assistant conservation officers. Town Hall Extension, Argyle St, London WC1H 8NL. *Tel*: (020) 7314 1944. Publications on all of Camden's 33 conservation areas are currently in progress. The following have appeared: Bloomsbury, Camden Town, Charlotte Street, Denmark Street, Kentish Town, King's Cross, Kingsway, Park Hill and Upper Park (Belsize Park area), Seven Dials, West End Green.

Head of Parks and Open Spaces: Martin Stanton, Crowndale Centre, 218 Eversholt St, London NW1 1BD. *Tel*: (020) 7911 1693. Publishes a monthly 'What's on in Camden Parks'.

Nature Conservation Office: Waterlow Park, London N6. *Tel*: (020) 7272 3588. Leaflets are planned for 1999: a tree trail in Waterlow Park, guides to monuments and trees in St Pancras Cemetery, and a conservation activities calendar.

Reference Library: Swiss Cottage Library, 88 Avenue Rd, London NW3 3HA. *Tel*: (020) 7413 6533.

* SOME NON-COUNCIL CONTACTS *

Residents associations:
CAMDEN FEDERATION OF TENANTS AND RESIDENTS ASSOCIATIONS. 11-17 The Marr, Camden St, London NW1. *Tel*: (020) 7383 2227.

Voluntary organisations:
VOLUNTARY ACTION CAMDEN/COUNCIL FOR VOLUNTARY SERVICE. 207 Kings Cross Rd, London WC1. *Tel*: (020) 7837 5544.

* LOCAL PRESS *

Camden Chronicle. 161 Tottenham Lane, London N8. *Tel*: (020) 8340 6868.
Camden Citizen. Monthly council magazine, edited by Christine Bramble at Town Hall, Judd St, London WC1H 9JE. *Tel*: (020) 7413 6944.
Camden New Journal. Weekly, independent free newspaper. 40 Camden Rd, London NW1. *Tel*: (020) 7419 9000.
Hampstead and Highgate Express. 100a Avenue Rd, London NW3 3HF. *Tel*: (020) 7433 0000.

CITY OF LONDON

* CORPORATION OF LONDON *

[30] **GUILDHALL LIBRARY**. *Hours*: Mon-Sat 9-5. One of the nation's great public libraries, with collections of great historical depth, open to all. It covers not only the city and the whole of Greater London, but British local history and topography as well as British national history. A booklet guide to holdings is available. *Fax for whole library*: (020) 7600 3384. *Principal reference librarian* (heading team of some six assistants): Irene Gilchrist. *Inquiry desk Tel*: (020) 7332 1868/1870. An extensive stock of reference books and London books of general interest is on open access. The catalogue has now become computerised.

Prints and drawings department: *Tel*: (020) 7332 1839; *Former keeper*: Ralph Hyde; *Assistants*: John Fisher, Jeremy Smith, Lynn Macnab. Some 30,000 items in the collection can now be accessed via the Internet: http://collage.nhil.com. The department also includes photographs. Exhibitions are organised.
Ralph Hyde is a prolific author. His career began with the publication of his FLA thesis *Printed maps of Victorian London 1851-1900* by William Dawson in 1975. He has just retired.

Manuscripts Department: *Tel*: (020) 7332 1863. *Keeper of Archives*: Stephen Freeth. *Deputy Keeper*: Philippa Smith. Its catalogues of holdings are listed below. The first volume in Greater London Archives Network's new series will be on the holdings of this department. The department has a website: http://ihr.sas.ac.uk./ihr/ghmnu/html.

Guildhall Library Publications:
These fall into several distinct categories: guides and handlists of resources, specialist books, reproductions of maps, prints and pictures; back issues of the *Guildhall Miscellany* (1952-1973), and its continuation *Guildhall Studies in London History* (1973-1981); maps panoramas and portfolios, and facsimiles of early playing cards in association with Harry Margary (Lympne Castle, nr Hythe, Kent CT21 4LQ, *Tel*: (01303) 267571). Other associated publishing organisations: Guildhall Art Gallery; Corporation of London; London Metropolitan Archives; London Topographical Society.

(i) **Guildhall Library Research Guides series**:
1: *A guide to genealogical sources in Guildhall Library.* 4th edition, 1997 (compiled by Richard Harvey).
2: *The British overseas: a guide to births, marriages and deaths of British persons overseas before 1945.* 3rd edition, 1995 (compiled by Geoffrey Yeo).
3: *City Livery companies and related organisations: a guide to their archives in Guildhall Library.* 3rd edition, 1989.
4: *City of London parish registers: a handlist of parish registers, register transcripts and related records at Guildhall Library.* 6th edition, 1990. (7th edition to be published summer 1999).
5: *Greater London parish registers*: registers of Church of England parish outside the City of London, non-parochial registers, registers of foreign denominations, burial grounds and marriage documents. 7th edition, 1995.
6: *A handlist of non-conformist, Roman Catholic, Jewish and burial ground registers at Guildhall Library.* 2nd edition, 1993.
7: *A guide to the Lloyd's Marine Collection and related marine sources at Guildhall Library*, compiled by Declan Barriskill. 2nd edition, 1994 (compiler on staff of reference library).

Supplementary series:
1: *A guide to archives and manuscripts at Guildhall Library.* 2nd edition, 1990.
2: *A handlist of business archives at Guildhall Library*, compiled by Joan Bullock-Anderson, 2nd edition, 1991.

(ii) **Books**:
Recent publications are *Vanished churches of the city of London*, by Gordon Huelin, 1996; and *William Herbert 1772-1851: actor, antiquary and first librarian of the Guildhall Library*, by Donovan Dawe and F.W. Padwick (former librarians), 1998. (Both Gordon Huelin and Donovan Dawe died recently). In 1974 Guildhall Library published *The medieval Guildhall of London* by Caroline M. Barron.

(iii) **Maps and panoramas**:
Includes: Ten colour lithographs of potable views and places in London, published by R. Ackermann, 1851; Benjamin Read's *Splendid Views*, 1829-39 (six aquatinted fashion plates).
sheets: *Bank's Balloon View, 1851* (London from a balloon over Hampstead); *Cross's New Map of London, 1835*; *Fish-eye view of London, c. 1845* (anamorphic view of London from top of St Paul's Cathedral); *London from the roof of the Albion Mills* (Robert and Henry Aston Barker's panorama of 1792-3), six sheets with notes; *John Rocque's map of London, 1745; John Speed: Middlesex, 1610; C.J. Visscher - long prospect of London, 1616; London and its environs, 1813; Jewish East London.*

(iv) **Atlases and maps and reproductions (in association with Harry Margary)**:
A series of five bound volumes with notes and indexes: *A-Z of Elizabethan London* (contains: The Copperplate Map, c. 1558; Braun & Hogenberg's map, 1570's; The 'Agas' map, 1562); *A-Z of Restoration London* (John Ogilby and William Morgan's survey of the City of London, 1676); *A-Z of Georgian London* (John Rocque's map, 1746); *A-Z of Regency London* (Richard Horwood's survey, 1807); *A-Z of Victorian London* (G.W. Bacon's atlas, 1888).

Maps produced as sets of sheets: *Collection of early maps of London, 1553-1667* (copperplate maps, 1553-59); Braun and Hogenberg, 1572; 'Agas' map, 1562, Faithorne & Newcourt, 1658; Hollar, 1658; Leake's post fire, 1667); *An exact survey of London, Westminster and the Borough of Southwark 1741-45*, John Rocque; *Morgan's survey of the cities of London, Westminster and the Borough of Southwark, 1682*; *Morden's counties, 1676* (playing cards); *Ogilby & Morgan's survey of the City of London, 1676*; *A plan of the cities of London, Westminster and the Borough of Southwark and the continuous buildings*, John Rocque; *Rocque key map, London & 10 miles around, 1762*; *Stanford Library map of London and its suburbs, 1862*.

Panoramas and portfolios: *The Barbican before the Blitz* (12 local street scenes 1901-20, by Robert Randoll); *Grand panorama of London from the Thames*, c. 1848; *Industry and Idleness*, 1747, Hogarth's 'Apprentice series'.

8 facsimile packs of early playing cards: Arms of the English peers, 1688; The Beggar's opera, c. 1730; Cries of London, c. 1754; Knavery of the Rump, 1697; Marlborough's victories, 1707; Morden's Counties, 1676; South Sea Bubble, 1720; Transformation cards, 1811 (suit marks concealed in each design).

Corporation of London publications:
Books currently available: *The Barbican sitting on history*, 1990, by Jennifer Clarke; *City gardens*: an open spaces survey in the City of London, by Brian Plummer and Don Shewan, co-published with the Belhaven Press, 1992; *The Mansion House*, by Sally Jeffery, 1993, published for the Corporation by Phillimore; *Sheep over London Bridge*: Freedom of the City of London by Caroline Arnold, 1996.
Official guides to: Bunhill Fields, 1991; Burnham Beeches, 1993; Epping Forest, 1993; The Guildhall, 1992; Hampstead Heath, 1993; Kent and Surrey Commons, 1992; The Monument, 1994; The Old Bailey, 1992; The Mansion House, 1994.
Old Spitalfields Market 'Vale' is a portfolio of three prints after drawings of the old market by Geoffrey Fletcher; and there is a series of nine colour postcards of views of the Guildhall, interior and exterior, Smithfields Market, interior, Prince Henry's Room, 15 Fleet Street (collection of Pepysiana within barristers' chambers), the Monument.

[31] **GUILDHALL LIBRARY BOOKSHOP/GUILDHALL LIBRARY PUBLICATIONS**. *Manager*: Lloyd Childe. *Tel*: (020) 7332 1858. *Fax*: (020) 7600 3384. *Email*: bookshop@ms.corpoflondon.gov.uk. Stocks a wide range of current academic and general interest titles. Lloyd Childe is responsible for seeing through to press books with the Guildhall Library imprint.

[32] **GUILDHALL ART GALLERY**. *Curator*: Vivian Knight; *Assistant*: Jeremy Johnson. *Tel*: (020) 7332 1632. A new building in Guildhall Yard to house and display the collection is due to finally open in July 1999. The collection is documented in *The works of art in the Corporation of London*, published in 1986 by Woodhead Faulkner. A series of more general interest catalogues is currently in preparation. In 1991 C.U.P. published the catalogue of the Harold Samuel collection, Dutch and Flemish painters. Reproductions of a number of works are available as prints, postcards and greetings cards.

[33] **CORPORATION OF LONDON RECORDS OFFICE**. *City archivist*: James R. Sewell. PO Box 270, Guildhall, London EC2P 2EJ, *Tel*: (020) 7332 1251; *Fax*: (020) 7710 8682; *Email*: CLRO@ms.corpoflondon.gov.uk. *Hours*: Mon-Fri, 9.30-4.45. The searchroom is in the North Office Block, Guildhall. The archives can be consulted without prior appointment (except to see rate books) and free of charge.
Free publications: *City archives* (introductory leaflet); 3 research guides: 1: *City Freedom archives*; 2: *Sworn brokers' archives*; 3: *Transportation and emigration*.
16 information sheets: 1: *Jack the Ripper*; 2: *Publications for sale*; 3: *Using the CLRO*; 4: *Archive copying services*; 5: *The city arms*; 6: *Open spaces*; 7: *Committee records*; 8: *The Court of Common Council*; 9: *Free publications order form*; 10: *Records of hospitals in CLRO*; 11: Coroner's inquests in CLRO; 12: *Lists of City of London inhabitants*; 13: *City of London cemetery*; 14: *Sessions records in CLRO*; 15: *School records in CLRO*; 16: *'King's freemen' and their records in CLRO*.
An introductory guide to the Corporation of London Records Office, by H. Deadman and E, Scudder, published in 1994, is now out of print.

Calendars and histories (some are in short supply now):
Calendar of wills proved and enrolled in the Court of Husting, London 1258-1688: Part I 1258-1358 (1889); Part II 1358-1688 (1890).
Calendar of Coroners rolls of the City of London 1300-78 (1913).
Calendars of plea and memoranda rolls: 1437-57 (1954); *1458-82* (1961).
The Fire Court, Calendar to the decrees of the Court of Juricature on disputes as to rebuilding after the Great Fire; Vol I 1667-68 (1966); Vol 2 1667-68 (1970).
Southwark and the City (1969), edited by D.J. Johnson.
Lastly there is a set of 14 colour postcards of images from the Corporation's records.

The [34] **GUILDHALL HISTORICAL ASSOCIATION** brings together staff and others concerned with the records of the Corporation.

[35] **CITY OF LONDON INFORMATION CENTRE**. *Manager*: Carol Ripca. St Paul's Churchyard, London EC4M 8BX. *Tel*: (020) 7332 1456. *Hours*: Mon-Sat 9-5.

* MUSEUMS AND VISITOR ATTRACTIONS *

[36] **BANK OF ENGLAND MUSEUM**. *Curator*: John Keyworth. Bartholomew Lane, London EC2R 8AH. *Tel*: (020) 7601 5545. Curator's office: (020) 7601 3866. *Archivist*: Henry Gillett, *Tel*: (020) 7601 4889. The museum opened in 1988 and traces the history of the bank from its foundation by Royal Charter in 1694 to its present day role as the nation's central bank. Important architectural features of the museum are the reconstructed Bank Stock Office, designed by Sir John Soane and built in 1793, and Sir Herbert Baker's Rotunda, with its original Soane caryatids. A free guide leaflet is issued, and there is a small shop.
Public Enquiries for present day affairs: *Tel*: (020) 7601 4878; Corporate hospitality: *Tel*: (020) 7601 4388.

[37] **CITY OF LONDON POLICE MUSEUM**. *Curator*: Roger Appleby. Wood Street Police Station, London EC2. *Tel*: (020) 7601 2705. A small museum of exhibits on the history of the City of London Police is maintained, and can be viewed by appointment. The complex includes a twelve storey tower and was designed by Donald McMorran 1962-66.

[38] **MANSION HOUSE**. Walbrook, London EC4N 8PH. *Tel*: (020) 7626 2500. The residence of the Lord Mayor, designed by George Dance the elder 1739-52 and altered by George Dance Junior at the end of the 18th century. A series of impressive reception rooms have been recently restored and can be viewed in group tours, Tues, Wed Thurs, at 11.00 and 2.00 when the mayor is out. Applications in writing to: the Principal Assistant Diary Officer, (minimum of people in group: 15; maximum: 40).

[39] **PRINCE HENRY'S ROOM**. 17 Fleet St, London EC4Y 1AA. *Tel*: (020) 7936 4004. Collection of Pepysiana within barristers chambers; open to public Mon-Sat 11-2.

[40] **ST BARTHOLOMEW'S HOSPITAL MUSEUM AND ARCHIVES**. *Archivist*: Marion Rea. West Smithfield, London EC1A 7BE. *Tel*: (020) 7601 8033/8152. The museum is open Tues-Fri 10-4 and relates the history of one of the world's oldest and most distinguished hospitals founded in 1123 by a monk named Rahere, and granted by Henry VIII to the City of London in 1546. Archives, works of art, surgical instruments, etc. are displayed. A pictorial guide *St Bartholomew's Hospital: nine centuries of health care* was published in 1997; and there is also a full scale history *The Royal Hospital of St Bartholomew, 1123-1973*, edited by Victor Cornelius Medvei, and John L. Thornton, as well as more specialist publications. The museum overlooks the 18th century square designed by James Gibbs, and adjoins the grand staircase, with its celebrated Hogarth murals, which leads to the Great Hall. The archives are open by appointment only. *Tel*: (020) 7601 8152; *Fax*: (020) 7606 4790, and are detailed in a booklet *Resources in the archives department: a guide for users*. Archives include those of hospitals and other bodies connected administratively with St Bart's.

Guided tours: Guided tours of Historic Bart's and Smithfield are organised by members of the City of London Guide Lecturers Association. *Tel contact*: (020) 7837 0546, and take place every Friday at 2pm (meet at main gate).

[41] **THE TOWER BRIDGE EXPERIENCE**. Tower Bridge, London SE1 2UP. *Tel*: (020) 7378 1928; for details on the raising of the bridge: *Tel*: (020) 7378 7700; educational services, and special events, *Tel*: (020) 7407 9191; corporate hospitality: (020) 7407 9222. The entrance is situated on the North pier, and visitors have access to the scenic high-level walkways as well as the engine rooms.

[42] **TOWER OF LONDON**, *Tel*: (020) 7680 9004. *Hours*: Mon-Sat 9-6; Sun 10-6.

* HISTORICAL/ENVIRONMENTAL SOCIETIES *

[43] **CITY HERITAGE SOCIETY**. *Contact*: Mrs Ann Woodward, 404 Gilbert House, London EC2Y 8BD. *Tel*: (020) 628 7307. Est. in 1973 as an amenity society for the city of London: conservation of historical buildings, and scrutiny of all important planning applications. There is an annual award for the best refurbishment project. Programme of lectures, walks, visits and annual dinner at one of the City Livery halls. Annual report issued. Currently some 100 members.

[44] **CITY OF LONDON GUIDE LECTURERS ASSOCIATION**. *Secretary*: Paul Taylor, 34 St John's Court, Finchley Rd, London NW3 6LL. *Tel/Fax*: (020) 7625 9163. *Chairman*: Derek Melluish, 55 Church Walk, Worthing, West Sussex BN11 2LT. *Tel*: (01903) 234639. *Membership secretary*: Len Phillips, 124 Foundling Court, Brunswick Centre, London WC1N 1AN. *Tel*: (020) 7837 0546. *Newsletter editor*: Hilda Denne, 2 The Woodlands, Chelsfield Park, Orpington, Kent BR6 5HL. *Tel*: (01689) 851701. Est. in 1983, currently with 190 members all of whom have qualified by examinations run currently by the City University. The course is part-time and runs from October to June. A newsletter is issued, and there is also a list of members with details of their special interests.

[45] CITY OF LONDON HISTORICAL SOCIETY. *Clerk*: Pauline Mitchell, 406 Mountjoy House, Barbican, London EC2Y 8BP. *Tel*: (020) 7920 9630. *Chairman*: Desmond Fitzpatrick. *President*: Michael Farrow. Est. over 10 years ago, currently with some 100 members. Meetings in committee room at Guildhall; tours, outings.

[46] FRIENDS OF ALL HALLOWS. All Hallows-by-the-Tower, Byward St, London EC3R 5BJ. *Tel*: (020) 7481 2928. Came into being after World War II to speed the rebuilding work after bombing. Friends help to maintain the building and recent projects have involved refurbishment of the Lady Chapel, the Undercroft and redesigning the North Porch. There are social functions throughout the year and an occasional newsletter is issued. The church is most historic, founded in 675 by the Abbey of Barking. Its history is illustrated in the Undercroft Museum. The mariner's chapel has models of ships. There are special links with churches in Philadelphia and New York, and with Cyprus and the Gulf.

[47] FRIENDS OF ST BOTOLPH'S ALDERSGATE AND POSTMAN'S PARK. *Membership secretary*: Mrs Carole Chandler, St Botolph's Church, Aldergate St, London EC1A 4EU. Est. in 1982 to support and help maintain the church. There is an occasional newsletter *St Botolph's alive!*. Postman's Park was created in the latter part of the last century from the churchyard of St Botolph's and two adjoining burial grounds. It is noteworthy for its curious Memorial Cloister, designed by G.F. Watts, with its plaques commemorating individuals who gave their lives to save others. There has been a church on this site since c. 1050; the present day, third church dates from 1788 with an outstanding interior designed by Nathaniel Evans.

[48] FRIENDS OF ST PAUL'S CATHEDRAL. The Secretary, Chapter House, St Paul's Churchyard, London EC4M 8AD. *Tel*: (020) 7246 8308. A world-wide association of supporters of the cathedral. There is an annual magazine, *The Dome*, and newsletters are issued. Some other cathedral contacts: *Library*: open Mon, Tues, and Fri mornings; Librarian: Joseph Wisdom (also on staff of Guildhall Library), *Tel*: (020) 7246 5345. *Retail shop*: situated in the crypt (where there is also a cafe), *Tel*: (020) 7246 8314/5/6. *Tourism and marketing*: Peter Mitchell, *Tel*: (020) 7246 8313; there is a conference room in the crypt, with the adjacent 'beehive room'. *The Triforium tour*: gallery area which includes the library, the geometrical staircase and the trophy room (includes Wren's model of the cathedral he wanted to build, Mon, Thurs, 11.30 and 2.30, advance booking: (020) 7245 8319.
The cathedral's annual report contains the Dean's report, the fabric report, financial report, a selection of events, and senior personnel.

[49] THE FRIENDS OF THE CITY CHURCHES. Postal address: St Margaret Pattens, Rood Lane, London EC3M 1HS. *Tel*: (020) 7626 1555. *Another contact (Treasurer)*: Roger Faulkner-Corbett, 3 Loudwater House, Rickmansworth, Herts WD3 4HN. *Tel*: (01923) 775695. Aims to bring together all who love and value these churches to ensure that they are preserved intact for posterity; helps to arrange regular opening hours, providing volunteers where necessary, providing literature, encouraging use for special services, and publicising events.

The City of London churches individually and collectively have been written about extensively: photographic evocations such as *Monuments of another age*: the City of London churches, with original photographs by Malcolm Quantrill, Quartet Books, 1975; visitors guide such as John Betjeman's *City of London churches* (Pitkin); and *City of London churches: a walker's guide*, by John Barron and Alexandra Moore, 1998 (9 Bartholomew Close, Winchester SO23 7DL); academic studies such as *The City churches of Sir Christopher Wren*, by Paul Jeffery, Hambledon Press, 1996; inventory-type documents such as *A survey of the churches of the City of London*, compiled by Alan Baxter Associates (14 Cowcross St, London EC1) for the Diocese of London, the City Corporation and English Heritage in 1997; studies of demolished buildings, such as Gordon Huelin's *Vanished churches of the City of London*, Guildhall Library Publications, 1996. An important new photographic survey is *The City of London churches*, by Peter Guillery, photographs by Derek Randall, published in 1998 by English Heritage in association with Collins and Brown.

[50] TOWER HILL IMPROVEMENT TRUST/WAKEFIELD TRUST. *Secretary*: Jim Connolly, Atlee House, (Toynbee Hall), 28 Commercial St, London E1, *Tel*: (020) 7377 6614. Est. in 1938. Some of the background to the setting up of the organisation, with Lord Wakefield of Hythe as its president can be found in *Tower Hill regained?* by P.B. Clayton and B.R. Leftwich published by Longmans, Green & Co. in 1934.

* SOME OTHER CITY OF LONDON CONTACTS *

City of London directories:
The City of London directory and livery companies guide concentrates on the livery companies and is published annually by the City Press, Colchester, Essex, *Tel*: (01206) 545121. *Crowfords directory of City connections*; and *Olivers guide to the City of London* are published by AP Information Services of London, *Tel*: (020) 8455 4550.

City Business Library. 1 Brewers Hall Gardens, Londn EC2, *Tel*: (020) 7638 8215.

Planning Department publications (Department of Planning, Corporation, PO Box 270, Guildhall, London EC2P 2EJ. *Tel*: (020) 7332 3794. *Fax*: (020) 7332 1806). There are several useful publications on conservation areas: *A directory of conservation areas, listed buildings and scheduled monuments in the City of London*; (Tel contact: (020) 7332 1716); *Conservation areas in the City of London: a general introduction to their character*; and the related series of booklets Conservation Area character summaries on: Dyers' Buildings, Fleet Street, Lovat Lane, Leadenhall Market, Middlesex Street, Newgate, Postman's Park, Smithfield, Whitefriars. (Tel contact: (020) 7332 1721).
There are also interesting brochures on twentieth century sculpture and fountains. Archaeological remains and their administration are discussed in *Archaeology and planning in the City of London* (Tel contact: (020) 7332 1447).
Some 150 years of architecture are surveyed in an especially informative publication: *Continuity and change: building in the City of London, 1834-1984*, published by the Corporation in 1984, illustrated with many photographs and old engravings.

The arts:
City of London Festival, Bishopsgate Hall, 230 Bishopsgate, London EC2M 4QD, *Tel*: (020) 7377 0540; *Fax*: (020) 7377 1972; *Email*: cityfest@dircon.co.uk. Part of the City Arts Trust, it receives its core funding from the Corporation. The 1998 festival was very musical: orchestral, choral and chamber concerts; jazz at St Katharine's Dock, world music in a variety of venues, and weekend architectural visits and walks.

* LOCAL PRESS *

City of London papers (non-financial affairs):
City Events, published monthly by the Diocese of London, Diocesan House, Causton St, London SW1, *Tel*: (020) 7932 1241; *Editor*: Leigh Hatts. Covers events, activities, services in the City of London churches.
City of London Times, 13 Coopers Row, London EC3N 5BQ, *Tel*: (020) 7488 3888. *Editor*: Dennis Delderfield. Contains historical articles. Editor describes it as a 'parish pump' type paper.
City View, quarterly magazine, edited by Michael Walsh, on Corporation of London affairs, from the Guildhall, London EC2P 2EJ. *Tel*: (020) 7606 3201.

ISLINGTON

* LONDON BOROUGH OF ISLINGTON *

[51] **ISLINGTON LOCAL HISTORY COLLECTIONS**: There are currently two sites, but they may merge to form one collection in due course: Central Reference Library, 2 Fieldway Crescent, London N5 1F, *Tel*: (020) 7619 6900. *Librarian*: Vada Hart; Finsbury Library, 245 St John St, London EC1V 3NB, *Tel*: (020) 7278 7343. *Librarian*: David Withey. NB: appointments necessary for both collections.
The two librarians compiled the Islington collection of old photographs from Sutton Publishing, 1995.
The publishing programme of the 1980's has not been sustained this decade due to funding cuts, but in 1993 the Islington Libraries published *People, places and plaques* by Roy Hidson, a former librarian (117 St Thomas Rd, London N4). His article on the Islington Antiquarian and Historical Society was published in the August 1998 newsletter of the I.A.H.S.
The following published in the 1980's are still in print: *In sweet St James' Clerkenwell*, 1984, by John Adlard (about the musical coalman Thomas Britton); *Islington cinemas and film studios*, 1989, by Chris Draper; *Islington entertained*, 1990, by Bill Manley; *Islington's people: changes in our working lives*, a photographic exhibition by Ed Barber; *Like it was yesterday*, 1989 (childhood memories of older residents, compiled by Daphne Chamberlain); *North London childhood 1910-1924*, by Louise M. Blundell, 1985; *The Sickerts in Islington*: catalogue, compiled by David Withey, 1987, of the works of Walter Sickert, Therese Lessore and the Sickert family in the Local Collection. The library also sells *Agricultural Hall: the building that would not go away* (the former Royal Agricultural Hall in Liverpool Rd, now the Business Design Centre), by Taduez Grajewski, 1989.

Postcards/maps:
There are two postcard sets: Angel, c. 1902; and Walter Sickert and the music hall; cards depicting Grimaldi; set of four Islington water-colours. Maps of the Parish of St Mary, Islington, 1805 (rev. 1828), 1841, c. 1853.

* TOURISM/GUIDES *

[52] **CLERKENWELL/ISLINGTON GUIDES ASSOCIATION.** *Contact*: Marion Larsen, 68a Primrose Mansions, Prince of Wales Drive, London SW11 4EG. *Tel*: (020) 7622 3278; *Email*: www.hawkins.ndirect.co.uk/clerkenwell_guides. Operates with the Mayor of Islington's official tourist guides. Walks on the Angel, Clerkenwell, Smithfield, Canonbury.

[53] **CLERKENWELL VISITORS CENTRE.** *Contacts*: Chris Graham; Cyril Oliver, 6 Clerkenwell Close, London EC1R 0DY. *Tel*: (020) 7253 7438. *Hours*: Mon-Sat 11-6. Opened December 1998. Chris Graham also runs the July Clerkenwell Festival from here. The contact for Historic Clerkenwell (which organises events) is Trisha Kerr-Cross (*Tel*: (020) 7251 6311). Dennis Avis, *Tel*: (020) 7226 1446 is the contact for the Clerkenwell Historic Trail (supported by local businesses) which came into being in 1998. It is a founder member of the world-wide Association of City Trails. A contact for Clerkenwell guides is Marion Larsen, *Tel*: (020) 7622 3278. Contemporary Clerkenwell, contact: John Eichler (proprietor of the Three Kings pub) promotes local businesses.
A *Clerkenwell Historic Trail* is published with water-colour illustrations by Trisha Kerr-Cross.

[54a] **DISCOVER ISLINGTON**; Visitor Information Centre. *Chief Executive*: Helen Carpenter, 44 Duncan St, London N1 8BW, *Tel* (tourist information): (020) 7278 8787; *Tel* (Admin): (020) 7837 5435; *Fax*: (020) 7833 21993; *Email*: VIC@islvic.demon.co.uk. *Website*: www.real-london.com. The organisation aims 'to generate both economic benefit and civic pride by promoting and developing local tourism in partnership with the public and private sector'. It has helped with the development of new hotels, the refurbished Angel underground station, the new Sadler's Wells theatre, and many small attractions such as bars and restaurants. The Discover Islington Network has a membership of some 200 businesses.

* MUSEUMS/VISITOR ATTRACTIONS/HISTORIC PROPERTIES *

[54b] **HOUSE OF DETENTION.** Clerkenwell Close, London EC1R 0AS, *Tel*: (020) 7253 9494; *Head office*: (020) 7493 1089; *Fax*: (020) 7493 1502. *Hours*: 7 days a week, 10-6. The underground remains of Victorian London's busiest prison; built in 1845 on the site of two seventeenth century prisons; closed in 1890.

[55] **ISLINGTON MUSEUM FOYER GALLERY**, (foyer of the old public hall), Town Hall, Upper St, London N1 2UD, *Tel*: (020) 7354 9442; *Office*: (020) 7477 3235. *Curators*: Alison Lister, Val Munday. Previously based at 268 Upper St, the museum reopened at the above address in 1998. There is a programme of temporary exhibitions including art and photography. In January and February 1998, there was a show 'Glad rags: Islington street fashion 1918-1947'. In 1997 the museum published a booklet *Beneath our feet: the geology of Islington*, by Diane Clements.
The museum is controlled by the trustees: Christopher Elrington (former editor of Victoria County History), Derek Sawyer and Pat Haynes (councillors), Mary Cosh, Alex Forshaw (Islington conservation officer), Lord Desai, Dr John Milner, Tim Burnett and Bruce Tattersall.
There is also a Friends organisation, *Contact*: Jim Ladgen, 20 Constantine Rd, London NW3 2NG, *Tel*: (020) 7267 9100.

[56] **MUSEUM OF THE ORDER OF ST JOHN.** *Curator*: Pamela Willis, St John's Gate, St Johns Lane, Clerkenwell, London EC1, *Tel*: (020) 7253 6644; *Fax*: (020) 7336 0587. *Hours*: tours of the gatehouse and the 12th century crypt at 11.00 and 2.30, Tues, Fri and Sat. Gatehouse built as the main entrance to the Priory of the Knights of St John in 1504, and now houses the headquarters and museum of the modern British Order of St John, parent body of the St John Ambulance and the St John Ophthalmic Hospital Jerusalem. They obtained the building in 1874. The grand priory church, reconstructed after World War II damage is in St John's Square, and there is a cloistered garden (study on the priory published by MoLAS in summer 1999).

[57] **UNION CHAPEL PROJECT.** The Vestry, Compton Ave, London N1 2XD, *Tel*: (020) 7226 3750.

[58] **WESLEY'S CHAPEL.** The Museum of Methodism, John Wesley's House, 49 City Rd, London EC1Y 1AU. *Tel*: (020) 7253 2262; *Fax*: (020) 7608 3825. *Hours*: 10-4, Mon-Sat; 12-2 Sun. Chapel built in 1778, the house in 1770, Wesley lived here for the last eleven winters of his life. Museum has a large collection of Wesleyan ceramics and paintings. There are also temporary exhibitions. There is a Friends organisation. The non-conformist cemetery Bunhill Fields is nearby; the graves of Susanna Wesley, mother of Charles and John, Daniel Defoe, William Blake and John Bunyan are here.

* HISTORICAL AND AMENITY SOCIETIES *

[59] **AMWELL SOCIETY.** *Chair*: Dr Hilway Rose, 4 Lloyd Square, London WC1X 9BA. *Secretary*: Richard Reddaway, 27 Wharton St, London WC1X 9PJ. *Membership and Treasurer*: Jane Wainwright, 8 Cumberland Gardens, London WC1X 9AG.

Est. in 1972 'to protect the amenities and architectural attractions of the conservation areas bounded by King's Cross Road, St John's Street, Pentonville Road and Rosebery Avenue'. Has over 250 members. It is currently concerned with plans for King's Cross, the future of the New River Head and with traffic flows in the area. There are walks, lectures and visits. There is a bi-monthly newsletter and a guided walk *A village in London*.

[60] **ANGEL ASSOCIATION.** *Secretary*: Vicky Wisher, 19 Haverstock St, London N1 8DL. *Tel*: (020) 7253 0243. *Chairman*: John MacGowan, 14 Sudeley St, London N1 8BP. *Tel*: (020) 7837 0312. The conservation, amenity and environmental society/pressure group for the whole of St Peter's Ward, from the Angel corner itself to New North Road. The ward is largely residential and is rich in listed buildings, mostly in Georgian and Victorian terraces. It contains the famous Camden Passage antiques market and the Regents Canal and City Road Basin, as well as garden squares and early backland 'industrial estates', some of which have been converted into mews-style houses. It also runs an annual art award for local primary schools; there is a quarterly newsletter. *Another contact*: Peter Brades, 12 Charlton Place, London N1 8AJ, *Tel*: (020) 7226 9560. The *Angel Trail* guided walk is published by Discover Islington. a folding leaflet, with map, listing businesses in Camden Passage has been issued by Camden Passage Traders Association, *Tel*: (020) 7359 9969.

[61] **BARNSBURY WOOD CO-OP.** *Contact*: Patrick Firebrace, 25 Thornhill Crescent, London N1, *Tel*: (020) 7609 1571, Now council-run, the nature reserve is in a triangular area between Huntingdon Street, Hemingford Road and Thornhill Crescent.

[62] **CANONBURY SOCIETY.** *Chairman*: John Lapthorne, 59 Canonbury Rd, London N1 2DG. *Tel*: (020) 7359 5144. Est. in 1971 to contest a scheme to redevelop a number of properties in the heart of the conservation area (designated in 1969). Annual summer garden party since 1989. Annual newsletter.

[63] **FINSBURY PARK ACTION GROUP** (Haringey/Hackney/Islington). Alexandra National House, 330 Seven Sisters Rd, London N4. *Tel*: (020) 8802 2612.

[64] **FINSBURY PARK COMMUNITY TRUST.** 1 Ashley Rd, London N17. *Tel*: (020) 8808 6086; 306 Seven Sisters Rd, London N4. *Tel*: (020) 8211 0121.

[65] **FRIENDS OF THE NEW RIVER WALK.** *Contact*: John Tasker, 3 Hope Close, Wallace Rd, London N1 2YS, *Tel*: (020) 7354 3363. Concerned with support and the raising of matching funding for the successful lottery bid to restore the New River Walk and its ponds.

[66] **HIGHBURY COMMUNITY ASSOCIATION.** c/o 83 Highbury Hill, London N5 1SX. *Contact*: Alison Carmichael. *Tel*: (020) 7359 5731. Represents residents and businesses in Highbury, Finsbury Park and Stoke Newington on traffic, conservation, planning and community matters. Newsletter issued.

[67] **HIGHBURY FIELDS ASSOCIATION.** *Chairman*: Martin Jones, 16 Highbury Park, London N5, *Tel*: (020) 7226 2145.

[68] **ISLINGTON ARCHAEOLOGY AND HISTORY SOCIETY.** *Chair*: c/o Flat 2, 67 Ferme Park Rd, London N8 9RY; *Membership and enquiries about events*: Catherine Brighty, 6 Wynyatt St, London EC1V 7HU, *Tel*: (020) 833 1541; *Fax*: (020) 7278 4802. *Newsletter editor*: Janet Wootton, 19a Compton Terrace, London N1 2UN, *Tel*: (020) 7354 3631; *Fax*: (020) 7354 3989. Programme of walks, visits and talks. Publications currently in print: *Criminal Islington*, edited by Keith Sugden (written by Flashback Project), 1989; *An historical walk along the New River*, 2nd edn, 1988; *An historical walk through Barnsbury*, 1980; and *An historical walk through Clerkenwell*, 2nd edn, 1987, all three by Mary Cosh; *A history of Highbury*, 2nd edn, 1984, by Keith Sugden. *A history of St Stephen's Church, Canonbury*, 1989, by Mary Cosh; and her two-volume study *The squares of Islington*, 1990 and 1993. There are also two sets of postcards. Mary Cosh (10 Albion Mews, London N1 1JX, *Tel*: (020) 7607 9305) is a freelance author. She has completed a history of the Kings Head Theatre, and is working on an account of the greens of Islington.

[69] **ISLINGTON BUILDINGS PRESERVATION TRUST.** *Contact*: David Gibson, architect, 131 Upper St, London N1 1QP, *Tel*: (020) 7226 2207; *home* (020) 7607 8193. The Trust works to save neglected and threatened buildings by raising money and providing specialist services. Completed cases include: 3 Highbury Place; Lloyd's Dairy; Amwell Street; industrial chimney, 64 Matilda Street; 2-4 Leigh Road; Friern Manor Dairy; Crouch Hill; St Luke's churchyard, Old Street. Continuing cases include: Finsbury Park Astoria (the Rainbow cinema); The Hat and Feathers, Clerkenwell Road; Finsbury Town Hall; Caledonian Market railings; Jewish burial ground, Kingsbury Road; Thornhill Square.

[70] **ISLINGTON LOCAL HISTORY EDUCATION TRUST**. *Contact*: Councillor Pat Haynes, 105 Mildmay Rd, London N1 4PU, *Tel*: (020) 7477 3078/7249 3679. The trust was active in publishing in the past: *The Illustrated Islington History Journal* ran from 1984 to 1997 and contained many specialist articles. Marjorie Edwards (48 Freegrove Road, London N7) was its publisher for numbers 28-52. In 1989 she published her own book *Up the Cally: history and recollections of London's old Caledonian Market*. Part of a book on Holloway Road exists in manuscript. The work of the Trust has now been absorbed by the I.A.H.S.

A major publication was *Streets with a story*: the book of Islington, by former Islington local history librarian Eric A. Willats, published in 1983, based on almost 40 years' work, an encyclopaedic history of the streets of Islington, with indexes of buildings, noteworthy residents, writers, artists and architects. In 1989 the Trust published Jim Connell's *An illustrated history of Upper Street*. He himself published Part 2 in 1991. He died several years ago. With Dick Whetstone, he also compiled two collections of old picture postcards, *Islington and Clerkenwell*; and the *Parish of St Mary Islington*, both published by S.B. Publications. Roy Hidson's account *The birth of a library service: Islington 1855-1904* was published in 1990.

[71] **ISLINGTON SOCIETY**. *Chairman*: Harley Sherlock, 13 Alwyne Place, London N1 2NL. *Tel*: (020) 7226 3404. *Vice-chairman*: David Gibson, 131 Upper St, London N1 1QP, *Tel*: (020) 7225 2207. *Secretary*: Sondra Beecroft, 24 Islington Park, London N1 1PX, *Tel*: (020) 7226 7429. *Chair of conservation, planning and transport committee*: Gordon Wigglesworth, 53 Canonbury Park South, London N1 2JL, *Tel*: (020) 7226 7734. *Editor of 'Islington News'*: Kathleen Frenchman, 7 Barnsbury Square, London N1 1JL, *Tel*: (020) 7607 2665. Est. in 1960 'to preserve the borough's existing historic fabric and individual buildings and to ensure harmony with the old'. It is also concerned with the natural environment, the whole community generally, traffic and transport. The Geoffrey Gribble (a former society conservation officer) Award is made annually for the best new building or restoration. The annual James Ogilvy-Webb Memorial Lecture commemorates the first chairman for some 20 yeas. Another annual event is the Bill Manley Memorial Pub Crawl (to commemorate the local historian and the pubs where he ate, drank, talked and wrote).

The *Angel Improvement Trust* (est. in 1982, responsible amongst other matters for the annual Sam Morris Civic Pride Shopfront Award) has now merged with the Islington society, and likewise *Friends of Islington Libraries*, est. in 1991 under the chairmanship of Michael Ignatieff. A newsletter *Islington News* is issued three times a year (has information on other societies). An article *Islington and the Islington Society* by Harley Sherlock was published in the November 1998 issue of the Angel Magazine (20 Parkfield St, London N1, *Tel*: (020) 7359 3434).

[72] **KINGS CROSS CONSERVATION AREAS ADVISORY COMMITTEE**. *Contact*: Bill Lee, St Pancras Traders Association, 9 Midland Rd, London NW1, *Tel*: (020) 7837 2709.

[73] **KINGS CROSS PARTNERSHIP** (regeneration). 31a Wicklow St, London WC1, *Tel*: (020) 7713 1177; *Fax*: (020) 7713 7177.

[74] **KINGS CROSS RAILWAY LANDS GROUP**. 207 Kings Cross Rd, London WC1, *Tel*: (020) 7837 6824. Est. in 1987. Quarterly newsletter *Carrion*.

[75] **NEW RIVER ACTION GROUP**. *Contact*: Frances Mussett, 24 Lavender Rd, Enfield, Middx EN2 0ST, *Tel*: (020) 8363 7187. *Another contact*: Dorothy Ravenswood, 29 Hogarth Hill, London NW11 6AY, *Tel*: (020) 8458 2958. Umbrella organisation aiming to preserve the New River and its reservoirs and filter beds for public enjoyment, recreation and as wildlife habitats. Members are individuals and organisations (some 45 currently). There is a quarterly newsletter.

[76] **ST PAUL'S CONSERVATION AND RESIDENTS SOCIETY**. *Chairman*: John Darrah, 48 St Paul's Rd, London N1 2QW. *Tel*: (020) 7226 1370. Est. in the 1960's to protect the environment of the St Paul's area, Canonbury. Involved with planting street trees, restoration projects and funding organisations, as well as road and rail transport.

[77] **SMITHFIELD TRUST** (incorporated the Smithfield Association, local businesses). *Administrator*: Vince Marshall, 55-56 Turnmill St, London EC1M 5QR. *Tel*: (020) 7566 0041. Est. in the 1970's to protect the unique character of the Smithfield area; and is involved with all planning issues. There are visits, walks and tours; research into local history and articles appear in the occasional newsletter *The Smithfield Turret*.

[78] **WHITTINGTON HISTORY PROJECT**. Est. in 1983, aiming 'to collect and rescue archives and artefacts, set up an archive and museum, exhibit photographs and memorabilia, publish books and postcards'. *Contact*: Ron Lendon, Voluntary Services Co-ordinator, F Block, St Mary's Wing, Whittington Hospital, Highgate Hill, London N19 5NF. *Tel*: (020) 7272 3070, ext. 4114. In 1992 a revised edition of its illustrated booklet *The hospital on the hill* was published.

In addition to the above active groups, there are many less active groups for Islington localities which tend to respond to issues as and when they arise:

For squares, for example, the Lonsdale Square Association, the Thornhill Square Residents Association.

For localities, there are many neighbourhood associations: Archway Neighbourhood, N19; Clerkenwell Neighbourhood; Cloudesley Association, N1; Copenhagen Neighbourhood, N1; Drayton Park Neighbourhood; Elthorne Park Neighbourhood, N19; Finsbury Neighbourhood; Hemingford Road Association, N1; Highbury Neighbourhood; Nag's Head Neighbourhood, N19; Rosetower Neighbourhood, N7; St Mary Magdalene Association, N7; St Peter's Neighbourhood, N1; Shakespeare Residents Association, N19; Tollington Neighbourhood and Tollington Park Action Group, N4; Whittington Neighbourhood, N19; Whitehall Park Conservation Group, N19; Woodbridge Preservation Group.

They all have representatives on Islington Council's Conservation Advisory Committee, *Contact*: Conservation Officer, Alex Forshaw, Planning Department, PO Box 3333, 222 Upper St, London N1 1YA, *Tel*: (020) 7477 2774.

* SOME OTHER COUNCIL CONTACTS *

Agenda 21: Helena Naidoo, University of North London, Ladbroke House, 62-66 Highbury Grove, London N1 2AD, *Tel*: (020) 7753 3186.

Arts and Heritage: Michael Hambridge, Town Hall, Upper St, London N1, *Tel*: (020) 7477 3338. Islington Arts Resources is at: Ashburton House, Ashburton Grove, London N7 7AA, *Tel*: (020) 7477 4855 (open: Mon, Wed, Fri 9.30-4.30).

Conservation officer: Alex Forshaw, 222 Upper St, London N1 1YA, *Tel*: (020) 7477 2774. There are 33 conservation areas, and leaflets have been issued on some of them.

Ecology: Islington Ecology Centre, Drayton Park, London N5, *Tel*: (020) 7354 5162. Publications include the *Islington Wildlife Diary*.

Information: The Library Information Unit at Central Library, 2 Fieldway Crescent, London N5 1PF, *Tel*: (020) 7619 6920. Maintains the 'Cardbox' database on local organisations and council services; it can be accessed at some 11 information access points in neighbourhood offices throughout the borough. The borough's central reference library is also at the above address.

* SOME NON-COUNCIL CONTACTS *

Arts:
ISLINGTON INTERNATIONAL FESTIVAL. 7 Islington Green, London N1, *Tel*: (020) 7354 2535.

Business:
ISLINGTON CHAMBER OF COMMERCE AND TRADE. 64 Essex Rd, London N1 8LR, *Tel*: (020) 7226 1593. The Islington branch of Business Link (City, Hackney, Islington) is here, *Tel*: (020) 7354 6400, and publishes a directory.

Voluntary organisations:
ISLINGTON VOLUNTARY ACTION COUNCIL. 322 Upper St, London N1, *Tel*: (020) 7226 4862.

* LOCAL PRESS *

Highbury and Islington Express. 1 Aztec Row, Berners Rd, London N1, *Tel*: (020) 7539 4886.
Islington magazine published quarterly by the Council, Town Hall, Upper St, London N1, *Tel*: (020) 7477 3344.
Islington Gazette. 161 Tottenham Lane, London N8, *Tel*: (020) 8340 6868.

KENSINGTON AND CHELSEA

* ROYAL BOROUGH OF KENSINGTON AND CHELSEA *

[79] **KENSINGTON LOCAL STUDIES DEPARTMENT**. Central Library, Phillimore Walk, London W8 7RX. *Tel*: (020) 7361 3038; *Fax*: (020) 7361 2976. *Hours*: Tues, Thurs 10-8; Wed closed; Fri, Sat 10-5. *Librarians*: Carolyn Starren; Kathryn McChord. Carolyn Starren is the author of *Kensington Past* (Historical Publications), and *Kensington and Chelsea in old photographs* (Sutton), both written with Barbara Denny.

In 1995 the department published *The warden's post 1939-1945*, a 12 page catalogue of World War II memorabilia.

It has still in print *An historical atlas of Kensington & Chelsea* (20 maps), 1971; *Kensington & Chelsea street names*, 1977; and *Lord Leighton's letters catalogue*, 1983. It also sells the publications of the KCCHG, and some independently produced items: *Guide to Bayswater: upstairs, downstairs*, by John Wittich, from Sunrise Press; *Lexham Gardens*, by David Weeks published by Gracewing, 1996; *Rachman, riots and Rillington Place*, by Tom Vague (c/o Wong - Singh Jones, 253 Portabello Rd, London W11 1LR, *Fax*: (020) 8968 5030); and *The Yellow Room*: the story of 15 Chepstow Place, London, by Alan Pattillo.

Postcards are also sold, including the Holland Park murals (RBKC); composer's houses (Boltons, Cheyne Walk, Harrington Road, Holland Park) and views of Holland Park and Kensington. There is also a video *Relentless perfection* about Leighton House.

The Chelsea Local Studies collection is at:
Chelsea Reference Library, Old Town Hall, Kings Rd, London SW3 5EZ, *Tel*: (020) 7352 6056. *Librarian*: David Walker. *Hours*: Mon, Tues, Thurs 10-8; Wed 10-1; Fri, Sat 10-5. Has an important collection of Chelsea prints and paintings.

* HISTORIC PROPERTIES *

[80] **APSLEY HOUSE, THE WELLINGTON MUSEUM,** *Director/Curator*: Alicia Robinson; *Assistant curator and education officer*: Katharine Hugh; *Marketing and administration*: Leah Tobin. 149 Piccadilly, Hyde Park Corner, London W1V 9FA. *Tel*: (020) 7495 8525; (020) 7499 5676. *Hours*: Tues-Sun 11-5. House designed by Robert Adam and the home of the Duke of Wellington since 1817. The family is in residence here, but the V & A administer it, and the Department for Culture, Media and Sport is responsible for its physical upkeep. There was a major conservation and restoration programme 1992-95. Specialist tours and talks were held in 1998 and may be repeated 1999/2000. There is a guide book, 1995, by former curator Jonathan Voak, and a catalogue of paintings, 1982, by Michael Kauffman.

[81] **CARLYLE'S HOUSE**. The Custodian, 24 Cheyne Row, Chelsea, London SW3 5HL. *Tel*: (020) 7352 7087. *Hours*: April-Nov, Wed-Sun 11-5. A National Trust property. The home of writer and historian Thomas Carlyle, from 1834 until his death in 1881. Also a restored Victorian walled garden. Annual Carlyle Memorial lecture: performances of works by Chelsea writers and readings from his letters; guided walks around Chelsea with the Chelsea Society.

[82] **LEIGHTON HOUSE**. *Curator*: Daniel Robbins; *Assistant curator*: Reena Suleman. 12 Holland Park Road, London W14 8LZ. *Tel*: (020) 7602 3316. *Hours*: Mon-Sat 11-5.30. After 6.30pm the house is available for hire - the Kensington & Chelsea Music Society for example has a monthly concert here. Leighton House was built in 1864 for the painter Frederick, Lord Leighton, a leading exponent of 19th century classical art, and President of the Royal Academy. The outstanding house contains work by Leighton and his contemporaries, paintings, furniture, ceramics and is especially famous for its 'Arab Hall'. There is a varied programme of temporary exhibitions. A major exhibition on the Holland Park Circle (1850-1900) is planned for December 1999 to February 2000. The annual Leighton Open Exhibition is for artists living, working or studying in the RBKC.
The Friends of Leighton House organisation can be contacted at the Central Library, Phillimore Walk, London W8 7RX, *Tel*: (020) 7361 3027. Established in 1969, it plays an important role in the work of the house: enabling interior restoration and acquisition of major works for the collection.
The staff at Leighton House also run [83] **LINLEY SAMBOURNE HOUSE**, 18 Stafford Terrace, London W8 7BH, *Tel*: (020) 8994 1019. *Hours*: March to October, Wed 10-4; Sun 2-5. This is the former home of a leading 'Punch' cartoonist and illustrator of the Victorian and Edwardian period, and is an outstanding artist's house of its time, with all original decorations, furniture and pictures. There is a guide book and a 'historical workbook' for teachers and children. The Countess of Ross (founder here of the Victorian Society, who lease the property) was the last owner and the house was sold in 1989 and is now owned by RBKC.

* GARDENS/PARKS/CEMETERIES *

[84] **CHELSEA PHYSIC GARDEN**. *Curator*: Sue Minter. *Head gardener*: Fiona Crumley. *Education officer*: Dawn Sanders. 66 Royal Hospital Rd, London SW3 4HS, *Tel*: (020) 7352 5616. *Fax*: (020) 7376 3910. *Hours*: April-October, Wed 12-5 & Sun 2-6; 12-5 during week of the Chelsea Flower Show and the Chelsea Festival.
A walled 'secret' garden, founded in 1673 by the Society of Apothecaries, and one of Europe's oldest botanic gardens, where research is still carried out. In 1983 it was established as an independent charity under its own trustees and opened to the visiting public. The Friends scheme also started then to enable supporters of the Garden to contribute to its maintenance and development. Two newsletters a year are issued.

[85] **FRIENDS OF BROMPTON CEMETERY**. *Contact*: Emma Arbuthnot. 58 Ilfield Rd, London SW10, *Tel*: (020) 7352 3974. Cemetery has an unusually formal layout with classical chapel and cascades designed by Benjamin Baud. Purchased by the government in 1850 and now managed by the Royal Parks Agency.

[86] **FRIENDS OF HOLLAND PARK**. *Chairman*: C.W. Wood, 21 Kenton Court, 356 Kensington High St, London W14 8NN, *Tel/Fax*: (020) 7602 0304. *Membership liaison secretary*: Thomas Lowry, 110 Woodsford Square, London W14 8DT, *Tel*: (020) 7602 0501. *President*: Sir Peter Parker. Established in 1978 the organisation now has over 1,000 members. Over £30,000 has been donated in the last five years for a variety of environmental improvements, including the murals in the arcade. Events include: a monthly bird walk, tree walks, an autumn fungi foray, concerts, carol concerts, an annual art exhibition in the Orangery, a party with raffle, talks, etc. There is a quarterly newsletter and historical articles from it are available as a photocopied volume. There is a booklet on the Kyoto Garden, opened in 1991, posters, prints, and 11 postcards of the murals. The official guide to the park and house and a woodland guide are published by RBKC (Directorate of Leisure and Waste Management). Exhibitions are organised at the Orangery and the Ice House; there is also the outdoor theatre.

[87] **FRIENDS OF HYDE PARK AND KENSINGTON GARDENS**. *Membership secretary*: Dr Hilary Walker, 9 Rutland Mews South, London SW7 2NZ, *Hon. secretary*: Pat Leathem. *Life president*: Philip Joseph. The society was established in 1991 and holds an annual meeting for all members. There are also events and lectures. There is a newsletter twice a year. The society has its headquarters at Hyde Park Corner Lodge, which the society also operates as an information centre on behalf of the Royal Parks Agency, *Tel*: (020) 7235 1850.

[88] **FRIENDS OF KENSAL GREEN CEMETERY**. *Secretary*: Henry Vivian-Neal, 17 Buchanan Gardens, London NW10 5AD, *Tel*: (020) 89960 1030. *President*: Julian Litten. *Membership secretary*: Sam Bull, Flat 1, Cranfield Court, Homer St, London W1H 1HE, *Tel*: (020) 7402 2749. Established in 1832, grounds landscaped by Richard Forrest, chapels and colonnaded catacomb designed by John Griffith, the cemetery is operated by the General Cemetery Company (Harrow Rd, London W10 4RA), and is the longest surviving cemetery remaining in private ownership. It has more free-standing mausolea than any other cemetery in England, the majority having been constructed when the owners were still alive. It is the resting place for many of the Victorian great and good. *Hours*: during summer 9-6, Sundays 10-6; during winter 9-5, Sundays 10-5. The Friends were established in 1990 and they have fully restored the Dissenters' Chapel, now used by the Friends for lectures and other events. There are guided tours every Sunday at 2.00pm, beginning at the Anglican Centre situated at the centre of the cemetery. Publications include postcards, greetings cards, a magazine three times a year, a short guide and a substantial book *Paths of Glory*: a select alphabetical and biographical list (with line drawings).

[89] **SIR HANS SLOANE SCHEME**. *Contact*: The Duchess of Hamilton, 52 Elm Park Gardens, London SW10 9PA. Part of the Duchess' Flora-for-Fauna organisation (local plants for local places campaign); established to raise funds for: re-greening Chelsea, maintaining the Sloane collections at the National History Museum, supporting the Chelsea Physic Garden. Sir Hans Sloane (1660-1753) was a physician, collector and President of the Royal Society. He bought the Manor of Chelsea in 1712 and went to live there in 1741.

* AMENITY AND HISTORICAL SOCIETIES *

[90] **THE BOLTONS ASSOCIATION**. *Contact*: Philip English, 14 Milborne Grove, London SW10 9SN, *Tel*: (020) 7370 2341. Established in 1970, currently with about 350 members, to protect the area based around the Boltons Conservation Area - from Old Brompton Road south to Fulham Road, and from Roland Way west to Redcliffe Gardens.

[91] **THE BROMPTON ASSOCIATION**. *Membership secretary*: at 51 Thurloe Square, London SW7 2SX. Established in 1973 to protect the conservation area around the Oratory and Brompton Square to the north of Brompton Road, around Thurloe Square, Egerton Gardens and Ovington Square to the south.

[92] **CHELSEA SOCIETY**. *Hon. secretary*: Hugh Krall, 51 Milmans St, London SW10 0DA (a qualified architect and a talented artist/etcher; there was an exhibition of his topographical etchings at Chelsea Old Town Hall in April 1994). *Membership secretary*: at 10/12 Elm Park Gardens, London SW10 9PE. *Chairman*: David Lelay (a practising architect). Former hon. editor of the annual report Tom Pocock also writes under the name Guy Topham. Established in 1927 by Reginald Blunt (portrait at Chelsea Library), to protect and foster the amenities of Chelsea. Currently there are some 1,200 members. There are committees for planning, the future of Kings Road, and the Chelsea Museum (artefacts in store at Chelsea Library). There is a season of lectures on Chelsea during the winter months, and an evening garden party in the summer. There are also Chelsea guided walks in the summer. The annual report includes a variety of short articles and an index to these annual reports 1927-1996 has been published.
1993: includes articles on: Sir Charles Dilke; the Chelsea Physic Garden; the art dealers Michael Bryan and Michael Parkin.

Michael Bryan runs his water-colour art dealing business from: 20a Cheyne Walk, *Tel*: (020) 7351 0147, and has issued two specialist catalogues: for shows held at the Alpine Gallery in 1984 and 1989: *In Cheyne Walk and thereabouts*; *Old Chelsea and Thames*.

1994: includes articles on: The boat people (by Louis Kennedy); the Duchess of Hamilton and her Flora-for-Fauna organisation; the history and future of Crosby Hall (by new owner Christopher Moran).

1995: includes articles on: the healing arts at the Chelsea & Westminster Hospital (by Susan Loppert); the Cosy Dining Room; the Kings Road (by Simon Bendall); the Chelsea Book Club (by Jane Dorrell); Chelsea Football Club (by Nesta Macdonald; her publications include a history of the pheasantry, Kings Rd, 1760-1977, self-published).

1996: includes articles on: a portrait of Nicholas Sprimont, Chelsea porcelain manufacturer (by Guy Topham); the forgotten schools of Chelsea (by Simon Bendall).

1997: includes articles on: Roman Chelsea, excavations behind Chelsea Old Church (by Alison Kain); the Veronese 'Resurrection' painting in the chapel of the C. & W. Hospital; Lion's Corner House - Lady Sibyl Colefax literary salon in Kings Rd (by Kirsty McLeod); 1891 naval history exhibition in grounds of the Royal Hospital (by Alan Russett).

Some recent publications on Chelsea include: *Chelsea today*, by Roger George Clark, published by Robert Hale in 1991 (a photographic evocation); *Chelsea seen from its earliest days* (photographs and prints selected by John Bignell) published by Robert Hale in 1987 (second edition); *Hidden Chelsea*, by J.W. Figg, published by Chelsea Rare Books (Leo and Philippa Bernard proprietors; shop now closed) in 1996 (collection of photographs of Chelsea curiosities). The author has built up a large collection of some 2,000 slides and photographs (see article in Chelsea Society 1997 report): *Paradise Walk, Chelsea*, written and published by Lesley Bairstow (5 Chelsea Manor Court, Chelsea Manor St, London SW3 5SA).

[93] KENSINGTON AND CHELSEA COMMUNITY HISTORY GROUP. *Contact*: Liz Bartlett, Methodist Church Centre, 240b Lancaster Rd, London W11 4AH. *Tel*: (020) 7792 2282; *Fax*: (020) 7792 4426. A registered charity which publishes books on the history of the local area and its communities. Ongoing work includes an inter-generational project which enables older people to contribute to the history curriculum in schools. In a Reminiscence at Home scheme trained volunteers visit homebound people and from the recollections produce a quarterly newsletter *Memories shared*.

The following reminiscence groups in which older people meet regularly to collaborate on projects and publications are currently running:

Chelsea Looking Back Group, tutor: Josephine O'Gorman; meet at Kingsmill House, Cale St, London SW3.

Gloucester Court Reminiscence Group, tutor: Eddie Adams; meets at 2 Basset Rd, London W10.

North Kensington Memories Group, tutor: Liz Bartlett; *Spanish Memories Group*, tutor: Cristina Mateo; *Windrush Memories Group*, tutor: Eric Huntley, all meet at 240b Lancaster Road.

Recent publications:

1993: ADAMS, Eddie, and BARTLETT, Liz, *editors*: *History in our bones*: Notting Hill lives remembered. 36pp, illus. Winner of an Arts Council photography prize; based on a collection of personal and family portraits of Gloucester Court Reminiscence Group.

1995: TWEDDLE, Christine, *editor*. *Changed destinies/destinos cambiados*. 64pp, illus. Memories of the Spanish community in London, with drawings by Cai Martinez, and many personal photographs. Text in English/Spanish.

1996: BARTLETT, Liz, and WHETLOR, Shaaron. *Portobello: its people, its past, its present*. 55pp, illus. Arts Council community publishing prize, 1997. The history of Portobello Road, and the story of the Carnival.

1998: WHETLOR, Shaaron. *The story of Notting Dale: from potteries and piggeries to present times*. 88pp, illus.

The KCCHG also distributes two publications from the Notting Dale Urban Studies Centre (now no longer in operation): *The Caribbean at war: British West Indians in World War II*. 30pp, illus.; and *Looking back: Notting Dale 1900 onwards*. 32pp. Members of a Notting Dale family, interviewed in the late 70's, speak about life prior to the Second World War.

[94] KENSINGTON HIGH STREET ASSOCIATION. PO. Box 295, London W8 5SU. *Tel*: (020) 8743 4559.

[95] KENSINGTON SOCIETY. *Hon. secretary*: Ethne Rudd, 15 Kensington Square, London W8 5HH. *Membership secretary*: c/o Campden Hill Court, Observatory Gardens, London W8 7HX, *Tel*: (020) 7937 2750. *President*: Sir John Drummond. Established in 1953 'to preserve and improve the amenities of Kensington for the public benefit by stimulating interest in its history and records, promoting good architecture and planning in its future development and by protecting, preserving and improving its buildings, open spaces and other features of beauty or historic or public interest'. Visits to historic places are organised, and there is a short newsletter. The annual report contains illustrated articles and reports on residents and area associations (some described in this chapter).

[96] KNIGHTSBRIDGE ASSOCIATION. *Contact*: Mrs C. Seymour-Newton, 6 Montpelier St, London SW7 1EZ. *Tel*: (020) 7823 9103.

[97] **LADBROKE ASSOCIATION**. *Contact*: P.E. Bastick, 75 Ladbroke Grove, London W11 2PD. Established in 1969 for the Ladbroke Estate Conservation Area, regarded as the finest example of early Victorian town planning of its kind in Britain.

[98] **NORLAND CONSERVATION SOCIETY**. *Chairman*: Robin Price, Flat 2, 5/7 Princedale Rd, London W11, *Tel*: (020) 7727 6359. *Secretary*: Claire Kemp, 11d Queensdale Rd, London W11. *Membership secretary*: Susan Bird, 20 St Ann's Villas, London W11. Established in 1969, currently with some 260 members. There is an annual lecture.

[99] **NORTH KENSINGTON AMENITY TRUST**. 1 Thorpe Close, London W10. *Tel*: (020) 8969 7511; (020) 8960 3020. North Kensington Arts also at this address, *Tel*: (020) 8964 3329; *Fax*: (020) 8964 4419.

[100] **ONSLOW NEIGHBOURHOOD ASSOCIATION**. *Chairman*: Hugh Brady, 16 Selwood Terrace, London SW7 3QG, *Tel*: (020) 7370 1078; *Membership secretary*: Richard Skinner, 8 Neville St, London SW7, *Tel*: (020) 7584 5489. Established in 1972 to protect the amenities of the area bounded to the north by Old Brompton Road, and to the south by the Fulham Road, 'Brompton Cross' to the east, and Thistle grove to the west. Annual summer garden party, usually in Onslow Square.

[101] **PEMBRIDGE ASSOCIATION**. *Chair*: Ms Vicky Butler, 4 Ledbury Mews North, London W11 2AF, *Tel*: (020) 7727 6099; *Fax*: (020) 7727 6255. The amenity society, currently with some 220 members, for the Pembridge Conservation Area - to north and south of Pembridge Square. Newsletter issued.

* SOME OTHER COUNCIL CONTACTS AND PUBLICATIONS *

The RBKC Council is especially effective at publishing attractive, highly informative literature about its services and the local heritage:
Inside information: a guide to the organisation, May 1998 is a lucid account of the council's five groups, and their departments and divisions, with telephone extensions of senior personnel.

Directories published on an ongoing basis include: *Directory of Voluntary Organisations* (from the Projects and Partnership Unit, *Tel*: (020) 7361 2239); an *Arts Directory* from Kensington & Chelsea Arts Council (Canalside House, 383 Ladbroke Grove, London W10 5AA, *Tel*: (020) 8960 5494); and a *Business and Services Directory* from the Research and Information Unit, Town Hall, Hornton St, London W8 7NX, *Tel*: (020) 7361 2615 (new 1999 edition is being compiled and published by Burrows).

General interest publications include: the *Directory of streets and services* (indexed maps, lists of council services, and adverts): *Residents of renown*: a guide to blue plaques; and *Places of Worship*, June 1998.

Built and natural environment:
A folding leaflet *Walking around the Boval Borough of Kensington & Chelsea* describes 5 walking routes in the borough, with map. Published by the Environmental Research Unit, Council Offices, 37 Pembroke Rd, London W8 6PW. Attractive guided walks of architectural nature are produced by the Planning Department: *Chelsea; Kensington; North Kensington; Notting Hill, Riverside - Thames path* (updated version, 1996, of those produced for European Architectural Heritage Year in 1975).
Information on leisure facilities, parks and open spaces is available in an illustrated booklet *Leisure information and citizen's charter*, issued by the Leisure Services Department, The Stable Yard, Ilchester Place, Holland Park, London W8 6PU, *Tel*: (020) 7471 9813.

The RBKC Council operates an ecology service from the Visitor Centre at Holland Park. *Ecology officer*: Dr Erica Constantine; *Ecology assistant*: Thomas Peel-Yates, *Tel*: (020) 7471 9810. It collects borough-wide scientific data and publishes a number of general interest leaflets: on bats, mammals and birds in Kensington and Chelsea. There are teachers packs on Holland Park, and Kensal Green Cemetery. The Holland Park centre and the Canalside Ecology Centre, next to the Grand Union Canal in North Kensington are both available for pre-booked environmental educational activities. There is an annual programme of environment and wildlife illustrated talks and walks, special open days, and training events.

* LOCAL PRESS *

The Hill (Notting Hill area), monthly magazine. Astley House, 33 Notting Hill Gate, London W11 3JQ, *Tel*: (020) 7792 2626.
Kensington and Chelsea News. From London Newspaper Group, Newspaper House, Winslow Rd, London W6, *Tel*: (020) 8741 1622.
Kensington and Chelsea Times (free). 134-136 The Broadway Way, London W13, *Tel*: (020) 8479 3131.
The Royal Borough, quarterly newsletter produced by the Council, Town Hall, Hornton St, London W8 7NX, *Tel*: (020) 361 2025.

WESTMINSTER

* CITY OF WESTMINSTER COUNCIL *

[102] **CITY OF WESTMINSTER ARCHIVES**, 10 St Ann's St, London SW1P 2XR, *Tel*: (020) 7641 5180; *Fax*: (020) 7641 5179. *Archivist*: Jerome Farrell. *Deputy archivist*: Susanna Rayner. (Team of nine professional archivists and librarians who deal with enquiries). *Hours*: Mon, Tues, Thurs, Fri, 9.30-7.00; Wed, 9.30-9.00; Sat, 9.30-5.00). A large open access collection of books, booklets and cuttings is maintained; there is a publications sales unit in the entrance foyer. A flourishing programme of courses, day schools, talks, walks and exhibitions is run. Historical walks in Hyde Park, Regent's Park and St James', for example are planned for the summer of 1999. There is also a Friends organisation. This links members closely with the work of the department, they receive the annual journal, the quarterly newsletter (contact: Local Studies Librarian: Ilinos Thomas), are invited to at least one social function a year, and get 20% discount on course, lectures and publications.

Two information sheets have been issued: 1: parish registers; 2: nonconformist and Roman Catholic registers. There are two guides to sources for researchers: *Tracing the history of your home*, by Alison Kenney, 1996, 34pp; and *Guide to sources for family history*, by Elizabeth Cory (responsible for the Grosvenor Estate collection and for readers services), 1997, 20pp.

Contents of Westminster History Review No. 1 1997:
A writer of comedy with a pencil: William Hogarth in Westminster (Anthony Clayton); Royal shrine and seat of justice: Westminster and the V.C.H. (Tim Baker); The most visible poor in England? - constructing pauper biographies in early modern Westminster (Jeremy Boulton); John Johnson and the Wyatts in Portman Square (Nancy Briggs); Box, privet and point plants: the urban gardens of Georgian Westminster (Ivan Hall); Lord Harley and his friends (Ann Saunders).

Other recent publications from the department:
1997: *Six views of Victorian Westminster* (reproductions, in folder, of engravings of central London views).
1997: STOUT, Adam. *Pimlico: deep well of glee*. 81pp, illus. maps. An historical account of Pimlico by author with life-time association with area.
1998: two folding leaflets: *Discovering Westminster: a lunchtime walk through Queen Anne's Gate*; and a similar one for the heart of Westminster.
Still in print are: *Artizans and avenues: a history of the Queen's Park Estate*, by Erica McDonald and David J. Smith, 2nd edition, 1990; *Blitz over Westminster*, by Roy Harrison, 1990 (City of Westminster Civil Defence bomb incident photographs 1940-44); *Pineapples and pantomimes: a history of Church Street and Lisson Green*, by E. McDonald and D.J. Smith, 1992.
Also sold, from Historical Publications: *Covent Garden past*, by John Richardson, 1995; *Soho past*, by Richard Tames, 1994; *Westminster and Pimlico past*, by Isobel Watson, 1993; and *The Westminster Corridor*, by David Sullivan, 1994 (the Anglo-Saxon history of Westminster Abbey and its nearby lands and people).
From Sutton Publishing (Britain in old photographs series): *Marylebone and Paddington*, by Richard Bowden; and *Westminster*, by Jill Barber.
From Tempus (Archive Photographs series): *Marylebone,* by Brian Girling; *Piccadilly Circus*, by David Oxford; *Westminster's villages*, by Brian Girling.
Brian Girling (17 Devonshire Rd, Harrow, Middx HA1 4LS) has also compiled collections on Kensington and the City of London for the same publisher, and has in preparation for 1999 one on Holborn, Bloomsbury and Clerkenwell, and one on Paddington.

Books on sale from more specialist sources include: *Down Memory Lane*, a collection of articles from the Reminiscence Group at the Village Hall, Allitsen Rd, St John's Wood, London NW8, compiled and edited by Daphne R. Broatch; Geology guides to Westminster and Trafalgar Square from Earthscan/British Geological Survey (Keyworth, Nottingham NG12 5GG).
The growth of St Marylebone and Paddington, by Jack Whitehead (55 Parliament Hill, London NW3), 2nd edition, 1990; *Lord North Street 1725-1996: a Westminster portrait* by Bunny Smedley (published by Hyde Park Antiquarian, 17 Hyde Park Square, London W2 2JR); *Norfolk Rd, St John's Wood, celebrating the first 150 years*, also by Bunny Smedley; *Regent's Park*, by Ann Saunders, 2nd edition, 1981 (study of the development of the area from 1086 to the present day), and *The Regent's Park villas*, also by Ann Saunders, 1981, both published by Regents College.

Education service:
The archives centre has an education officer: Jill Barber, direct line: (020) 7641 3482. The service aims to help teachers develop the skills and knowledge they need for National Curriculum requirements; courses and workshops are run on a range of topics. A range of postcards is planned, as well as a new series of resource material.

* AMENITY, COMMUNITY, HISTORICAL ORGANISATIONS * (arranged by area)

Bayswater:
[103] **BAYSWATER RESIDENTS ASSOCIATION**. *Contact*: Mr C. Fawcett, c/o Fauchier Partners, 97-99, Parker Street, London WIY 3HA.

[104] **SOUTH EAST BAYSWATER RESIDENTS ASSOCIATION**. *Chair*: Mr J.W.S. Walton, 70 Gloucester Terrace, London W3 3HH. Newsletter issued.

Bond Street:
[105] **BOND STREET ASSOCIATION** (for shops, galleries, companies in and around Bond Street). *Contact*: Penny Kennedy Scott, c/o 1 New Bond Street, London W1P 9PE, *Tel*: (020) 7821 5955; *Fax*: (020) 7821 7320. The association was responsible for a sculpture 'The Allies' (of President Roosevelt and Sir Winston Churchill) by Lawrence Holofcener unveiled in 1995.

Covent Garden:
[106] **COVENT GARDEN MARKET MANAGEMENT OFFICE**. 41 The Market, Covent Garden, London WC2E 8RF, *Tel*: (020)7836 9136; *Fax*: (020) 7240 5770. A glossy brochure *Covent Garden Market: a decade of entertaining shopping* contrasts pictures of the past and present. Information sheet issued on present-day street entertainment.

[107] **IN AND AROUND COVENT GARDEN**. *Publisher and Managing Director*: Kim Church, 19 Shorts Gardens, Covent Garden, London WC2H 9AT, *Tel*: (020) 7240 9731; *Fax*: (020) 7836 3137, *Email*: info@coventgarden.uk.com. *Internet*: www.coventgarden.uk.com. Set up to support and promote Covent Garden which it does principally through a free magazine *In and Around Covent Garden* first published in 1992. Distributed from around 300 points in the area it contains short articles and directory listings for businesses and event. The monthly Inside information Newsletter is intended for business members; businesses are also helped through the Covent Garden Business Forum established in 1997. A 'Living' newsletter is a notice board for community and social issues.
The British Oxygen Company sponsored [108] **COVENT GARDEN FESTIVAL** is now in its 7th year, and features many performances of opera and music theatre, often in unconventional venues. *Director*: Kenneth Richardson, 47 The Market, The Piazza, London WC2, *Tel*: (020) 7379 0870.

Fitzrovia:
[109] **FITZROVIA NEIGHBOURHOOD ASSOCIATION**. 39 Tottenham Street, London W1P 9PE, *Tel*: (020) 7580 4576; *Fax*: (020) 7580 2057. Formed in 1974 as a voice for the Fitzrovia community, a unique village around Charlotte Street straddling the boundary between the City of Westminster and the London Borough of Camden. The neighbourhood centre at the above address provides free advice and help in English and Bengali, a focus for a wide variety of community activities, a community information resource, and office of the quarterly *Fitzrovia News*. Mike Pentelow (Flat 5, 21 Nassau Street, London W1N 7RE, *Tel*: (020) 7636 5569) is a regular contributor to the paper on historical topics - statues, pubs, personalities etc. and has recently completed a book *Characters of Fitzrovia: a mixed bunch*. There is also an annual report. The 1998 report has informative articles on many areas including the newly formed Friends of the Parks of Fitzrovia, the Fitzrovia Trust, and the Fitzrovia Festival (commemorative booklet produced for the 25th festival). Supporters of the centre and association can join the Friends of Fitzrovia organisation.

[110] **FITZROVIA TRUST**, Melbourne House, 1 South Parade, London W4 1JU, *Tel*: (020) 8995 9146.

Hyde Park:
[111] **HYDE PARK ESTATE ASSOCIATION**. *Chair*: Mrs P. Budge, 8 Gloucester Square, London W2 2RA. Newsletter issued.

Knightsbridge:
[112] **KNIGHTSBRIDGE ASSOCIATION**. *Contact*: Mrs C. Seymour-Newton, 6 Montpelier Street, London SW7 1EZ, *Tel*: (020) 7823 9103.

Marylebone:
[113] **MARYLEBONE ASSOCIATION**. *Chairman*: John Millard, *Tel*: (020) 7486 4525. *Secretary*: Audrey Lewis, 7 York House, Upper Montague Street, London W1H 1FR, *Tel*: (020) 7402 4863. Est. in 1984, currently with some 630 members, to deal with all amenity and planning matters in the area south of Marylebone Road. There is a bi-monthly newsletter.

[114] **ST MARYLEBONE SOCIETY**. *Secretary*: Mrs Gwyneth Hampson, 3 Wyndham Yard, London W1H 1AR, *Tel*: (020) 7723 4160. *Chairman*: Mr A.C. Keen, 20 Upper Montagu Street, London W1H 1RN, *Tel*: (020) 723 7783. *President*: Cllr. Jenny Bianco. *Patron*: Lord Montagu of Beaulieu. Est. in 1948 to 'stimulate public interest in, and care for and preserve the history, buildings and environment of the old borough of Marylebone; to study, and record its history, topography and social development.' There are talks, visits and social events. There is an annual competition for all gardeners in St Marylebone. A newsletter is issued three times a year. Ten historical publications were issued 1959-1969.

Mayfair:
[115] **RESIDENTS ASSOCIATION OF MAYFAIR**, c/o 25 South Audley Street, London W1Y 5DJ.

Oxford Street:
[116] **OXFORD STREET ASSOCIATION**. *Director*: Sally Humpheries. Selfridges, Oxford Street, W1A 1AB, *Tel*: (020) 7629 2738; M*obile*: (0831) 282809; *Fax*: (020) 7409 3168; *Email*: sallyoxfordstreet.w.uk. There is a monthly newsletter/magazine *Street Scene*.

Paddington:
[117] **NORTH PADDINGTON SOCIETY**, *Contact*: Ms Jen McClelland, 29 Croxley Road, London W9 3HH. Est. in 1997 to improve local conditions and amenities.

[118] **PADDINGTON BASIN DEVELOPMENTS LTD**. 35-37 North Wharf Road, London W2, *Tel*: (020) 7402 5299; *Fax*: (020) 7723 0925. The regeneration of the basin, now underway will include new towpaths, bridges across the canal and open space; a four acre site off North Wharf Road is to be developed as a mixture of offices, housing, shops and restaurants.

[119] **PADDINGTON HOTELIERS ASSOCIATION**. Royal Norfolk Hotel, 25 London Street, London W2 1HH.

[120] **PADDINGTON REGENERATION PARTNERSHIP**. *Director*: Jackie Sadek, Room 108, Macmillan House, Paddington Station, London W2 1TF, *Tel*: (020) 7313 1011. A large folding brochure *A new era and a new definition* is issued, and there is an informative booklet *Paddington life: places to visit and enjoy*.

[121] **PADDINGTON RESIDENTS ACTIVE CONCERN ON TRANSPORT (PRACT)**. 70 Gloucester Terrace, London W2 3HH.

[122] **PADDINGTON SOCIETY**. *Chair*: Dr T. Hettena (Vice President of the Society of Women Writers and journalists). *Hon. Secretary*: G. Storren. All correspondence to: 30 Westbourne Park Villas, London W2 5EA, *Tel*: (020) 7229 3281. Est. in 1957, it covers the former borough of Paddington, and was one of the original 6 major societies consulted by the City Council. It has long been consulted by many local, regional, national and overseas bodies and researchers and has representatives on many London organisations. It is concerned with all aspects of the locality, past, present and future. Copies of reports published can be obtained for a fee send s.a.e).

[123] **PADDINGTON WATERWAYS AND MAIDA VALE SOCIETY**. *Chair*: Ms Y. MacAlpine, 29a Warwick Avenue, London W9 2PS. Concerned with the preservation of the amenities and heritage of the area bounded by Edgware Road/Maida vale, Kilburn Park Road, Shireland Road, Harrow Road, and the Paddington Basin. The area has numerous listed buildings, two Pearson churches, one by George Street, as well as three Grade I listed pubs. A newsletter is issued three times a year.
The Local History Group functions under the society, contact: Hans Norton, 19a Randolph Road, London W9 1AN, *Tel*: (020) 7289 0950; *Email*: Hans@hansnorton.demon.co.uk. It has a small membership and publishes occasional papers and articles.

[124] **QUEEN'S PARK SOCIETY**. *Contact*: Mrs Mary Micholas, 41 Galton Street, London W10 4QW, *Tel*: (020) 8960 2586.

[125] **WESTBOURNE NEIGHBOURHOOD ASSOCIATION**. *Contact*: Mrs Pat Burn, 17 Bridstow Place, London W2 5AE.

[126] **ALEXANDER FLEMING LABORATORY MUSEUM**. St Mary's Hospital, Praed Street, Paddington, London W2 1NY, *Tel*: (020) 7725 6528. *Hours*: Mon-Thurs. 10-1, other times by appointment only. A reconstruction of the laboratory where Fleming discovered penicillin.

Regent Street:
[127] **REGENT STREET ASSOCIATION**. *Contacts*: Annie Walker, Sarah Millar, Regent House, 235-241 Regent Street, London W1R 7AG, *Tel*: (020) 7491 4429.

Regents Park:
[128] **BEDFORD COLLEGE**, Regents Park. The college, originally the Ladies' College at 47 Bedford Square, was founded in 1848 and moved to new premises, designed by Basil Champneys in Regents Park in 1913. It merged with Royal Holloway College in 1985. To celebrate its 150 years two books have been published: *Bedford College: memories of 150 years*, edited by J. Mordaunt Cook (departmental histories); and *Educating women*: a pictorial history of Bedford College, University of London 1849-1985, by Linna Bentley; also reproductions of two prints by A.E. Wardle; available from the College Shop, Royal Holloway, University of London, Egham, Surrey, TW20 0EX.

[129] **FRIENDS OF REGENTS PARK AND PRIMROSE HILL**. *Secretary*: Valerie St Johnston, 30 Fitzroy Road, London NW1 8TY, *Tel*: (020) 7722 5932; *Fax*: (020) 7209 4836. *Treasurer*: Malcolm Kafetz, *Tel*: (020) 7935 1143. Est. in 1991, currently with some 800 members, to 'help preserve the tranquillity of the open spaces and prevent any further building upon them. Members receive a quarterly newsletter and attend activities including lectures, concerts, visits to the open air theatre, and buildings and gardens within and adjacent to the park; they contribute funds towards tree planting and occasional works, for instance the restoration of the 'ready money' fountain, which has received a heritage lottery grant.

St John's Wood:
[130] **ST JOHN'S WOOD SOCIETY**. *Treasurer*: Miss Eileen Penman, 15 Hamilton Close, London NW8 8QY. *Archivist*: Malcolm Brown, 8 Garden Court, Garden Road, London NW8 9PP. (author of article 'St John's Wood: the Eyre Estate before 1830', in London Topographical Record, 1995). The society is primarily concerned with conserving the historic character of the area, much of which is laid out in paired villas. *St John's Wood: an abode of love and the arts*, by Stella Margetson was published by the society in 1998. A newsletter is issued twice yearly. There are some 1500 members.
A new book by Richard Tames *St John's Wood and Maida Vale past* has been published recently by Historical Publications.

[131] **LORDS CRICKET GROUND**. St. John's Wood, London NW8 8QN, *Tel*: (020) 7432 1611. Established by Thomas Lord in 1787. Home of the Marylebone Cricket Club. Tours daily, 12.00 and 2.00, *Tel*: (020) 7266 3825. Includes the famous Long Room and museum.

Soho:
[132] **SOHO RESTAURATEURS ASSOCIATION**. c/o The Manager, Kettners, 29 Romilly Street W1V 6HP, *Tel*: (020) 7734 6112.

[133] **SOHO SOCIETY**. Office at: St Anne's Tower, 55 Dean Street, London W1V 5HH, *Tel*: (020) 7439 4303 (office open Mon-Fri. 2-4). *President*: Bryan Burrough (work tel: (020) 7210 4296. *Chair*: Nina Tempia. Est. in 1972, currently with over 1000 members. A museum and archive is in store at the above address and volunteers are needed to clean, conserve and catalogue it, contact: Wendy Monkhouse, or Bryan Burrough. The community based Soho Festival happens in early July. A quarterly magazine/newsletter the *Soho Clarion* is issued.

Strand and area:
[134] **STRAND, ALDWYCH AND TRAFALGAR SQUARE ASSOCIATION**. *Executive*: Richard Devonald-Lewis, 7 Burleigh Street, London WC2, *Tel*: (020) 7379 1788. Est. in the 1950's, and resuscitated in about 1987 by the Savoy Hotel. Membership of some 150 diverse businesses and institutions. Quarterly newsletter.

Old Westminster:
[135] **THORNEY ISLAND SOCIETY**, and **FRIENDS OF ST JAMES'S PARK AND THE GREEN PARK**. *Founder and chairman*: June A. Stubbs, 39 Westminster Mansions, Great Smith Street, London SW1P 3BP, *Tel*: (020) 7222 2449. *President*: Lord Rees-Mogg. *Vice Chairman*: Owen Luder. The society takes its name from the island upon which Westminster Abbey was first built and was formed in 1985 to save the Great Smith Street library, which it did. It is a conservation and amenity group, concerned with the interests of both residents and businesses. It is particularly active in local history and research and an archive has been established at Old Pye Street. Oral history is collected. Dinners are held once a month with guest speakers; there are visits and an annual Christmas bazaar.

[136] **WESTMINSTER SOCIETY**. *Secretary*: Mr P.R. Handley, Third Floor, Emanuel House, 10 Rochester Row, London SW1P 1BS, *Tel*: (020) 8693 2290. *Membership Secretary*: Mrs. I. Tanbunyuen, 108/24 John Islip Street, London SW1P 4LQ,

Tel:(020) 7828 5061. *President*: The Dean of Westminster, *Patron*: HRH Duke of Gloucester. Est. in 1959 'to preserve the amenities of Westminster'. There are meetings, visits and lectures

Reminiscence:
[137] **WESTMINSTER PENSIONERS ASSOCIATION**. 284 Harrow Road, London W2 5ES, *Tel*: (020) 7289 1849; *Fax*: (020) 7266 4207. Also at: 99, Tachbrook Street, SW1, *Tel*: (020) 7630 5530.

Parliament:
[138a] **HOUSE OF COMMONS**, London SW1A OAA; **HOUSE OF LORDS**, London SW1A OPW. *Telephone contacts*: Main switchboard: (020) 7219 3000; information on business, procedure, history: Commons: (020) 7219 4272; Lords: (020) 7219 3107.
Parliamentary Education Unit: (020) 7219 2105
Parliamentary Bookshop, 12 Bridge street, London SW1, *Tel*: (020) 7219 3890.
Record Office (archives), *Tel*: (020) 7219 3074.
Parliamentary web site: www.parliament.uk.
HISTORY OF PARLIAMENT TRUST. 15 Woburn Square, London WC1, *Tel*: (020) 7862 8800. See chapter 'Academic Research organisations' for details of its ongoing research publications.
Less monumental studies on parliament, published recently include: a two volume history *House of Commons*; *House of Lords*, published in 1994 by Smith Peerage (Heron Place, 3 George Street, London W1H 6AD): a study on the *House of Lords* by Clive Aslett and Derry Moore, published by Harper-Collins in 1998; and *Art in Parliament: the permanent collection of the House of Commons* by Malcolm Hay and Jacqueline Riding published by Jarrold in 1996.

[138b] **WESTMINSTER ABBEY**. *Tel*: (020) 7222 5152; guided tour reservations, *Tel*: (020) 7222 7110; *Fax*: (020) 7233 2072; *Email*: press@westminster-abbey.org; *Internet*: http://www.westminster-abbey.org. *Hours*: Mon-Fri. 9-4.45; Sat. 9-2.45. College Garden open to the public on Tuesdays and Thursdays. The Chapter House, Pyx Chamber (in use as the treasury), and the Abbey Museum are operated jointly. The museum is housed in the vaulted undercroft beneath the former monks' dormitory and is noteworthy for its collection of royal and other effigies. Chapter Library in the East Cloister is open Wednesday, May-September 11-3.00. The *Abbey Bookshop*, *Tel*: (020) 7222 5565 stocks a wide range of books and souvenirs.

---

* SOME OTHER COUNCIL CONTACTS *

Business information*:*
The *City of Westminster Business Directory and Guide* is a joint initiative between the council and Business Link London Central. Available from: Economic Enabling Unit, 18th Floor, Westminster City Council, 64 Victoria Street, London SW1E 6QP.
Conservation and listed buildings: Assistant Head of Development Planning Services (including both contemporary and old buildings): Rosemary McQueen, *Tel*: (020) 7641 2455. Westminster has some 11,000 listed buildings and 51 conservation areas. A section of some 12 staff operate within three area teams: Central, contact: Rob Ayton, *Tel*: (020) 7641 2978; South, contact: Mike Gray, *Tel*: (020) 7641 2931; North: contact: Mike Lowndes, *Tel*: (020) 7641 3014. There are three series of publications for all the conservation areas: mini-guides, directories of listed buildings, and 'audits' (on policy, etc). Many guidelines on architectural features are also issued. Contact for publications: Semtov Samuel, *Tel*: (020) 7641 2652.
A contact for the *Westminster Amenity Societies Forum* is Richard Clifton, Senior Administration Officer, Development Planning Services, *Tel*: (020) 7641 2520.
Three leaflets on cemeteries have been issued recently by the Department of Planning and Environment: East Finchley Cemetery (formerly managed by St Marylebone B.C.); Hanwell Cemetery (formerly managed by M.B. of the City of Westminster), and Mill Hill Cemetery (formerly managed by M.B. of Paddington).
An interesting booklet *Historic Parks and Gardens in Westminster* was published in 1997 with information on relevant legislation and the Councils' policies within the Unitary Development Plan.
Nature conservation/ecology: a contact is Jonathan Hughes, Environmental Initiatives Officer, Westminster City Hall, *Tel*: (020) 7641 5977. A strategy report *Nature conservation in Westminster* was published in 1995; and there are also leaflets issued on *Birds, bees, butterflies* (their favoured habitats); *Amazing weeds*; and on the St John's Wood church ground nature reserve.
Reference libraries*:* Central Reference Library, 35 St Martin's Street, London WC2, *Tel*: (020) 7641 4636; Marylebone Reference library, Marylebone Road, London NW1, *Tel*: (020) 7641 1039.

* SOME NON-COUNCIL CONTACTS *

Voluntary organisations:
VOLUNTARY ACTION WESTMINSTER, 37 Chapel Street, London NW1, *Tel*: (020) 7723 1216; F*ax*: (020) 7723 8929.

* LOCAL PRESS *

Westminster and City Mail. Published by Ealing and West London Newspapers Group, 134 Broadway, London W13 0TL, *Tel*: (020) 7381 6262.

Westminster and Pimlico News. Published by the London Newspaper Group, Newspaper House, Winslow Road, London W6. *Tel*: (020) 8741 1622.

Westminster Reporter. colour magazine published monthly by council; editor: Jane Murray, 17th Floor, City Hall, 64 Victoria Street, London SW1E 6QP, *Tel*: (020) 7641 3041; *Fax*: (020)7641 2948; *Email*: press@westminster.gov.uk; *Internet*: www.westminster.gov.uk.

Westminster Times. Also published by the Ealing and West London Newspapers Group.

OLD SCHOOLHOUSE · Rokesly Avenue

HAMPSTEAD GARDEN SUBURB
RESIDENTS ASSOCIATION

NORTH LONDON BOROUGHS:

Barnet, Brent, Enfield, Haringey

Bruce Castle

BARNET

* LONDON BOROUGH OF BARNET *

[139] **BARNET LOCAL STUDIES AND ARCHIVES**: at Hendon Catholic Social Centre, Chapel Walk, Egerton Gardens, London NW4, *Tel:*(020) 8359 2876. Staff (Pamela Taylor, Joanna Corden, archivists, and assistant Alison Condé) are resigning - March 1999; Information advisor David Bicknell will be the contact until replacements. *Hours:* Tues, Wed, Sat, 9.30-5.00; Thurs, 12.30-7.30. Postal address for library is: c/o Hendon Library, The Burroughs, London NW4 4BQ. Postal sales of publications: Barnet Libraries, Educational Sales, Friern Barnet Lane, London N11 3DL. *Tel:* (020) 8359 3169, *Fax:* (020) 8359 3171. Books from commercial publishers and local societies are sold in addition to its own publications.
The library has not published in recent years, but the following titles are available:
Bygone Hendon, 1989 (in association with Hendon Publishing); *Avenue House, Finchley, before the fire*, 1989: *Finchley Common: a Notorious Place*, by Fred Davis, 1981; *Milk for the millions: the Express Dairy in the Borough of Barnet*, by Brigid Grafton Green, 1983; *St Mary-at-Finchley: a short history and guide*, by Fred Davis, 1983; and *St Mary's School*, also by Fred Davis, 1989.

Fred Davis (15a Church Crescent, London N3, *Tel:* (020) 8346 1935) is a Finchley local historian, with some 50 years experience of the area (a former teacher, and head teacher for some 12 years). He contributed articles on Finchley in the 1970's to the Finchley Press and holds much unpublished information on the area: his *Finchley Index* is an A-Z of families, roads and buildings; also information (which can be made available in bound format) on Finchley estates and pubs. His survey *Finchley Charities 1488-1988* was published in 1988 by the organisation to celebrate 500 years. His booklet on *Finchley Manor* was published by Barnet Libraries in 1982.

Dr Pamela Taylor (former archivist, President of the Barnet & District Local History Society) is the author of three histories, all published by Phillimore: *Barnet, Edgware, Hadley and Totteridge: a pictorial history* (with Joanna Corden), 1994; *Hendon, Childs Hill, Golders Green and Mill Hill: a pictorial history* (with Stewart Gillies), 1993; and *Finchley and Friern Barnet a pictorial history* (with Stewart Gillies), 1992. Stewart Gillies is a former Barnet Local studies librarian.

John Heathfield (a retired senior inspector of schools), *Tel:* (020) 8368 5345 is another important local historian. Sutton have published his *Around Whetstone and North Finchley in old photographs*, 1994; and with Percy Reboul, *Barnet at war*, 1995; and *Barnet past and present*. A book on Barnet in the twentieth century is to be published by Sutton as part of their new Millennium series. He also self-publishes booklet histories of schools: *All Saints School, Whetstone; Cromer Road School, New Barnet; Trent School, Cockfosters;* and *Woodhouse School, Finchley* were all published in the 1990's.
Also: *Parish and people: history of St John's Church, Whetstone.*

Percy Reboul was a former publicity manager for BP. He is an amateur photographer (the contemporary photographs of Barnet in *Barnet past and present* are his); he is also chairman of the Plastic Historical Society.

* MUSEUMS *

[140] **BARNET MUSEUM**. 31 Wood Street, Barnet, EN5 4BE, *Tel:* (020) 8440 8066. *Secretary:* Gillian Gear. *Hours:* Tues, Wed, 2-4.30; Sat, 10.30-12.30, 2.00-4.00. Run by the Barnet and District L.H.S., the museum illustrates the archaeology and history of Barnet and surrounding area. There are displays on social history and the decorative arts. A bookstall sells a range of titles.

[141] **CHURCH FARMHOUSE MUSEUM**. *Curator:* Gerard Roots, Greyhound Hill, Hendon, London NW4 4JR, *Tel:* (020) 8203 0130; *Fax:* (020) 8359 2666. *Hours:* Mon-Thurs, 10-12.30, 1.30-5.00; Fri. closed; Sat. 10-1; 2-5.30; Sun. 2-5.30. Housed in the oldest surviving dwelling house in Hendon, built in c. 1660, it remained the centre of a hay and dairy farm until the 1930's. Opened as a museum in 1955. The house has three 19th century period furnished rooms: kitchen, (c.1820), laundry room (c. 1890), and dining room (c.1850), the last decorated for a Victorian Christmas every year. There is a small local history room with changing displays of materials from Barnet archives. There is a continuous programme of unique temporary exhibitions and recent subjects have included: Victorian and Edwardian wedding photographs, the Pullman railway carriage, industry in Barnet, board games, the writer Dannie Abse. Forthcoming exhibitions will look at Barnet's supernatural and occult connections, and the early days of punk rock in North Finchley. The museum provides a free outreach service for local schools, based on its extensive 19th and 20th century domestic life collections.

* HISTORICAL AND AMENITY SOCIETIES *

[142] **BARNET AND DISTRICT LOCAL HISTORY SOCIETY.** *Secretary:* Gillian Gear, Nichols Farms, Lybury Lane, Redborn, St Albans, Herts, *Tel:* (015820) 792603. *Membership Secretary/Librarian:* Doreen Willcocks, 27 Manor Road, Barnet, *Tel:* (020) 8449 6153. Historical account of the society *60 years of local history* published in 1987. Recent publications are: *Barnet's history in its street names* by Doreen Willcocks, 1995; *Geoffrey de Mandeville and London's Camelot*, by Jennie Lee Cobban, 1997; and to be published in 1999 *800 years of Barnet Market*, by Doreen Willcocks and Jennie Lee Cobban. The society issues a bulletin on specific topics. Recent issues:
20: The Red Lion; *21:* How Barnet got its railways; *22:* Ravenscroft Family (Barnet branch); *23:* Education in East Barnet in the 19th century; *24:* Church Farm Industrial School, East Barnet; *25:* The story of Geoffrey de Mandeville; *26:* The Salisbury; *27:* Chipping Barnet's Old Town Centre. *28:* The Old Red Lion, Underhill; *29:* Ravenscroft past and present; *30:* Food supplies in World War I: East Barnet example; *31:* A Barnet choirboy; *32:* The Victorians answer to 'nuisance disposal' in East Barnet; *33:* Beating the bounds - Chipping Barnet and adjacent parishes; *34:* Local wartime memories.

Gillian Gear is the author of *Barnet and the Hadleys in old photographs,* from Sutton. She has published a book *East Barnet village* and her work also appears in the society's bulletins: *Church Farm Industrial Schools, East Barnet,* 1986; *Education in East Barnet in the 19th century,* 1984; and *Food supplies in World War I: the East Barnet example,* 1992.

William Gelder is an elderly local historian, and his self-published books on Hadley, and Barnet and Monken Hadley (copyright owned by the society). The bulletin published his work *Ravenscroft, past and present* in 1991.

Brian Wise (lives on the Isle of Wight) has written on Barnet for the bulletin: *The Salisbury Hotel,* 1988: *The Old Red Lion, Underhill Barnet* 1990; and with Jennie Lee Cobban *Chipping Barnet's old town centre,* 1989.

Richard Selby, 16 Somerset Road, New Barnet, *Tel:* (020) 8440 7497 self-published his 180pp book *Barnet pubs,* in 1995. Based on holdings in the Barnet Museum it traces the growth of inns and pubs in Barnet town since the 1300's.

[143] **FINCHLEY COMMUNITY NETWORK.** Church End Baptist Church, East End Road N3, *Tel:* (020) 8343 3576.

[144] **FINCHLEY SOCIETY.** *Secretary:* Mr R. C. Winton, MBE (a retired chemical engineer), 224 Creighton Avenue, London N2 9BD, *Tel/Fax:* (020) 8883 2633. Established in 1971, currently with some 600 members. Aims 'to protect, preserve and improve buildings, transport, roads and open spaces in Finchley and Friern Barnet.'

[145] **HAMPSTEAD GARDEN SUBURB RESIDENTS ASSOCIATION.** *Chairman:* Richard Wakefield, 26 Hampstead Way, London NW11 7JL. *Tel:* (020) 8455 9132; *Vice-chairman:* David Rapson, 165 Hampstead Way, London NW11 7YA *Tel:* (020) 8458 5094; *Secretary:* Graham Cunnold, 55 Meadway, London NW11 6SH, *Tel:* (020) 8458 9741. *Internet:* www.hgs.org.uk. Hampstead Garden Suburb was founded in 1907 by Dame Henrietta Barnett (of Toynbee Hall), and is now a conservation area, with three Lutyens buildings in the Central Square, and over 500 listed properties. The residents association was founded in 1910 and is extremely active today with committees for conservations and amenities, events, allotments, membership, publications, roads and traffic, trees and open spaces. *Suburb News,* edited by Richard Wakefield is issued quarterly and there is also a very useful *Suburb Directory* and annual report.
There is a gallery in Hampstead Way which sells pictures, ceramics, cards, maps, books. Books available there on the area include: *The artisan's quarter,* a walk around the old suburb, by Stephen Brookhouse; *Directory of suburb roads* (giving dates when houses were built, and names of original architects; *Hampstead garden suburb* by Mervyn Miller and A. Stuart Gray (published by Phillimore, 1992); *Hampstead Garden Suburb: archive photographs* by Mervyn Miller (Tempus); *Hampstead Garden Suburb: the care and appreciation of its architectural heritage,* by HGS Design Study Group; *Hampstead Garden Suburb, 1907-77, a history,* by Bridget Grafton Greene; *Hampstead Heath: how the Heath was saved for the public,* by C.W. Ikin; *Henrietta's Dream: a chronicle of the Hampstead Garden Suburb,* by Kathleen M. Slack.

[146] **HENDON AND DISTRICT ARCHAEOLOGICAL SOCIETY.** *Secretary:* Denis J. Ross, 13 Reynolds Close, London NW11 7EA, *Tel:* (020) 8458 1352. *Membership secretary:* Ms Vicky O'Connor, 2a Dene Road, London NW1 1ES, *Tel:* (020) 8361 1350. Monthly *newsletter editor:* Dorothy Newbury, 55 Sunningfields Road, London NW4 4FA, *Tel:* (020) 8203 0950. *Chairman:* Andrew Selkirk (publisher of *Current Archaeology*). Established in 1961, currently with some 300 members. Currently available publications include: *The blue plaques of Barnet* (new edition in preparation), *The chroniclers of the Battle of Barnet,* 1971; *A place in time: the London Borough of Barnet up to c.1500,* edited by Pamela Taylor, 1989; *Those were the days (memories of the 1920's and 1930's),* 1980; *Victorian jubilees in the Borough of Barnet,* 1977.

An archaeological report published in 1991 was on the excavations of the Mesolithic site on West Heath, Hampstead 1976-1981. More recent archaeology has been at a Roman pottery site at Brockley Hill Edgware.

[147] **MILL HILL HISTORICAL SOCIETY**. *Secretary*: Richard S. Nichols, 29 Maxwelton Avenue, Mill Hill, London NW7 3NB, *Tel*: (020) 8959 3485. Established in 1929, the society has done much work recording and researching the past of Hendon and Mill Hill, and a large collection of material is maintained at the Archives and Local Studies Centre. A celebratory volume *60 years of local history* was published in 1988. In 1990 the society published the revised edition of John Collier's *The story of Mill Hill* and in 1993 *Mill Hill: a thousand years of history*, by Ralph Calder was published by Angus Hudson Ltd in association with the society.

Other publications on Mill Hill include *Mill Hill: a history of Mill Hill in its environment* by Bernard Oak, 1994, published by the Pentland Press in 1994. Richard Nichols is the author and publisher of *The diaries of Robert Hook* (the 'father' of English meteorology and microscopy); and *The Royal Commercial Travellers School, Hatch End, 1945-1965* (the author was a former pupil there).

[148] **MILL HILL PRESERVATION SOCIETY**. *Secretary*: Miss Marion Dewing, 7 High Street, Mill Hill, London NW7 1QY. *Tel/Fax*: (020) 8959 5013. *Chairman*: John Turtle, 46 Burtonhole Lane, Mill Hill, London NW7 1QY *Tel*: (020) 8959 8783; *Fax*: (020) 8906 8329. *Email*: i mhps@hotmail.com; *internet*: www.users.dircon.co.uk/jet/mhps.htm. Established in 1949, the society has over 1,100 members; it aims to promote and protect natural, historical and architectural features of beauty and interest. There are two annual footpath walks; an annual report and newsletters are issued. There is also a footpath map, with notes.

An important centre for the Jewish community (with part of the Jewish Museum attached, is the [149] **STERNBERG CENTRE FOR JUDAISM** (and the Manor House Society), 81 East End Road, London N3 2SY, *Tel*: (020) 8346 2288.

* SOME OTHER COUNCIL CONTACTS *

Conservation officer/listed buildings: contact Architecture group, Barnet House, 1255 High Road, London N20, *Tel*: (020) 8359 2000.
Parks, *Tel*: (020) 8359 4600.
Information office (council information), Town Hall, The Burroughs, Hendon, London NW4 4BQ, *Tel*: (020) 8359 2277.
Reference libraries: Hendon Reference Library, as above, *Tel*: (020) 8359 2883; Church End Reference Library, Finchley, N3, *Tel*: (020) 8346 5711: Chipping Barnet Reference Library, *Tel*: (020) 8359 4039. Information on community organisation is held on computer database.

* SOME NON-COUNCIL CONTACTS *

Arts:
BARNET BOROUGH ARTS COUNCIL, c/o All Saints Arts Centre, 122 Oakleigh Road North, Whetstone, London N20 9EZ, *Tel*: (020) 8445 8388.

Business:
BARNET CHAMBER OF COMMERCE, 23 Hendon Lane, N3, *Tel*: (020) 8343 3833. *Fax*: (020) 8343 6455.

Residents associations:
FEDERATION OF RESIDENTS ASSOCIATIONS OF LONDON BOROUGH OF BARNET (FORAB), 4 Eysham Court, 69 Station Road, New Barnet, EN5 1PS, *Tel*: (020) 8449 0807 (contact: Mrs D.P. Pannell).

Voluntary organisations:
BARNET BOROUGH VOLUNTARY SERVICE COUNCIL, 28 Church End, London NW4, *Tel*: (020) 8202 7225.

* LOCAL PRESS *

Barnet Borough Times, 71 Church Road, London NW4, *Tel*: (020) 8203 0101 (classified adverts).
Barnet Press, Hillview Gardens, London NW4, *Tel*: (020) 8205 5102..
Community News, council paper, produced by Press and Public Relations, *Tel*: (020) 8359 2325.

BRENT

* LONDON BOROUGH OF BRENT *

[150] **BRENT COMMUNITY HISTORY LIBRARY AND ARCHIVES**: at Cricklewood Library, 152 Olive Road, London NW2 6UY, *Tel*: (020) 8937 3540. *Assistant archivist*: Ian Johnston. *Hours*: Mon. 105; Tues. 10-5; Thurs; 1-8; Sat. 10-5. There is a Friends of Brent Archives organisation, contactable at the above address. The library has published a small amount: in 1979 a major work *A history of Wembley*, edited by Geoffrey Hewlett, 259pp, illus. bibliog. was published, based on research work by members of the W.H.S. Earlier, in 1977 it published *Brent place names*. by Valerie Bott; and in 1975 *From Bacon Lane to Yuletide Road: a guide to Brent street names*, by Michael Drewe and Ann Sansom. In 1984 a booklet *Aviation in and around Brent*, by Geoffrey Hewlett was published.

[151] **GRANGE MUSEUM**. Neasden Lane, London NW10 1QB, *Tel*: (020) 8452 8311. *Curator*: Stephen Allen. A converted 18th century stable block. Information sheets are produced; in 1987 the museum published *The metropolitan railway and the making of Neasden*, in association with Transport History.

* HISTORICAL SOCIETIES *

[152] **WEMBLEY HISTORY SOCIETY**. *Secretary*: Robin Morgan, 54 Wood Lane, Kingsbury, London NW9 7NY, *Tel*: (020) 8200 0481. *Chairman/Publications*: Des Barber, 13 Milton Avenue, Kingsbury, London NW9 0EU, *Tel*: (020) 8204 4815. *Journal editor*: Geoff Hewlett (a planning officer with Brent Council), 39 Wemborough Road, Stanmore, HA7 2EA, *Tel*: (020) 8952 6462. Booklets in print include: *Aerodrome estate alleyways* (Stag Lane, Edgware); *Ealing College; F.A. Wood; Harlesden Green; John Copeland; North Wembley (walk); Old St Andrew's, Kingsbury; Queensbury: a short history; St John's, Wembley; Tokyngton: a walk; Welsh Harp Reservoir 1835-1985*.

[153] **WEMBLEY STADIUM**. Empire Way, Wembley, *Tel*: (020) 8902 8833. Tours at regular intervals.

[154] **WILLESDEN LOCAL HISTORY SOCIETY**. *Secretary*: Vera Thompson, 12 Kynaston Close, Harrow Weald, Middlesex HA3 6TD, *Tel*: (020) 8954 1312. Established in 1974, the interests of the society extend to Cricklewood, Harlesden, Kensal Rise, Kilburn, Neasden, Stonebridge, Park Royal. There are meetings, walks and outings. An annual journal has been issued since 1983, and an index up to the present is available.
An important member of the society, and the editor of the journal, is Cliff Wadsworth (a retired engineer), 51 West Ella Road, Harlesden, London NW10 9PT, *Tel*: (020) 8965 7230. He has self-published in the 1990's a range of booklets: *George Furness: Willesden's greatest resident? Harlesden in the 1870's*. (Local history notes by Amos Beeson, edited by Cliff Wadsworth), *Ken Valentine: a master local historian* (author of *Neasden: a historical study*, 1989, and *Our Lady of Willesden*, W.L.H.S.); *The quiet waters by* (the grand Junction Canal in Willesden); *Robson the roadmaker* (Willesden's surveyor 1875-1918); *Roundwood Park*: notes on its history: *St Mary, Willesden: a history and guide*; *A walk around St Mary's churchyard*; *The waterways of Brent.*
Another important local historian is Len Snow, *Tel*: (020) 8902 3721. Phillimore published his *Brent: a pictorial history* (with Wembley, Willesden and Kingsbury) in 1990; and his *Willesden Past* in 1994. He is a former Brent mayor and councillor. Adam Spencer, former curator at the Grange Museum compiled two collections of old photographs for Sutton: *Wembley and Kingsbury*; and *Willesden*.

* SOME OTHER COUNCIL CONTACTS *

Conservation officer: Paul Ricketts, Brent House, 349-357 High Road, Wembley, HA9 6BZ, *Tel*: (020) 8937 5227.
The Architectural heritage of Brent   was published by the Council in 1984.
Park Rangers: at Roe Green, off Kingsbury Road, London NW9, *Tel*: (020) 8206 0492; another office is at Gladstone Park, NW2. Nature leaflets can be obtained at the Barham Park office, *Tel*: (020) 8937 5619.
Information: *One stop shop* (telephone inquiries only); at Brent House, *Tel*: (020) 8937 1200. Mainly council, but some community information depending on local input.
Reference library: at Willesden Library, 95 High Road, Willesden, London NW10 2SU, *Tel*: (020) 8937 3400.

* SOME NON-COUNCIL CONTACTS *

Arts:
BRENT ARTS COUNCIL. Stables Arts Centre, Gladstone Park, London NW2, *Tel*: (020) 8452 8655.

Regeneration:
BRENT REGENERATION AGENCY, York House, Empire Way, Wembley, *Tel*: (020) 8937 6400.

Voluntary organisations:
BRENT COUNCIL FOR VOLUNTARY SERVICE/BRENT VOLUNTEERS BUREAU, 181 Mortimer Road, London NW10, *Tel*: (020) 8960 4052.

* LOCAL PRESS *

Brent Magazine, free council paper, edited by So Lin Jeffery, Town Hall, Forty Lane, Wembley HA9 9HX, *Tel*: (020) 8937 1066
Kilburn Times, 2 Cricklewood Broadway, NW2, *Tel*: (020) 8450 5272. Also at this address *Wembley and Brent Times.*

ENFIELD

* LONDON BOROUGH OF ENFIELD *

[155] **ENFIELD LOCAL HISTORY UNIT**, Town Hall, Green Lanes, London N3 4XD, *Tel*: (020) 8379 2724. *Local history officer*: Graham Dalling. *Assistant*: Kate Godfrey. *Hours*: Mon, Tues, Thurs, Fri, 10-5, *by appointment only.* Graham Dalling has spent some 30 years with the London Borough of Enfield. He has written on street names: *Southgate and Edmonton street names*, EHHS occasional paper no. 52, 1990; and *A guide to Enfield street names*, 1982 from the Enfield Preservation Society. Historical Publications have issued his *Southgate and Edmonton past*, 1996 and in October 1999 will publish his *Enfield past* (historical account up to 1965). He is also a railway enthusiast and the London Borough of Enfield published his booklet *All stations to Enfield Town: the Great Eastern Railway in Enfield*, in 1986. He has also compiled two collections of old postcards for London Borough of Enfield: *Lower Edmonton in pictures*, 1994, 55pp: and *Upper Edmonton in pictures*, 1998, 53pp.
Another important local author is Alan Dumayne (now deceased), born in 1929 he worked for the family building business, which was sold in the mid 1980's. He self-published his histories of Palmers Green, Southgate and Winchmore Hill; his compilations of old photographs of Enfield, and Southgate were published by Sutton.

* MUSEUMS *

[156] **FORTY HALL MUSEUM**. Forty Hill, London EN2 9HA, *Tel*: (020) 8363 4046. *Curator*: John Griffin. Built in 1629 the building exhibits collections of furniture and paintings, as well as holding temporary exhibitions. Phone first before visiting; future of museum uncertain at time of compilation. Museum holdings include some 2,000 nineteenth and early twentieth century water-colours of Enfield.

* HISTORICAL AND AMENITY SOCIETIES *

[157] **BROOMFIELD HISTORICAL BUILDINGS TRUST**. *Contact*: Colin Pointer, Waltham cottage, Forty Hill, Enfield EN2 9EU *Tel*: (020) 8366 2406.

[158] **ENFIELD ARCHAEOLOGICAL SOCIETY**. *Secretary and Membership secretary*: John Stevens, 3 Scarborough Road, Edmonton, London N9 8AT, *Tel*: (020) 8804 6918. *Chairman*: Professor Dennis Hill, 72 Belmont Avenue, Cockfosters, Herts EN4 9LA, *Tel*: (020) 8440 1593. *President*: Harvey Sheldon. Established in 1955. Excavations, research and recording of all periods. There is a quarterly bulletin.
Former chairman Geoffrey Ray Gillam (born in Edmonton, worked for the Eastern Electricity Board) has published two booklets with the society on World Wars I & II: *Enfield at war 1939-1945*: events in Edmonton, Enfield and Southgate during the second world war, 1985: and *Enfield at war 1914-1918*: events in Edmonton, Enfield and Southgate during the first world war, 1982. His *Theatres, music halls and cinemas in the London Borough of Enfield* was published in 1986. His other interests are shown in *Prehistoric and Roman Enfield*, published in 1973; and *Industrial archaeology in Enfield*, 1971. The Society has recently published his *Forty Hall, Enfield*, 64pp, illus.

[159] **EDMONTON HUNDRED HISTORICAL SOCIETY**. *Secretary*: David Pam, 44 Chase Green Avenue, Enfield, EN2 8EB. *Membership secretary*: Miss Pinkham, 102 Northfield Road, Waltham Cross, Herts, EN8 7RD. Established in 1936 to

promote and foster local history in: Edmonton, Enfield, Potters Bar, Southgate, South Mimms, Monken Hadley, Tottenham, Wood Green. Also concerned with preservation of buildings and sites. Programme of monthly talks on wide variety of topics.

The following occasional papers are currently available:
10: McILVEN. R. *The Edmonton Board of Health*: 16: HOARE, E. *Work of the Edmonton Vestry, 1739-43*; 20: WEINER, M. *John Eardley-Wilmot: a man of his time*; 23: BURNBY, J.G.L. *John Sherwen and drug cultivation in Enfield*; 24 KNIGHT, G.W. *Non-conformist churches in Enfield*; 32: BURNBY J.G.I. *and* ROBINSON, A.F. *And they blew exceeding fine: a biography of Robert Uvedale of Enfield, schoolmaster and horticulturist*; 38: DALLING, G. *David Waddington and the Great Pew Controversy*; 40: ROBINSON, J. *The history of Tottenham Grammar School*; 41: HAWKES, H.G. *The Reynardsons and their almshouses*; 44: PHILLIPS, P.L. *Upon my word I am no scholar*: the Elizabeth Canning kidnapping case of 1753; 45: BURNBY, J.G.L. *and* ROBINSON, A.E. *Now turned into fair garden plots*: the growth of market gardening in Tottenham, Edmonton and Enfield. 47: COLLICOTT, S. *Enfield School Board*. 48 DOREE, S. *Domesday Book and the origins of Edmonton Hundred*; 50: BURNBY, J.G.L. *and* ROBINSON, A.E. *Guns and gunpowder in Enfield*: the origins of the Royal Small Arms Factory; 51: BURNBY, J.G.L. *Drovers and tanners of Enfield and Edmonton*; 52: DALLING, G. *Southgate and Edmonton street names*; 53: HAWKES, H.G. *Some reflections on education in Tottenham*; 54: GOUGH, T.W. *War-time letters from the Tottenham home front*; 55: AVERY, D. *Heinous and grievous offences*: crime and justice in the Jacobean Hundred of Edmonton. 56: BURNBY, J.G.L., editor. *Elizabeth times in Tottenham, Edmonton and Enfield.*

Other EHHS publications available are: *Recollections of old Enfield*; HOY, Dennis: *From fields to flats*: a history of Bush Hill Park and St Stephen's Church.
Affiliated to the EHHS is the *Jewish Research Group, Secretary*: Jeffery C. Baum. 43 Churchill Court, Ainsley Court, Edmonton, London N9 9XJ, *Tel*: (020) 8364 3518. The group publishes an occasional journal *Heritage* (No 1, 1982), with articles on synagogues, institutions and personalities.
No 5, 1998: Jews of Tottenham (1900-1930), a further study; The early life of Q.D. Leavis (1906-1981); The campaign for Soviet Jewry in Southgate; The Jews of Woodfield Way, New Southgate.

[160] **ENFIELD PRESERVATION SOCIETY**. *Secretary*: Mrs Beryl Dorrington, 77 London Road, Enfield, Middx EN2 6ES. *Tel*: (020) 8366 7326. HQ/Correspondence address/answerphone: Jubilee Hall, 2 Parsonage Lane, Enfield EN2 0AJ, *Tel*: (020) 8363 9495. Former Secretary Irene Smith and driving force behind the society for many years died in 1996. The society was established in 1936, one of the oldest amenities societies in the country and now has some 2,300 members. One of the society's earliest campaigns in 1938 successfully opposed an attempt to build on Chase Green, one of the last vestiges of Enfield Chase remaining as public open space close to the heart of Enfield. Membership increased dramatically in 1961 when the society led a seven year battle against a devastating road scheme which would have sliced through St Andrew's ancient churchyard. All planning applications are carefully monitored and the society is strongly represented on the study groups responsible for safeguarding the borough's conservation areas. The 15 mile network of public footpaths pioneered by the society is regularly inspected and new paths suggested. There are regular guided walks, and several annual outings. A quarterly newsletter is issued. The society is especially active in publishing, and in 1977 produced *Enfield's architectural heritage*. Victor H. Allemandy's book *Enfield: past and present* first published in 1914 was reissued in 1984. David Pam's book on *Enfield Chase* was published in 1984; and a book on *Gentleman's Row* (by Donald Potter and others) was published in 1986. There have been two heritage walks: No 1: *Forty Hill and Bull's Cross*, by Valerie Carter, 1985, and No 2: *Enfield Town*, by Graham Dalling and Valerie Carter, 1988. A major project has been the three volume *History of Enfield* by David Pam: Vol. I: A parish near London (before 1837); Vol. II: A Victorian suburb (1837-1914); Vol. III: A desirable neighbourhood (1914-1939); published in 1990, 1992 and 1996 respectively.
A history of the society *Fighting for the future*, 279pp, illus., maps, by Valerie Carter was published in 1997.
A limited edition coloured print 'Heart of Enfield' by local artist Derrick Stone was issued in 1996. A revised *footpaths map* has been published recently.
Finally, there is *The Enfield Book: a guide for young explorers*, written by an EPS editorial team, and first published in 1992.

[161] **SOUTHGATE AND DISTRICT CIVIC TRUST**. *Secretary*: Miss Frances Cook, Eversley, 2b Oakwood Crescent, London N21 1PB. *Publications*: Peter Hodge, 64 Houndsden Road, Winchmore Hill, London N21 1LY, *Tel*: (020) 8360 6465. *Contact for local history group*: Mrs A. Cathcart, 64 Wellington Road, Bush Hill Park, EN1 2PH.
There are two guided walks, first published in 1978: *A walk in Southgate*; *A walk in Winchmore Hill*. There is a set of 15 colour postcards of Southgate and district and a reproduction of the 1st edition, 25 inch to a mile OS plan of Winchmore Hill, 1865. *Oakleaves, No 2, Local History Bulletin, 1996* has articles, photographs and maps relating to the local history of Southgate and district.
In 1994 the trust published *Broomfield: an illustrated history of the house*, by Steven Brindle (an English Heritage officer).
Forthcoming for 1999 is *The Cresswells of Winchmore Hill: a gifted Victorian family*, by Peter Hodge.
Henrietta Creswell's 1912 book *Winchmore Hill: memories of a lost village* was reissued in 1982.

The Trust covers Southgate, New Southgate, Cockfosters, Palmers Green and Winchmore Hill, and was established in 1962 as a result of public concern over the threatened demolition of the Georgian cottages on Southgate Green. It has three main groups: town planning and conservation areas, trees and open spaces; and local history.

* SOME OTHER COUNCIL CONTACTS *

Arts: Cultural Services Manager: Clare Chidley, at Civic Centre, *Tel*: (020) 8379 3659.
Conservation areas/listed buildings: Christine White, Civic Centre, *Tel*: (020) 8379 3852.
Information: There are First Stop Information services (council and community information) at Central Library, *Tel*: (020) 8379 8341; Edmonton Centre, *Tel*: (020) 8967 9369; Ordnance Road Library, *Tel*: (01992) 787008; and Palmers Green, *Tel*: (020) 8982 7228.
Central Reference Library, Cecil Road, Enfield, *Tel*: (020) 8379 8391; also reference collections at Palmers Green, *Tel*: (020) 8379 2710; Edmonton Green, *Tel*: (020) 8379 2609.
Nature conservation/ecology, *Tel. contact*: (020) 8379 3143.
Tourism: Tourism development officer: Helen Winchester, Civic Centre, *Tel*: (020) 8379 3738.

* SOME NON-COUNCIL CONTACTS *

Business:
ENFIELD BUSINESS CENTRE, 201 Hertford Road, Enfield EN3 5JH, *Tel*: (020) 8443 1701. An Enfield Business Directory is compiled by the Marketing and Communications Team, Civic Centre, *Tel*: (020) 4379 4439.

Voluntary organisations:
ENFIELD VOLUNTARY SERVICE COUNCIL. 341a Baker Street, Enfield, *Tel*: (020) 8342 1898.

* LOCAL PRESS *

Enfield Advertiser (free) *Enfield Gazette* (paid for), 281 Ballards Lane, London N12, *Tel*: (020) 8449 5577. *Enfield Independent* (free), 440 Hertford Road, London N9, *Tel*: (020) 8805 8844.
Enfield News, fortnightly Enfield Council paper produced by the Marketing and Communications Team, Civic Centre.

HARINGEY

* LONDON BOROUGH OF HARINGEY *

Local history collection and museum: [162] **BRUCE CASTLE MUSEUM**, Lordship Lane, London N17 8NU, *Tel*: (020) 8808 8772; *Fax*: (020) 8808 4118. *Curator*: Penny Wheatcroft; *Local history officer*: Rita Read. *Hours*: Wed-Sat. 1-4.45, but telephone first; archives can be consulted by appointment only.
Bruce Castle is one of only two Grade I listed buildings in Haringey, once the manor house of Tottenham, it dates from the late 16th century. It was bought by the Hill family in 1827 and became a school for boys. It opened as a museum in 1906.
The museum has a major collection of postal history material (formed because of Bruce Castle's historic association with Sir Rowland Hill, reformer of the British postal system). Also: Victorian costume and domestic equipment, a reconstruction of a 1930's office, an original Roman kiln, excavated from Highgate; collection of local photographs, paintings and prints. Also temporary exhibitions.

There is a small sales point within the museum, selling postcards, prints, pamphlets and books on local and postal history. There is also a Friends organisation (contact: Penny Wheatcroft). A booklet history of Bruce Castle *From manor house to museum*, by Jean Pegram was published in 1990. Haringey Libraries have published only a small amount of local history: in 1977 *Urban growth of Haringey*, 17pp, by Ian Murray; *Lost houses of Haringey*, 1986, by Alan Aris and others (Haringey Community Information, in association with the Hornsey Historical Society); *Connections*, 1986, by Sylvia Collicott on Haringey local/national-world links (Haringey Community Information in association with the Multicultural Curriculum Support Unit); *Local herstory*: lives of women in Haringey was published in 1987.

* HISTORICAL SOCIETIES *

The main publications source is [163] **HORNSEY HISTORICAL SOCIETY**. Official address/HQ and shop: The Old Schoolhouse, 136 Tottenham Lane, London N8 7EL, *Tel*: (020) 8348 8429 (answerphone). Normally staffed on Thursday mornings, and all day on Saturdays. *Hon. officials*: *President*: Dr Joan Schwitzer; *Chairman*: Peter Barber (British Library Maps Curator); *Secretary*: Elizabeth Israel.

The schoolhouse itself is the subject of a booklet *The little school*, 1994 by HHS President Joan Schwitzer. The society was established in 1971 and covers the western side of Haringey borough from Highgate to Wood Green. There are lectures, walks and visits and a flourishing publications programme, including an annual bulletin, and newsletter.

Books currently available include: *All Highgate is a garden*, 1989 (history of the Highgate Horticultural Society, founded in 1859); *From forest to suburb*, 1988, by Ken Gay (the formation of the Parish of Hornsey, and the urbanisation on Crouch End, Finsbury Park, Muswell Hill and Highgate); *Haringey before our time*, 1994, by Ian Murray; *Home fires*, edited by Joan Schwitzer with Ben Travers (Bulletin No. 33, 1992); *In Times Past*, 1989, (more than 100 old photographs), compiled by Peter Curtis; *Making history together: the first 25 years of Hornsey Historical Society*, 1998, by Joan Schwitzer; *Palace on the hill*, 1992 by Ken Gay; *People and places: lost estates in Highgate, Hornsey and Wood Green*, edited by Joan Schwitzer (with maps and 60 illus.), 1996.

There is a series of popular guided walks; *Highgate village: four walks*, by Joan Schwitzer; *A walk around Muswell Hill*, by Ken Gay; *Crouch End: a walk*, by Bridget Cherry and Ken Gay; *Hornsey village: a walk* by Ken Gay; *A walk along ancient boundaries in Kenwood*, by Malcolm Stokes; *A Stroud Green walk*, by Ken Gay; *Discovering Wood Green a walk*, by Albert Pinching.

There are three booklets in the 'portrait' series: *Crouch end clock tower*, by Joan Schwitzer; *Hornsey Town Hall*, by Bridget Cherry; *Finsbury Park*, by Ken Gay.

There are seven OS map reprints, 1864 to WWII; a wide range of historic postcards, and a video *Our Northern Heights*, written and directed by Andy Attenburrow. A further video on Highgate is to be issued shortly.

KLA, a local company has made a video *A palace for the people*, and the same company is to issue another video *North London at war*.

The society also sells three commercially produced books of old photographs:
From Highgate to Hornsey, by Ken Gay and Dick Whetstone (SB Publications); *Highgate and Muswell Hill*, by Joan Schwitzer and Ken Gay, and *Hornsey and Crouch End*, by Ken Gay, both from Tempus. *Wood Green, Crouch End and Tottenham*, by Peter Curtis is a new collection from Sutton.
Ben Travers' book *The book of Crouch End* from Barracuda is now out of print

Contents listings for the Bulletin (excludes notes and queries):
No. 35, 1994: The Greig Family of Hornsey; The rink: a Hornsey cinema; Trams and things 1910-1930; The Queen's Head Tavern; Hornsey Home Guard; Ducketts in Stuart times; Armistice Day 1918; Hornsey in 1920; Hornsey air raids; Bruce castle: a brief history.
No. 36, 1995: The Limes, Highgate (Southwood Hospital); 'The Sage of Muswell Hill'; Memories of St Mary's School in the 1920's; Hornsey pumping station; Weekends at home when I was young; The story of my house (by Mary J. Groves); War-time treats; Coronation Day, June 10, 1910; Henry Tidmarsh, unknown artist of Muswell Hill; The Bounds Green incident.
No. 37, 1996: Hornsey's historic houses, No. 2: Grove Lodge, Muswell Hill; Growing up in the Depression; Girls can kick! Bounds Green Farm; The making of 'our northern heights'; Forge family memories; Highgate School; The story of the Hornsey Toll Gate (part 1).
No. 38, 1997: Local historic houses No. 3: Woodside House, Wood Green; Elgar and the 'mighty hunter' of Muswell Hill; Hornsey Historical Society: how it all began; The colour of the 2/7th Battalion, Middlesex Regiment; Hornsey Cameo Dramatic Society; Robert Paul, film pioneer of Muswell Hill; Changes I have seen (Ruth Rogers Essay winner 1996).
No. 39, 1998: Campsbourne School: 100 years in Hornsey; Hubert Henry Lansley - Meccano man of Fortis Green Road; The Hornsey halfpenny of 1797; Thomas Oakes and Westbury House; My favourite local place of refreshment (by Vic Pearce); Memories of Crouch End and the Ferme-Parkers. (This number dedicated to the memory of Peter Curtis (died February 1997), chairman 1991-1996 and print and production co-ordinator).

[164] **FRIENDS OF HORNSEY CHURCH TOWER**. *Chairman*: Peter Sanders, 54 Inderwick Road, London N8 9LD, *Tel*: (020) 8340 1879. Established in 1989, the group has issued five booklets: *Hornsey churchyard nature trail*, by David Bevan; *An introduction to St Mary's, Hornsey churchyard*, by Joan Schwitzer; *St Mary's Church, Hornsey*, by Ian Murray; *St. Mary's tombstone trail* (geological), by Eric Robinson; *St Mary's tower: a brief history and guide*, by Bridget Cherry.

[165a] **FRIENDS OF TOTTENHAM CEMETERY**. *Contact*: Ashley Grey, 1 Prospect Place, Church Lane, London N7 8AT: *work tel*: (020) 8489 4524. Cemetery owned by Haringey Council and covers 56 acres, encompassing the medieval parish church of All Hallows and graveyard. Two Gothic chapels designed by George Pritchett; Victorian architect William Butterfield is buried here.

* ENVIRONMENTAL/COMMUNITY GROUPS *

Alexandra Palace and Park:
Muswell Hill, London N22, *Tel*: (020) 8365 2121. Many organisations and individuals are involved with this site: the consultative committee, the London Borough of Haringey Advisory Committee (residents and councillors; contact: Nigel Lindsey, *Tel*: (020) 8862 2956) the Alexandra Park and Palace Conservation Area Advisory Committee and [165b] **SAVE THE ENVIRONMENT OF ALEXANDRA PARK AND PALACE**, (Stepp), *Contact*: Jane Hutchinson, 20 Grove Avenue, London N10, *Tel*: (020) 8883 8972.

[166] **C.A.S.C.H.** (residents association for: Crescent Road, Avenue Road, Stanhope Road, Stanhope Gardens, Claremont Road, Coolhurst Road and Hurst Avenue. *Secretary*: Frances Doporto, 27 Coolhurst Road, London N8 8ET. *Chair*: Lynda Limata-Adams, 44a Coolhurst Road, N8 8EU, *Tel*: (020) 8245 7112. Established in 1984 and since then the group has been active in a number of local campaigns and initiatives. A newsletter is issued.

[167] **CROUCH END OPEN SPACE (CREOS)**. *Secretary*: Ros Abrams, 97 Wood Vale, London N10. Established over 20 years ago as a local environmental group to protect Crouch End Playing Fields and open space in the area below Shepherds Hill (bounded by Park Road, Glasslyn Road, Cranley Gardens and Wood Vale from any undesirable development. There is a newsletter and a guidebook about the area is planned.

[168] **FINSBURY PARK ACTION GROUP**. Alexandra National House, 330 Seven Sisters Road, London N4 2PJ. *Tel*: (020) 8802 2612 (community development); (020) 8800 2630 (private tenants adviser/fax). The group works to improve the quality of life for all in Finsbury Park. It is funded by Hackney, Haringey and Islington Councils. It has helped to set up a variety of community organisations including *Finsbury Park Community Trust* (306 Seven Sisters Road, N4, *Tel*: (020) 8211 0121, and *Friends of Finsbury Park* (*Tel*: (020) 8800 0946). The regeneration of the Finsbury Park area is a current concern, and the *Finsbury Park Community Regeneration Initiative* was set up in 1997 to obtain lottery funding. The initiative is working with the University of North London on a community profile of the area (a directory of community groups, and a study of informal social networks). The *Finsbury Park Area Joint Working Party* is a joint body between the three councils and the community. (see annual report, October 1998). The group publishes a quarterly community newspaper *The Finsbury Parker*, edited by Patricia Zich, 15a Finsbury Park Road, London N4, *Tel*: (020) 7359 1109.

[169] **FRIENDS OF FINSBURY PARK**. *Chairman*: Alister Brinkley, 53 Alexandra National House, 330 Seven Sisters Road, London N4, *Tel*: (020) 8800 0946.

[170] **MUSWELL HILL AND FORTIS GREEN ASSOCIATION**. *Chairman*: Robert Andrewes, 11 Southern Road, Fortis Green, London N2, *Tel*: (020) 8883 3535. *Recruitment*: Monica Myers, 144 Dukes Avenue, Muswell Hill, N10, *Tel*: (020) 8444 8574. Established in 1946, currently with some 600 members, it is an amenity society concerned with all aspects of the quality of life and the environment in Muswell Hill and Fortis Green. It has played a key role in representing the view of local residents on the future of Alexandra Palace and Park. There are meetings and discussions on diverse subjects. A regular newsletter is issued.

* SOME OTHER COUNCIL CONTACTS *

Conservation officer: Steve Gould, 639 High Road, Tottenham, London N17, *Tel*: (020) 8489 5216.
David Lowe Watson is the chair of the joint Conservation Area Advisory Committees.
Central Library: High Road, Wood Green, London N22, *Tel*: (020) 8888 1292.
Nature conservation officer: David Bevan, Railway Fields (nature reserve), Green Lanes, London N4, *Tel*: (020) 7348 6005. (for correspondence: c/o Tottenham Town Hall, N15 4RY). There are leaflets on Railway Fields; on the Parkland Walk and on Coldfall Wood.
There are a number of friends of parks groups.

* SOME NON-COUNCIL CONTACTS *

Arts:
HARINGEY ARTS COUNCIL. The Chocolate Factory, Unit 104, Building B, Clarendon Road, Wood Green, London N22 6XJ, *Tel*: (020) 8365 7500.

Business:
A Haringey Business Directory is produced by Haringey Business Support Services, *contact*: Manoj Ambasra, Lee Valley Technopark, Ashley Road, London N17 9LN, *Tel*: (020) 8880 4472. Also at the same address: Business Link, North London (covering Haringey, Enfield, Barnet), *Tel*: (020) 8880 4475.

Voluntary organisations:
VOLUNTARY ACTION HARINGEY, 2 Factory Lane, Tottenham, London N17 9FL, *Tel*: (020) 8365 1873.

* LOCAL PRESS *

Haringey People, council magazine edited by Siobhan Crozier, Civic Centre, London N22, *Tel*: (020) 8862 2997.
Hornsey Journal; *Tottenham and Wood Green Journal.* 116 Tottenham Lane, London N8, *Tel*: 020) 8340 6868.

EAST LONDON BOROUGHS:

Barking, Hackney, Havering, Redbridge, Waltham Forest; Docklands, Newham, Tower Hamlets

BARKING

* LONDON BOROUGH OF BARKING *

[171] **BARKING LOCAL HISTORY COLLECTION**. At Valence Library, Becontree Avenue, Dagenham, RM8 3HT, *Tel*: (020) 8592 6537. *Librarian*: Myers Meredith.

[172] **VALENCE HOUSE MUSEUM**. Becontree Avenue, Dagenham, RM8 3HT, *Tel*: (020) 8595 8404. *Hours*: Tues-Fri 9.30-1; 2-4.30; Sat 10-4. To reach: Chadwell Heath British Rail, or Becontree Station (district line), then bus 62 to the junction of Valence Avenue and Becontree Avenue. In the 14th century Valence Manor was held by Aylmer de Valence, Earl of Pembroke, who gave the building its name. The museum houses the famous Fanshawe family portraits (presented to the borough by Captain Aubrey B. Fanshawe in 1963), by 17th and 18th century court artists such as Sir Peter Lely and Sir Godfrey Kneller. Exhibits show the history of the area: the important fishing industry for example, and the massive Becontree Estate. The O'Leary Gallery (named after librarian John Gerard O'Leary) opened in 1991 and houses temporary exhibitions throughout the year.
There is a souvenir shop and a herb garden, opened in 1992, based on a design by Virginia Nightingale. *A Guide to Valence House*, by Susan Curtis and Mark Watson is available. There is a Friends organisation with lectures, musical evenings, courses and social events; regular newsletter.

Another historic property is [173] **EASTBURY MANOR HOUSE**, Eastbury Square, Barking IG11 9SN, *Tel*: (020) 8507 0119, normally open on the first Saturday of each month. A guide book written by Susan Curtis is available. Owned by the National Trust, managed by LBB. Originally part of the estate of Barking Abbey.

Barking Libraries and Valence House Museum sell their own publications almost exclusively, written by members of staff. Recent publications:
1993: *On the move: views of transport in Barking and Dagenham 1890-1959*, by Susan Curtis. 82pp, illus.
1994: *D-Day remembered*. 44pp, illus. Memories of local veterans.
1995: CLIFFORD, Tony. *Barking pubs past and present*. 28pp, illus.
1995: *Danger over Dagenham*, by J.G. O'Leary, Dr C. Herington, H.O. Bigg, F.C. Strickland and P.T. Frost. First published 1947, reprinted 1995. 89pp. Dagenham during World War II.
1995: *A step back in time*. 11pp. Pamphlet to mark the 60th anniversary of Woodward Library. (An earlier publication, now out of print is *One hundred years of libraries in Barking*, by Alan Hill).
1996: CLIFFORD, Tony. *Dagenham pubs past and present*. 22pp, illus. Author is information technology officer in the Barking Libraries; also author of *Barking and Dagenham buildings*, 1992.
1996: HOWSON, James. *Recording the past*, edited by Alan Hill and Susan Curtis. James Howson was curator/archivist at Valence House from 1974-1986. A selection of his articles is printed in this collection.
The 6th edition of his *Brief History of Barking and Dagenham* was published in 1990.
1997: HOME, Dr Robert. *A township complete in itself*. 56pp, illus. The author is at the University of East London. This is a historical study of the planning and development of the Becontree Housing Estate.

Other publications still in print are: *Barking and Dagenham buildings past and present*, 1992 by Tony Clifford; *Barking and Ilford*: an extract from the Victoria History of Essex, by J.E. Oxley, 1987; *A brief history of Barking and Dagenham*, 1990, by James Howson; *Dagenham*: extract from the Victoria History of Essex, by J.G. O'Leary, 1988; *Fanshawe Family and other portraits*: a catalogue, by James Howson, 1983; *First in Essex*: one hundred years of library service in Barking 1889-1989, by James Howson; *A Miscellany of Marks Gate*, by A.E. Baker, 1990; *More views of old Barking and Dagenham*, 1991; *Views of old Barking and Dagenham*, 1990.

From commercial publishers: *Bygone Barking*, by Brian Evans published by Phillimore in 1991; and *Barking and Dagenham*, compiled by Gavin Smith, from Tempus.

* HISTORICAL SOCIETIES *

[174] **BARKING & DISTRICT HISTORICAL SOCIETY**. *Secretary*: Mrs Terri Runchman. 9 Armstrong Close, Dagenham RM8 1TF. *Tel*: (020) 8590 9684. *Membership secretary*: Mrs J. Lines, *Tel*: (020) 8598 8548. Est. in 1934, currently some 100 members. Miscellaneous publications have been produced: *Barking 100 years ago*, by A. Lockwood, 1990; *Helping hands: voluntary service organisations in Barking and Dagenham*, edited by Gwen Shields, 1982; *A short history of the Barking*

Church of England (aided) Primary School, by Harold Wand, 1990, and *Where was the first Barking Abbey*, by H.H. Lockwood, 1986. Visits and exhibitions. The society has a large collection of old photographs.

* SOME OTHER COUNCIL CONTACTS *

Arts development officer: Beverley Whitrick, Civic Centre, Dagenham. *Tel*: (020) 8227 2133.
Information: Reference Library, Central Library, Barking IG11 7NB, *Tel*: (020) 8517 8666, est. 3613.
Parks Rangers: at the Millennium Centre, The Chase, Dagenham Rd, Rush Green, Romford RM7 0SS, *Tel*: (020) 8595 4155.
Urban Regeneration Team: Manager: Jeremy Grint, at Town Hall, Barking, *Tel*: (020) 8227 3502.

* SOME NON-COUNCIL CONTACTS *

Business:
BARKING AND DAGENHAM CHAMBER OF COMMERCE, 16 Cambridge Rd, Baking, *Tel*: (020) 8591 6966.

Voluntary organisations:
COUNCIL FOR VOLUNTARY SERVICE, BARKING & DAGENHAM. The Faircross Community Complex, Hulse Avenue, Barking IG11 9UP, *Tel*: (020) 8591 5275.

* LOCAL PRESS *

Barking and Dagenham Post. 2 Whalebone Lane South, Dagenham RM8 7HB, *Tel*: (020) 8517 5577.
Barking and Dagenham Recorder. 539 High Rd, Ilford IG1 1UD, *Tel*: (020) 8478 4444.
The Citizen, council paper produced by public relations unit, contact: Paul Bailey, Civic Centre, Dagenham RM10 7BN, *Tel*: (020) 8592 4500.

HACKNEY

* LONDON BOROUGH OF HACKNEY *

[175] **HACKNEY ARCHIVES DEPARTMENT**. 43 De Beauvoir Rd, London N1 5SQ, *Tel*: (020) 7241 2886; *Fax*: (020) 7241 6688; *Email*: archives@hackney.gov.uk. *Hours*: Mon, Tues, Thurs 9.30-1; 2-5; 1st and 3rd Saturday of every month, same times. Recent information technological developments include *Hackney on Disk*, a visual database allowing access to illustrations and photographs. It is also accessible at Sutton House.
Borough archivist: David Mander; *Senior assistant archivist*: Martin Taylor. David Mander is the compiler/ author of a number of books from Sutton Publishing: *Hackney, Homerton and Dalston in old photographs*; *London Borough of Hackney in old photographs* Volume II (with Jenny Golden); *Stoke Newington, Stamford Hill & Upper Clapton in old photographs* (with Bill Manley). He has also written a three-part history: *More light, more power*: an illustrated history of Shoreditch; *Look back, look forward*: an illustrated history of Stoke Newington; *Strength in the tower*: an illustrated history of Hackney.
He is also the author of a booklet guide to sources: *Researching in Stock Newington*, published in 1993 by the London & Middx F.H.S; and the history of St John at Hackney. Jenny Golden is also the author of *Hackney at war*, also from Sutton.
These and others from more specialist sources including the Hackney Society are sold at the department, and include:
Furnishing the world: the East London furniture trade, 1830-1980, from the Geffrye Museum.
The German Hospital in London and the community it served, by Maureen Specht, from the Anglo-German History Society, 1987.
The growth of Stoke Newington, 1983 by Jack Whitehead, published by the author, (55 Parliament Hill, London NW3 2TB).
Hackney depicted: three centuries of topographical paintings and drawings of Hackney from the collection of Hackney Council's Archives Department. Catalogue of an exhibition at Sutton House, 1997.
The North London railway, by A.J. Chisholm, published by the North London Railway Historical Society. A reprint of an illustrated booklet of 1902.

[176] **FRIENDS OF HACKNEY ARCHIVES** was formed in 1985 to support the work of the archives department and can be contacted through the above address. Visits and other meetings are arranged from time to time. There is an annual lecture held in memory of the borough's first archivist, the late Stanley Tongue. There is a regular newsletter *The Hackney Terrier* (previously an outlet for articles), and the journal *Hackney History*. *Chair*: Isobel Watson.

Contents listing for Hackney History:

* MUSEUMS/HISTORIC PROPERTIES *

[177] **CLISSOLD HOUSE TRUST**. *Chair*: Will Richardson, Flat 12, 13 Stamford Hill, London N19, *Tel*: (020) 8802 9147.

[178] **FRIENDS OF THE HACKNEY EMPIRE**. 291 Mare St, Hackney, London E8 1EJ. Est. in 1988 by Alistair Fullerton, a puppeteer with Spitting Image, and Clive Manning, a teacher, to raise funds for the renovation of the theatre. A complete restoration of the theatre is currently being planned with funding from the National Lottery. Designed by Frank Matcham and built in 1901 it is considered one of the finest examples of a suburban variety theatre. Members receive a regular newsletter, advance notice of new productions, etc.

[179] **GEFFRYE MUSEUM**. *Director*: David Dewing. *Keeper of collections*: Saskia Partington, Kingsland Rd, London E2 8EA, *Tel*: (020) 7739 9893; *Fax*: (020) 7729 5647. *Hours*: Tues-Sat, 10-5; Sun and Bank Holiday Mon 2-5. The only museum in the UK to specialise in the furniture and domestic interiors of the urban middle-classes from 1600 to the present day. Museum opened in 1914 in the former Geffrye Almshouses built in 1715 by the worshipful Company of Ironmongers with funds bequeathed by Sir Robert Geffrye, former Lord Mayor of London and Master of the Company. New developments include the herb garden, opened in 1992 and the substantial extensions opened in 1998, with four new 20th century period rooms, a temporary exhibition gallery and a design centre; gardens are being developed to complement the interior displays. Guide book published in 1998. Local publications: *The Vaughans: East End furniture makers, 300 years of a London family*, by Anthony Vaughan, 1984; *Furnishing the world*: the East London furniture trade 1830-1980, by Pat Kirkham, Rodney Mace and Julia Porter, 1987; *Immigrant furniture workers in London 1881-1939*, by William I. Massil, 1997 (published with the Jewish Museum). A shop stocks a wide range of publications on the decorative arts and interior design.
There is a Friends organisation, membership secretary: Mrs Julie Davies, 39 Ockenden Rd, London N1 3NN, *Tel*: (020) 7226 7658.

[180] **HACKNEY MUSEUM SERVICE**. *Community education officer*: Claire Adler; *Assistant curator*: Alex Sydney, Parkside Library, Victoria Park Rd, Hackney, London E9 7JL, *Tel*: (020) 8986 6914; *Fax*: (020) 8985 7600. The Hackney Museum is currently closed, but will be reopening in the new Technology Learning Centre next to Hackney Town Hall in July 2000. Teaching sessions using objects and materials are held in local schools. There is a programme of touring exhibitions at four branch libraries and other venues: on the Vietnamese, and Turkish communities, on food, 1950's interiors of homes mainly in Hoxton and Shoreditch, music halls and theatres, etc.

[181] **SUTTON HOUSE**. 2 & 4 Hommerton High St, Hackney, London E9 6JQ, *Tel*: (020) 8986 2264; *Fax*: (020) 8533 0556; *Email*: tshgen@smtp.NTrust.org.uk. *Programme co-ordinator*: Ros Daniels. A National Trust property, now restored and open to the public as a result of the Save Sutton House Campaign initiated in 1987. It is a Tudor red-brick house, built in 1535 by Sir Rafe Sadleir, principal Secretary of State for Henry VIII with 18th century alterations and later additions. *Open*: 3 Feb - 24 Nov, and 2 Feb 2000 onwards: Wed, Sun, bank holidays, 11.30 - 5.30; Sat 2-5.30; gallery, shop and cafe/bar open Wed - Sun and bank holidays, 11.30-5, except 20th December - 11th Jan 2000. There are displays on the history of the house and of Hackney history: changing shows of contemporary art and sculpture. Also concerts (Sutton House Music Society), craft shows and other events.

* AMENITY AND HISTORICAL SOCIETIES *

[182] **ABNEY PARK CEMETERY TRUST.** *Chairman*: Greg McNeil; *Project co-ordinator*: Lisa Hook. The South Lodge, Stoke Newington High St, London N16 0LN, *Tel*: (020) 7275 7557. The cemetery was established in 1839 and is significant for its 2,500 different kinds of trees and shrubs supplied by Loddiges nursery. It was built in the grounds of Abney House, home of dissenter Sir Thomas Abney (1640-1722). William Booth (founder of the Salvation Army), wife and son are buried here, and there is a statue to hymn writer Isaac Watts. The trust is responsible for the management of the cemetery, on long lease from Hackney Council, since 1992. A visitor centre, and a community environment centre have been set up and there is close involvement with local schools on educational projects. There is a wide range of weekend events and workshops and a monthly history walk. A full length illustrated history and guide to the cemetery by Paul Joyce (a retired architect) was published in 1984 (reissued 1994). A booklet on Clissold Park (to the west of the cemetery) by David Solman was issued in 1992. There is also a poster map of the cemetery.
The trust was set up by [182b] **FRIENDS OF ABNEY PARK CEMETERY** (originally Save Abney Park Cemetery, est. in 1974). The current *Secretary and quarterly newsletter editor* is: Ann Jameson, 24 Middleton Rd, London E8 4BS, *Tel*: (020) 7241 3696. *Chair*: Joan Potter, 50 Olinda Rd, London N16 6TL, *Tel*: (020) 8800 2861.

[183] **CANALS IN HACKNEY USERS GROUP.** *Contact*: The Chair, Kingsland Basin, Whitmore Rd, London N1 5QG, *Tel*: (020) 7729 2915. Est. in 1981 by local people 'concerned about the canal through Hackney and anxious to improve it'. With funds from moorings in Kingsland Basin it has sponsored clean-up workdays, assisted in establishing wildlife habitats, taken part in campaigns against canal pollution and worked for save canal moorings and canalside safety. Has also sponsored work in schools, which has resulted in a number of local history publications, a teachers' resource pack, *London's canals, yesterday and today* (in collaboration with British Waterways), *The River Lea* a teaching pack for Hackney schools and memoirs of local people who remember the canal when it was in commercial use.

[184] **HACKNEY SOCIETY.** *Part-time researcher/development officer*: Sarah Vaughan-Roberts. The Round Chapel, 1d Glenarm Rd, London E5 0LY, *Tel/Fax*: (020) 8986 0029; *Email*: hac-soc@pop3.poptel.org.uk. *Membership secretary*: Ann Jameson, 24 Middleton Rd, London E8 4BS, *Tel*: (020) 7241 3696. *Publications and mail order*: Jack Youngmark, 21 Sanford Terrace, London N16 7LH, *Tel*: (020) 7249 2898. *Chairman*: Patrick Hammill, 115 Eleanor Rd, London E8 1DN, *Tel*: (020) 7249 0834. The society was founded in 1969 'to encourage the improvement of the environment of the London Borough of Hackney, its buildings, streets and parks'. It works closely with the council and is involved with the work of Conservation Area Advisory Committees wherever possible. There are monthly meetings at which talks are given.
The society has an important publications programme. A newsletter has been produced since 1987. Articles of interest have included:
Vol 1, No 1, Spring 1987: The Agapemonite Church, Clapton Common; *Vol 1, No 2, Autumn 1987, and Vol 1, No 3, Summer 1988*: Hackney Bred, by Bill Eltham; *Vol 1, No 3, summer 1988*: Haggerston Library and the Free Library Movement; *summer 1990* (Special edition): Hackney Baths, Lower Clapton Road; *Vol 1, No 7, Spring 1991*: The Stoke Newington reservoirs and the buildings in the reservoir area.
Recent books:
1993: MANDER, David. *St John-at-Hackney: the story of a church*. 60pp, illus. History of the present church, consecrated in 1797, the original church it replaced and a visitor's guide to the building and its monuments. (Published by the Parish of Hackney, 356 Mare St, London E8).
1993: MIELE, Christopher. *Hoxton: architecture and history over five centuries*. 44pp, illus. Traces Hoxton's developments from medieval times to the early decades of the 20th century. (Author is an architectural historian, currently working for Alan Baxter Associates).
1995: SOLMAN, David. *Loddiges of Hackney: the largest hothouse in the world*. 96pp, illus. An account of the most famous plant nursery in Europe from the 1750's to 1850's (stood on site close to today's Town Hall). Author is a director of the Abney Park Cemetery Trust.
1997: *A plan of Hackney Church and churchyard*. 1741 (historical map), by Roger Root. shows St Augustine's as rebuilt at the beginning of the 16th century.
1999: in preparation is: *20th century buildings in Hackney*, by Elizabeth Robinson. It will feature some 50 buildings, or groups of buildings, of all types and parts of the borough, ranging from the Hackney Empire Theatre to the present day Geffrye Museum extension, 1998 (Branson Coates Architects).
Walks leaflets cover: Clapton, Springfield Park; Central Hackney and Victoria Park; Stoke Newington; Shoreditch and Hoxton; Kingsland and Dalston; Barnsbury (Islington).
There are also currently 9 postcards showing 18th, 19th and 20th century views.
Other books in print include: *Buildings at risk in Hackney*, 1987; *Famous women of Hackney* (leaflet); *From tower to tower block*: the buildings of Hackney, 1979; *The German Hospital houses: a guide to improvement, conservation and maintenance,*

1987; *Lost Hackney*, 1989, by Elizabeth Robinson (Hackney's lost architectural heritage); *South Shoreditch: historic and industrial buildings*, 1986; *The Victorian villas of Hackney*, 1981, by Michael Hunter (Professor of History at Birkbeck College).

Lastly, there are 4 exhibitions available for loan: Buildings at risk in Hackney; South Shoreditch (both produced in parallel with publications); Stoke Newington Church Street; Renewing Hackney (new schemes submitted for Civic Trust awards up to 1990).

The society has initiated [185] **THE HACKNEY HISTORIC BUILDINGS TRUST**. *Contact*: Patrick Hammill, 115 Eleanor Rd, London E8 1DN, *Tel*: (020) 7249 0834. It was set up to carry out urgent works in order to rescue buildings in need. Its major project to date has been the refurbishment of the Round Chapel (Clapton Park United Reformed Church), built in 1871. The outstanding horse-shoe shaped interior is now a performing arts centre, available for hire; contact: Jill Truman (address, tel. as for Hackney Society office, above). An article on the Round Chapel can be obtained from Jack Youngmark (see above). The trust is also currently involved with the restoration of St Augustine's Tower.

[186] **HACKNEY BUILDING EXPLORATORY**. *Project director*: Polly Hudson, Professional Development Centre, Albion Drive, London E8 4ET, *Tel/Fax*: (020) 7275 8555. 'A developing exhibition about the built environment which is being put together by Hackney people across an enormous range of ages and ability. It offers local communities a unique resource for understanding how their homes and neighbourhoods have developed over past centuries and how people who live and work there now can help to shape future housing plans'.

* COMMUNITY HISTORY PUBLISHING PROJECTS *

[187] **CENTERPRISE TRUST LTD**. 136-138 Kingsland High St, London E8 2NS, *Tel*: (020) 7254 9632; *Fax*: (020) 7923 1951. The publishing programme flourished for some 20 years between 1972 and 1992/3. The following list is of titles still in print: **History and memoirs**: *The Austrian cockney*, 1980, by Martha Lang; *Doctor Jelley: the threepenny doctor of Hackney*, 1983; *The 43 Group*, 1993, by Morris Beckman (post World War II Jewish anti-fascist group in Hackney); *The Gibson Gardens history and cookery book*, 1984 (Gibson gardens is a small estate in Stoke Newington, built in 1880). *A Hackney memory chest*, 1983, by George Cook; *Hackney propaganda: working-class club life and politics 1870-1900*, 1980, by Barry Burke and Ken Worpole; *A Hoxton childhood*, 1969, by A.S. Jasper; *The Irish in London*, 1991, by Paddy Fahey (worked as a professional photographer documenting lives of London's Irish communities for 40 years); *The Island: the life and death of an East London community 1870-1970*, 1979 (memories of 15 former residents of a small self-enclosed community in Lower Clapton); *One over the baker's dozen*, 1985, by Betty Vodden (one of 14 children, she lived all her life on the borders of Hackney and Islington); *A second look*: a photographic record of a walk through Hackney in the 1890's and today, 1975; *Volla Volla Jew Boy*, 1988, by Cyril Spector.

Contemporary autobiographical writing:

Breaking the silence: writing by Asian women, 1984; *A comprehensive education*, 1978, by Roger Mills (school days in a Hackney secondary school, 1965-1971); *Every birth it comes different*: writings from Hackney Reading Centre, 1980 (experiences of childbirth in England, the Caribbean, Africa and Israel); *It can happen*, 1985, by Isaac Gordon (childhood in Jamaica, arriving in England in 1960); *Living and winning*, 1985, by Pauline Wiltshire (disabled Jamaican woman); *A misspent youth*, 1985, by Jim Baker; *Pure running*, 1982, by Louise Shore (autobiography of a Jamaican woman); *Wesley, my only son*, 1987, by Monica Jules (single mother of an autistic son); *Working lives*: Hackney 1945-1977, 1977 (autobiographies of 13 Hackney residents).

Creative writing:

As good as we make it, 1982 (stories, poems and autobiographical writing by people aged 14-25; *Flood at the door*, 1979, by Savitri Hensman (poems by a school student); *Not all roses*: poetry and prose, 1987, by Black Anthology Group; *Scribe sistren*, 1987 (poems by a young Rastafarian woman); *Some grit, some fire*, 1984, by Hackney women writers; *Stepney Words I & II*, 1973 (first edition of poems by school students led to dismissal of their teacher Chris Searle; subsequently over 15,000 copies were sold); *Sub animal yells*, 1984, by Sharon Dunham (poems); *Time to be bold*, 1981, by Lotte Moos; *Where there's smoke*: poems and stories, 1983 (by Hackney Writers Workshop); *Words from the women's cafe*: lesbian poetry from 'Word-up', 1993 (poems from Centerprise's monthly women's performance evening).

Centerprise is still involved with creative writing: the Centerprise Literature Development project offers a range of creative writing courses, events, writers' surgeries, advice and information resources, plus links with other writers and organisations. *Contact*: Eva Lewin, ext. 211, Tues, Thur, Fri.

* SOME OTHER COUNCIL CONTACTS *

Agenda 21: Kathryn Johnson, Town Hall, Mare St, London E8, *Tel*: (020) 8356 3390. A recent report issued is *Hackney tomorrow: shaping a better future*.

Conservation and design section is at 161 City Rd, London EC1V 1NR. *Principal conservation officer*: Katherine Owen, *Tel*: (020) 8356 8088; *Listed buildings at risk officer*: Catherine Bond, *Tel*: (020) 8356 8076.

First Stop Shop (source for many information leaflets). Entrance to Town Hall, Mare St, London E8, *Tel*: (020) 8356 3000. Another First Stop Shop at: Shoreditch Library, Hoxton St, London N1, *Tel*: (020) 8356 4360.

Reference Library: Rose Lipman Library, 43 De Beauvoir Rd, London N1, *Tel*: (020) 8356 2576. *Strategic Policy Unit*, at Town Hall, Mare St, London E8, publishes a *Directory of public service organisations in Hackney*. Contact: Mandy Woodhall, *Tel*: (020) 8356 3264.

Park Users Groups:
These have been set up for all the major open spaces in Hackney and can be contacted through Springfield Park, Upper Clapton, *Tel*: (020) 8806 1826.

In the south of the borough: Haggerton and Shoreditch parks; in the central area: London Fields, Hackney Downs, Millfields, Hackney Marsh; and in the north: Clissold Park and Springfield Park.

* SOME NON-COUNCIL CONTACTS *

Business information:
HACKNEY BUSINESS VENTURE. 1 Kingsland High St, London E8, *Tel*: (020) 7254 9595.
HACKNEY CHAMBER OF COMMERCE. 18 Ashwin St, London E8, *Tel*: (020) 7923 3783. Also at this address: Hackney branch of Business Link (City, Hackney, Islington), *Tel*: (020) 7275 6800.
SHOREDITCH BUSINESS INFORMATION (in same building as Shoreditch Library, and Shoreditch First Stop Shop), 80 Hoxton St, London N1, *Tel*: (020) 8356 4358.

Community trusts:
HOXTON TRUST (for community initiatives). 156 Hoxton St, London N1, *Tel*: (020) 7729 1480.
QUEENSBRIDGE TRUST. 6 Laurel Court, Queensbridge Rd, London E8 3BN, *Tel*: (020) 7923 7920.

Regeneration:
Hackney Regeneration Partnership. Executive director: Kevin Sugrue, 300 Mare St, London E8, *Tel*: (020) 8356 6666. Head of Regeneration Unit within Council: Chris Hadley.

Voluntary organisations:
HACKNEY COUNCIL FOR VOLUNTARY SERVICES. 18 Ashwin St, London E8, *Tel*: (020) 7923 1962.

* LOCAL PRESS *

Hackney Gazette. 138 Cambridge Heath Rd, London E1 5QJ, *Tel*: (020) 7790 8822. Part of the East London Advertiser Group which also publishes the free paper *Hackney Echo*. *Hackney Today*, the council's magazine is edited by Jenny Bloom at the Town Hall, Mare St, London E8. *Tel*: (020) 8356 3444.

HAVERING

* LONDON BOROUGH OF HAVERING *

[188] **HAVERING LOCAL HISTORY COLLECTION** at Reference Library, Central Library, St Edward's Way, Romford, Essex RM1 3AR, *Tel*: (01708) 772394. *Librarian in charge of reference library*: Julie Johns. *Hours*: Mon, Tues, Wed, Fri. 9.30- 8; Sat 9.30-4.
The Family History Centre based here issues a guide to materials available. The reference library compiles and publishes the *Havering list of local organisations* (16th edition: 1999/2000).
Recent publications are: *From country to Cockney: Romford Market within living memory*, by Norma Jennings, Nellie Sims, and George Saddington (with pupils from Redden Court School), published in association with Redden Court Enterprises,

1996. 56pp, illus. *Hornchurch and the New Zealand connection*, by Barbara Mannox, 1993, 68pp, illus. Other publications currently available include: *Childhood memories of Hornchurch, 1914-1936*, by Olive Edith Thomas, 1991; *A history of Havering-Atte-Bower*, by Harold Smith, 1925, reprinted 1990; *History of the Queen's Theatre, Hornchurch*, by Gordon Humby, edited by Joyce Meade and Karen Fisher, 1988, 47pp, illus; *Hornchurch and Romford* - extract from Volume VII of the Victoria County History; *Making of Emerson Park*, by Barbara Mannox, 1991, 131pp, illus; *A short history of Stubbers*, by Valerie Body, 1989 (historic garden associated with botanist William Coys); *Upminster: the story of a garden suburb*, self-published by Tony Benton (46 Waldegrave Gardens, Upminster RM14 1UX), 1996, 176pp.

Tony Benton is also the author of *Upminster and Hornchurch*, old photographs, from Sutton; also from Sutton: *Romford*, compiled by D. Hewson.

Phillimore publish a number of Havering titles: by Brian Evans: *Bygone Romford*, 1988; *Hornchurch and Upminster: a pictorial history*, 1995; and *Romford, Collier Row and Gidea Park*, 1994. *Havering Village to Harold Wood*, a pictorial history, 1995, is by Chris Saltmarsh and Norma Jennings.

---

* HISTORICAL AND AMENITY SOCIETIES *

[189] **FRIENDS OF RAINHAM MARSH**. *Contact*: Phil Butler, 218 Lodge Lane, Romford RM5 2EU. *Tel*: (01708) 754391. This SSSI is under threat from council promoted speculative industrial development. The Friends in coalition with other conservation bodies, including the London Wildlife Trust wishes to create a new nature reserve - the capital's largest, and a catalyst for regenerating Havering riverside.

[190] **FRIENDS OF WENNINGTON CHURCH**. *Contact*: Mr R.J. Petheram, 3 Spencer Rd, Rainham RM13 8HD.

[191] **GIDEA PARK AND DISTRICT CIVIC SOCIETY**. *Secretary*: Mrs J.M. Leicester, 9 Meadway, Gidea Park, Romford RM2 5NU, *Tel*: (01708) 743645. Seeks to protect the Gidea Park Conservation Area, including the Romford Garden Suburb, built in 1911 by more than 100 architects as an exhibition of houses and cottages in a vernacular 'arts and crafts' style and the houses in the 1934 'modern homes' exhibition.

[192] **INDEPENDENT HAVERING MUSEUM TRUST**. *Contact*: Owen Ware, c/o Central Library, Romford RM1 3AR. Working to create a new Havering Museum.

[193] **HORNCHURCH AND DISTRICT HISTORICAL SOCIETY**. *Secretary*: P.M. Butler, Little Silvers, 7 Mendoza Close, Hornchurch RM11 2RP, *Tel*: (01708) 447535. Aims 'to foster interest in and protection of the Hornchurch and Upminster area, its buildings and artefacts'. There are monthly meetings, and visits. The society opens the Upminster Windmill and the Upminster Tithe Barn once a month during summer. There is a newsletter and the annual *Havering History Review*.

Contents listings for recent issues of Havering History Review:

No 13, 1992: ..And Another Year ... 1991-92; The Brickworks of Upminster and Cranham; When You Go Down Hopping!; Roman Rainham - AD43 to 410 or later; Grays - Upminster Railway Centenary; Hornchurch in the late 19th-early 20th century from its artefacts; Heritage of Straw; The Crinkle-Crakle Wall at 'Stubbers', North Ockendon; Archaeology in Havering 1991-1992 - The Highlights.

No 14, 1993: Report from the Chair ... 1992-1993; Upminster Tithe Barn Folk and Agricultural Museum in 1992; Upminster - Romford Railway Centenary: 7th June 1993; The Tilbury Universal Machine (Tilbury Tanks); Upminster Parish Church: Rebuilding 1862; St Laurence Church Upminster; The Local Press and its Predecessors; The Queen's Theatre Hornchurch 1953-1993, 40th Anniversary Year; South Hornchurch Chapel; This is the Pits!

No 15, 1994: Another Year Passes ... 1993-1994; Upminster Tithe Barn Folk and Agricultural Museum in 1993; Cranham Beginnings; "On your Doorstep" RONEO to NEOPOST; War Work at the Roneo Works.

[194] **ROMFORD AND DISTRICT HISTORICAL SOCIETY**. *Secretary*: Mrs J. Raggett, 14 Thames Close, Rainham RM13 9HP, *Tel*: (01708) 520673. Publishes a newsletter and the annual *Romford Record*.

Contents listing for the Romford Record:

No 25: A community transformed, Part 2; What's in a name II; Romford in Parliament Part 2 (1945-70); Reliable goods, reasonably priced, pleasantly sold: 10 years of Pollards; Determining Havering's populating in 1327; Old iron: 60 years ago; Obituary - A.G. Edwards; Growing up in London and Leytonstone.

No 26: Kings, queens and 14th century Havering; Bridge over troubled waters: a look at Havering's water courses; James Owens VC; Boyhood strong, girlhood graceful: working class women on Harold Hill; Growth of local government in Romford and Hornchurch: some memories; Century of Romford's second railway: 100 years of the 'Push-pull'; Roneo remembered.

No 27: A notable tenant of Hare Hall; A lady of Havering Atte Bower; 15th century kings and Havering Liberty Charter; Reminiscences, Part II (by Glyn Richards); Boyhood strong, girlhood graceful, Part 2: Princess Caroline.

No 28: Recollections of the forties: Noak Hill and the coming of Harold Hill; How the 'pictures' came to Harold Hill; Trades and professions of Romford 1828/9; The dark lantern: the last chase of Inspector Simmons; A foot round London - Rip Van Winkle and the 'pathfinder' (May 1911); Gift of a park to Romford (16 August 1902 newspaper report); A Romford railway station that never was; Violinist in the workhouse; Crime in Junction Road (August 1914 report).

No 29: 1956 and all that; the gentle craft; Ruby anniversary: presidential address; Tudor kings and Havering; Romford 1956: a momentous year; A Romford life: late Victorian to early 20th century; Romford memories: 1920's, 1930's and the two world wars; London omnibuses and how they are managed (from Home Words, September 1891); Geoffrey J. Clements remembered.

No 30: Forty years on (by Geoffrey Clements); My Havering connection (by Marjorie McIntosh); Memories of the society; History recalled in Romford library; Romford in the early 1950's and St Edward's School; A glance at local medical services in the 1950's; Memories of happy times; How the old place has changed!; Looking at churches; Memories of the Romford area; A 'Dame School' in Hornchurch; Greetings from the far West (Cooke descendants); The difference a road makes; Romford at night (poem by Bill Pearce).

No 31: The hurricane in retrospect; Charles Thomas Perfect 1864-1939; Romford - late Victorian/early 20th century, Part 2; The Petre family and recusancy; Where there's a will; Romford directory, 1848.

No 32: In memorium: Laurie Matthews; Havering Palace: notes on the survey 1649-50, and plans from 1578, 1610; Tudor queens and Havering; Squirrels Heath Railway factory listed; Around Romford in the early 1900's; Tylers (Upminster) Commons; News from far and near; 'Pale hands I loved'.

[195] **UPMINSTER COMMON CONSERVATION ASSOCIATION**. *Secretary*: Mrs J. Page, 76 Shepherds Hill, Harold Wood, Romford RM3 0NJ.

* SOME OTHER COUNCIL CONTACTS *

Arts officer: Chris Cole, *Tel*: (01708) 773950.
Business: Eldon Chudley, Economic Profile Department, *Tel*: (01708) 772842.
Conservation officer: Mrs Sue Smith, Mercury House, Mercury Gardens, Romford RM1 3SL, *Tel*: (01708) 772655. There are 9 conservation areas.
Countryside service: Paul Vickers, *Tel*: (01708) 772698; Peter Williams, *Tel*: (01708) 772585.
Information: Information office at Town Hall, *Tel*: (01708) 772012; reference library at Central Library, Romford, *Tel*: (01708) 772394.

* SOME NON-COUNCIL CONTACTS *

Voluntary organisations:
HAVERING VOLUNTEER CENTRE. 9 Tadworth Parade, Elm Park, Hornchurch RM12 5AS, *Tel*: (01708) 479788.

* LOCAL PRESS *

Harold Gazette. 14 St Thomas St, Brentwood CM14 4DE, *Tel*: (01277) 219222.
Havering Magazine, published by council, *Tel*: (01708) 772427.
Havering Yellow Advertiser. 137 George Lane, South Woodford E18 1AJ, *Tel*: (020) 8530 3641.
Romford and Havering Post. 2 Whalebone Lane South, Dagenham RM8 1HB, *Tel*: (020) 8517 5577.
Romford Recorder. 3 River Chambers, High St, Romford RM1 1TD, *Tel*: (01708) 766044.

REDBRIDGE

* LONDON BOROUGH OF REDBRIDGE *

[196] **REDBRIDGE LOCAL HISTORY COLLECTION** at: Central Library, Clements Rd, Ilford IG1 1EA, *Tel*: (020) 8478 7145. *Librarian*: Ian Dowling. *Hours*: Mon-Fri 9.30-8; Sat 9.30-4.30. A museum is planned to open at the Central Library in 1999/2000. *Contact*: Vicky Knapman. The library sells a range of publications. Its own recent publications include: *Ilford past and present*, by George Tasker, published in 1901, reissued in 1992; *One hundred years of suburbia*: the Aldersbrook Estate in

Wanstead 1899-1999, by Katherine Morrison and Ann Robey (in association with the RCHME), 1999, 45pp, illus; and *Victory in 1945* by Ian Dowling and Peter Ledger, 1995, 55pp, illus.

Commercial publications on sale include: from Tempus two collections of old photographs on *Ilford*, compiled by Ian Dowling and Nick Harris; and one collection on *Wanstead and Woodford*, from same compilers. *Woodford: a pictorial history*, by Peter Lawrence and Georgina Green was published by Phillimore in 1995. From Sutton: collections on *Chadwell Heath*, and *Ilford to Hainault*, by D. Hewson. A new edition of Norman Gunby's self-published *A potted history of Ilford* was issued in 1997 (see advert).

* HISTORICAL AND AMENITY SOCIETIES *

[197] **CHADWELL HEATH HISTORICAL SOCIETY**. *Secretary*: Miss C. Wagg, 338 High Rd, Chadwell Heath RM6 6AJ, *Tel*: (020) 590 0013. *Chair*: Jill Cox, 2 Forsters Close, Chadwell Heath RM6 6DH, *Tel*: (020) 599 9805.

[198] **FRIENDS OF THE HOSPITAL CHAPEL** (the hospital chapel of St Mary the Virgin and St Thomas of Canterbury). *Secretary*: Mrs S. Leake, 6 Linden Crescent, Woodford Green IG8 0DG, *Tel*: (020) 8504 9395. *Membership secretary*: Mr M. Fairhurst, 46 Gaysham Avenue, Gants Hill, Ilford IG2 6TJ. Situated at 48 Ilford Hill, Ilford; founded c. 1145 as a leper hospital, the present building is 14th and 19th century; chapel has many interesting monuments, and Burne Jones windows.

[199] **FRIENDS OF VALENTINES PARK**. *Contact*: D.A. Johnson, 67 St Andrews' Rd, Ilford IG1 3PE, *Tel*: (020) 8518 1199.

[200] **ILFORD HISTORICAL SOCIETY**. *Secretary*: Mr J. Page, 71 Cranley Rd, Ilford IG2 6AF, *Tel*: (020) 8554 0493. *Chairman*: Peter Wright, 174 Aldborough Rd South, Ilford IG3 8HF, *Tel*: (020) 8590 9972. Monthly meetings at Ilford Reference Library. The society is developing a housing archive - a record of all types of dwellings in the town, and is recording the detailed growth of Ilford during the late 19th and early 20th centuries. There is a monthly newsletter, and a journal may commence in 1999. Transactions are issued occasionally: *Trams and trolleybuses in Ilford* by L.A. Thomson in 1979; a booklet on *Ilford conservation areas* in 1992.

[201] **SEVEN KINGS AND GOODMAYES HISTORICAL SOCIETY**. *Contact*: Frank Turvey, 636 Green Lane, Goodmayes, Ilford IG3 9RZ, *Tel*: (020) 9599 3287; another contact: Margaret Langwith, *Tel*: (020) 8599 9277. Est. in 1979. Meetings, outings. Occasional papers with articles of local and Essex interest issued.

[202] **WANSTEAD HISTORICAL SOCIETY**. *Contacts*: Clifford Hume, 28 Howard Rd, Ilford IG1 2EK, *Tel*: (020) 8514 8595. Brian Page, 122b George Lane, South Woodford E18 1AD; mobile: (0589) 834833. Est. in 1961. A journal is issued three times a year, and there is an annual newsletter. There are two indexes to the journal, for 1983-1991; and for 1992-1996. *Wanstead in pictures a the Passmore Edwards Museum*, compiled by George Collins, 1990, is a booklet guide to photographs, prints and postcards of Wanstead and Snaresbrook. Dennis Keeling booklet *Orphans of Commerce: The Commercial Travellers Schools in Wanstead* was published by the author in 1992.
Wanstead House was built between 1715 and 1722 and demolished in 1822. A booklet of an exhibition on the house, by Peter Wright, was published by the library in 1974. A surviving Doric temple in the park of Wanstead House has an exhibition of recently discovered 18th century artefacts. The park is now owned by the Corporation of London.

[203] **WOODFORD HISTORICAL SOCIETY**. *Secretary*: Georgina Green, 24 Henry's Walk, Hainault, Ilford IG6 2NR, *Tel*: (020) 8500 6045. *Chairman*: Peter Lawrence, 349 Chigwell Rd, Woodford Bridge, Woodford Green IG8 8PE, *Tel*: (020) 8491 6857. Est. in 1932, the society aims to stimulate interest in the history of Woodford and surrounding districts. There are lectures, visits and exhibitions and it supports archaeological work in the district. There is a newsletter twice a year. Proceedings and transactions have been published since 1933; during the 1980's: No 14: *Woodford: village to suburb*, by Margery M. Smith, 1982; No 15: *A century of Woodford memories*, edited by Ernest A. Fulcher, 1986; No 16: *Robert Knight, builder of Luxborough*, by F.J. Erith and *Luxborough*, by A.R.J. Ramsey and others (revised edition of No 7).
Publications are now issued separately, each with an individual style: *Woodford in the 1930's*, edited by Ernest A. Fulcher was published in 1992 as No 1 in the new series. Trails have been issued for Woodford Green, 1984; Church End, 1990, and George Lane 1991.

* SOME OTHER COUNCIL CONTACTS *

Business:
Business and Community Partnerships office, Town Hall, Ilford, ext. 2238. *Contact*: Isobel Weeks.

Conservation officer: Bridget Shepherd, Town Hall, Ilford, *Tel*: (020) 8478 2272. There are 13 conservation areas, and 7 more under consideration. A variety of guidance leaflets have been issued. In 1984 a 62 page guide *Conservation areas and listed buildings* was published.

Nature conservation: *Contact*: Pat Buttress, parks department, *Tel*: (020) 8478 3223. Hainault Forest Country Park, *Tel*: (020) 8500 7353, *contact*: Andrea Byerley.

Information: information centre at Town Hall, Ilford, *Tel*: (020) 8478 3020; reference library at the Central Library, Clements Rd, Ilford IG1 1EA, *Tel*: (020) 8478 7145.

---

* SOME NON-COUNCIL CONTACTS *

Arts:
REDBRIDGE ARTS COUNCIL. *Contact*: Miss Doreen Weller, *Tel*: (020) 8593 7994.

Business:
REDBRIDGE CHAMBER OF COMMERCE, 8th Floor, 197 High Rd, Ilford IG1 1LX, *Tel*: (020) 8514 8222. There is also a Redbridge Business Forum.

Voluntary organisations:
REDBRIDGE COUNCIL FOR VOLUNTARY SERVICE. Broadway Chambers, 1 Cranbrook Rd, Ilford IG1 4DU, *Tel*: (020) 8554 5049.

---

* LOCAL PRESS *

Borough News, issued twice a year, edited by Mazine Bradley, Town Hall, *Tel*: (020) 8478 9122.
Ilford Recorder. 539 High Rd, Ilford IG1 1UD, *Tel*: (020) 8578 4444.
Redbridge Guardian. Guardian House, 480-500 Larkhall Rd, Hyams Park, London E4 9GD, *Tel*: (020) 8498 3400.
Redbridge Post. 2 Whalebone Lane South, Dagenham RM8 1HB, *Tel*: (020) 8517 5577.
Yellow Advertiser. 137 George Lane, South Woodford E18 1AN, *Tel*: (020) 8530 3641.

WALTHAM FOREST

* LONDON BOROUGH OF WALTHAM FOREST *

[204] **WALTHAM FOREST LOCAL HISTORY LIBRARY**, at Vestry House Museum, Vestry Rd, Walthamstow, London E17 9NH, *Tel*: (020) 8509 1917. *Librarian*: Brian Mardall (part time, on clerical grade); *Archivist*: Josephine Parker. *Hours*: Tues, Wed, Fri: 10-1, 2-5.15; Sat 10-1, 2-4.45. The collection can be consulted *by appointment only*.
Photographs, prints, water-colours are the responsibility of the museum, as are publications.

[205] **VESTRY HOUSE MUSEUM**. Vestry Rd, Walthamstow, London E17 9NH, *Tel*: (020) 8509 1917. *Manager*: Nigel Sadler. *Hours*: Mon-Fri 10-1, 2-5.30; Sat 10-1, 2-5. Building is an early 18th century workhouse; its history 1730-1965 is described in a four page leaflet. The museum sells a range of books, posters, maps and souvenirs relating to the history of Waltham Forest, plus a number of replica toys and games.
VHM/LBWF publications currently available include: the autobiography of Robert Barltrop: *My mother's calling me*, 1984 (boyhood in the 1920's and early 1930's); *A funny age*, 1985 (The Manoux Grammar school, sports, politics, morals, Scouts, jobs); *Bright summer - dark autumn*, 1986 (jobs, boxing, football, World War II).
There are a number of World War II publications: *War over Walthamstow: the story of civil defence*. by Ross Wyld, reprinted 1989 (originally published 1945 by Walthamstow B.C.); *Second World War information pack* (postcards, HMSO/Civil Defence leaflets, newspapers, certificates, posters, etc.), published 1995; four HMSO Civil Defence leaflets are also available separately.
A C.O.'s war, by Percy G.C. Wilding, 1996, was published by the author, and relates his experiences as a conscientious objector during World War II.
Also available, and published by VHM: 8 World War II postcards, two sets of 8 postcards showing local scenes, one in colour, the other b/w; 'Mayfair' colour postcards, featuring old advertisements and posters. The museum also sells commercial publications: from Phillimore: *Bygone Walthamstow*, 1995. by Brian Evans; from Tempus: *Chingford*, compiled by Stephen Pewsey; *Leyton and Leytonstone*; and *Walthamstow*, both compiled by Keith Romig and Peter Lawrence.

[206] **WILLIAM MORRIS GALLERY**. Lloyd Park, Forest Rd, London E17 4PP, *Tel*: (020) 8527 3782; ;*internet*: www.lbwf.gov.uk/wmg. *Curator*: Nora Gillow. *Hours*: Tues-Sat and first sun of each month 10-1, 2-5. The Morris's family home from 1848 to 1956, and the only public museum devoted to William Morris and his diverse achievements, as well as his followers in the Arts and Crafts movement, 1880's to 1920's.

The Brangwyn Gift is of paintings, drawings and prints by the pre-Raphaelites and other Victorian and later artists, as well as works by Sir Frank Brangwyn himself. There is a gallery shop and a Friends organisation.

* HISTORIC PROPERTIES *

[207] **FRIENDS OF LOW HALL PUMP HOUSE**. *Secretary*: Mr L. Collier, 12 Penrhyn Grove, Walthamstow, London E17 5DE, *Tel*: (020) 8531 2627.

[208] **THE COPPED HALL TRUST**. *Contact*: Alan Cox, 112 Torriano Avenue, London NW5 2SD, *Tel*: (020) 7267 1679. The present house was built in 1753 for John Conyers, but the estate has a history which stretches back to Doomsday. The 18th century house was embellished by the Wythes family who built a very elaborate Italianate garden. The Corporation of the City of London purchased much of the park in 1992, removing the threat of a golf course, and after many vicissitudes the Trust purchased the freehold of Copped Hall in 1995. The Friends organisation helps to sustain the repair and restoration work of the trust. A short history of Copped Hall, by Raymond Cassidy was published by the Waltham Abbey Historical Society in 1983.

[209] entry withdrawn

* HISTORICAL AND AMENITY SOCIETIES *

[210] **CHINGFORD HISTORICAL SOCIETY**. *Secretary*: Mrs J. McGann, 55 Bretterham Rd, London E17, *Tel*: (020) 8531 1478. *Membership secretary*: Mrs H. Ansell, 3 Faversham Avenue, Chingford E4 6DT, *Tel*: (020) 8529 4365; *Chair*: Miss S. Beard, 42 Seymour Rd, Chingford E4 7LS. Est. in 1939; meetings, visits research. There is a newsletter *Chingford Notes*. Bulletins on specific subjects have been published since 1958, and currently in print are: *Chingford in history*, by Kenneth Neale, first published in 1967; *Chingford as it was*, 1977, a selection of photographs from the society's collection showing pre 1920's Chingford; and *The Chingflier*, 1996 (a collection of articles and information from the station magazine of the Chingford Royal Naval Air Station, published during WWI, 1916-1918), compiled by Leonard Davis.

[211] **WALTHAM FOREST CIVIC SOCIETY**. *Secretary*: David Boote, 85 Forest Drive West, London E11 1JZ, *Tel*: (020) 8558 1554. *Chairman*: Adrian Stannard, 19 Avon Rd, Walthamstow E17 3RB, *Tel*: (020) 8521 4400. The society evolved in 1987 from the foundations laid by the Leyton Society in 1972, and aims 'to preserve the best and improve the rest in Waltham Forest'. A newsletter is issued and a booklet on William Morris connections is in preparation.

[212] **WALTHAM FOREST ORAL HISTORY WORKSHOP**. *Secretary*: Mr R. Wilkinson, c/o Vestry House Museum, Vestry Rd, Walthamstow, London E17 9NH, *Tel*: (020) 8509 1917. A series of Waltham Forest Memories compiled from interviews has been published: *Touch yer collar, never swaller*, 1984; *Pig's head and pease pudding*, 1985; *Cottage loaves and plain bricks* (bakery trade), 1986; *Bullseyes*, 1988 (local confectionery trade); *We want Winns*, 1993 (a school strike in 1945); *One door closes, another opens*, 1984 (a personal experience of polio).

[213] **WALTHAMSTOW HISTORICAL SOCIETY**. *Secretary*: Mr P.C. Plummer, 24 Nesta Rd, Woodford Green IG8 9RG, *Tel*: (020 8504 4156. *Publications*: Mrs W.J. Ellingham, 82 The Charter Rd, Woodford Green IG8 9RE. Est. in 1914 as the Walthamstow Antiquarian Society. Publications currently in print: *Fit to drink* (history of water supply in Walthamstow), 1986; *The Forest in Walthamstow and Chingford*, by Anthony David Law, 1978; *George Monoux's School, Walthamstow* (1527-1977), by C.C. Pond, 1977; *Non-conformity in Walthamstow*, Part II, by M.E. Batsford, 1979 (Methodists and others). Part I, 1977 also by M.E. Batsford is on Congregationalists and Baptists; *Shoppers Paradise* (history of Walthamstow High Street), compiled by John Hawes and Anthony D. Law, 1991; *Some old Walthamstow houses*, 1998; *Victorian and Edwardian Waltham Forest* (photographs of the period 1846-1910), published in 1974; *Waltham Forest 1910-1940* (photographs of the period 1974); *Waltham Forest 1940-1975* (photographs of the period), 7th revised edition, 1994; *The Walthamstow tokens* (published 1927/29, reprinted 1988); *Walthamstow Village*, 5th revised edition, 1996.

* EPPING FOREST *

[214] **CONSERVATORS OF EPPING FOREST**. Wanstead Flats, London E12, *Tel*: (020) 8989 1234. The Workshop, Jubilee Retreat, Bury Rd, London E4, *Tel*: (020) 8559 4634.

[215] **EPPING FOREST DISTRICT MUSEUM.** 39/41 Sun St, Waltham Abbey EN9 1EL, *Tel*: (01922) 716882; *Fax*: (01992) 700427. *Hours*: Tues 12-5; Fri, Sat, Sun, Mon 2-5; Wed & Thurs, party bookings by appointment. Run by the Epping Forest District Council. Situated in two adjacent framed houses dating from c. 1520 to c. 1760 in the historic market town of Waltham Abbey, the museum interprets the social history of the whole of the Epping Forest district from the stone age to the present day. There is a Victorian Life Gallery and a Tudor Room, and temporary exhibitions cover a wide range of subjects. There are special events and adult workshops, and a lively education programme; also a shop and herb garden. A booklet is published on the history of the building; there is also a collection of old photographs *Epping*, from Tempus.

[216] **FRIENDS OF EPPING FOREST.** *Contact*: Mrs M. Britten, 9 Frederica Rd, Chingford, London E4 7AL, *Tel*: (020) 8529 8594.

[217] **QUEEN ELIZABETH'S HUNTING LODGE.** Rangers Rd, Chingford, London E4 7QH, *Tel*: (020) 8529 6681. *Hours*: Wed-Sun 2-5. Run by the Corporation of London. Displays show the history and former uses of the building dating back to 1543, and of Epping Forest in the days when it was a Royal Forest and the monarch hunted deer. A series of illustrated leaflets is published.

* SOME OTHER COUNCIL CONTACTS *   (NB: Telephone numbers are due to change in 1999).

Arts and Tourism: Clara Arokaisamy, Sycamore House, Forest Rd, London E17 4JF, *Tel*: (020) 8527 5544, ext. 4629.
Business/urban regeneration: David Franks, Department of Planning and Economic Development, The Ridgeway, Chingford E4 6PS, *Tel*: (020) 8527 5544.
Conservation officer: Guy Oxborne, The Ridgeway, as above, ext. 6316.
Information: Reference Library, at Central Library, High Street, Walthamstow E17, *Tel*: (020) 8520 3017. For council information there are First Stop Shops at the Town Hall, Forest Rd, London E17 4JF, *Tel*: (020) 8527 5544; and at Leyton and Leytonstone.
Nature conservation officer: Nick Evans, The Ridgeway, as above, ext. 6019.

* SOME NON-COUNCIL CONTACTS *

Arts:
WALTHAM FOREST ARTS COUNCIL, William Morris Gallery, Lloyd Park, Forest Rd, London E17 4PP. *Tel*: (020) 8527 8750.

WALTHAMSTOW VILLAGE FESTIVAL. *Chair*: at 33 Church Lane, Walthamstow E17 9RN, *Tel*: (020) 8521 3864.

Business:
WALTHAM FOREST CHAMBER OF COMMERCE, 306 Hoe St, London E17, *Tel*: (020) 8520 5494.

Regeneration:
ORIENT REGENERATION, Kirkdale House, 7 Kirkdale Rd, Leytonstone, London E11 1HP, *Tel*: (020) 8539 5333. *Fax*: (020) 8539 8074.

Residents associations:
WALTHAM FOREST FEDERATION OF TENANTS, COMMUNITY AND RESIDENTS ASSOCIATIONS. 195 Wood St, London E17, *Tel*: (020) 8509 3030. *Contact*: Linda McNeshis.

Voluntary organisations:
VOLUNTARY ACTION WALTHAM FOREST. Alpha Business Centre, South Grove, London E17, *Tel*: (020) 8521 0377.

* LOCAL PRESS *

There are Leyton/Leytonstone, Walthamstow and Chingford editions of the *Guardian* produced at: Guardian Gazette Independent and Citizens Newspapers, Guardian House, 480-500 Larkhall Rd, Chingford, London E4 9DD, *Tel*: (020) 8498 3460. Free newspapers *The Independent*, and *Yellow Advertiser* also from here.
Waltham Forest Today, council monthly newspaper, edited by Kasia Reardon, *Tel*: (020) 8925 5076.

DOCKLANDS

The *Docklands Business Directory* is published by Dorchester Productions, 5 Lanark Square, Glengall Bridge, London E14 9RE, *Tel*: (020) 7531 1146.

[218] **BECKTON RESIDENTS ACTION GROUP**. 60 Fleetwood Court, Evelyn Dennington Rd, Beckton London E6 4XZ, *Tel*: (020) 7473 1317.
Another Beckton contact is the St Marks Church and Community Centre, *Director*: David Pennock, Tollgate Rd, London E6 4YA, *Tel*: (020) 7511 3024.

[219] **CUSTOM HOUSE AND CANNING TOWN COMMUNITY RENEWAL PROJECT**. St Luke's Church and Community Centre, Tarling Rd, London E16, *Tel*: (020) 7366 6400.

[220] **DOCKLANDS EAST LONDON** (public sector, partnership body for the area's continuing development). Fourth Floor, Bellerive House, 3 Muirfield Crescent, London E14, *Tel*: (0870) 6060502.

[221] **DOCKLANDS ENGLISH PARTNERSHIP OFFICE** (Royal Docks). Compressor House, Royal Albert Docks, London E16 2QD, *Tel*: (020) 7540 5500.

[222] **DOCKLANDS FORUM**. Brady Centre, 192 Hanbury St, London E1 5HU, *Tel*: (020) 7377 1822; *Fax*: (020) 7247 5637; *Email*: docklandsforum@dial.pipex.com. *Website*: http://dockforum.gold.ac.uk. The forum was est. in 1974 and today represents some 130 community and voluntary groups throughout East and South East London. It works 'to protect and enhance the region's economic, social, natural and built environment'. The membership includes a wide range of organisations hitherto unrecorded in this publication, such as: Allotments for the future; Beckton Area Team; Bermondsey Forum; Bridge Project; Civilians Remembered (for a memorial park in Wapping); Clippers Quay Resident's Association; Community Economy; DLR Consultative Group; Downtown Community Development; East End Action Group; East London Community Training; Greenwich Experience; Hermitage Basin Environment Group; Islander Trust; Isle of Dogs Action Group; Joint Docklands Action Group; Limehouse Development Ground; London Churches Docklands Group; London Environment Centre; New Deal; Newham Docklands Forum; North Southwark Community Development Group; People Against the River Crossing; People of Poplar Against Roads; Residents Against Noise and Pollution; Riverside Communities and the Environment; Shadwell Basin Project; South East London Women's Environment Network; Tower Hamlets Churches in Community; Urban Learning Foundation.
A recent report publication from the forum is: *Millennium-partnerships for sustainable regeneration*.

[223] **DOCKLANDS HISTORY GROUP**. *Secretary*: Bob Aspinall, Museum in Docklands Library and Archives, Unit C14, Poplar Business Park, 10 Prestons Rd, London E14 9RL, *Tel*: (020) 7515 1162. Est. in 1979 to encourage the greater understanding of all aspects of the maritime, industrial and social history of the River Thames, the Port of London and Docklands. Currently some 80 members. Programme of talks and visits.

[224] **DOCKLANDS LIGHT RAILWAY LTD** (Holding company). PO Box 154, Castor Lane, London E14 0DX, *Tel*: (020) 7363 9898; *Press office*: (020) 7537 7023. Issues a quarterly newsletter *Light News*, and an illustrated report *Transport for the future*: the developing role of DLR Ltd.

[225] The operators **DOCKLANDS RAILWAY MANAGEMENT LTD** are also at the above address, responsible for customer services and for the information kiosk at Canary Wharf, *Tel*: (020) 7363 0500; *press office*: (020) 7363 9696.

[226] **ISLE OF DOGS COMMUNITY FOUNDATION**. PO Box 10449, London E14 8XT, *Tel*: (020) 7531 1200.

MUSEUM IN DOCKLANDS LIBRARY AND ARCHIVES. *See entry*: [753]

[227] **PORT OF LONDON AUTHORITY**. 58-60 St Katharine's Way, London E1 9LB, *Tel*: (020) 7265 2656; *Fax*: (020) 7265 2699. *Website*: www.portoflondon.co.uk. Publishes the monthly *Port newspaper*, editor: Roger Mutton.

[228] **ROYAL DOCKS MANAGEMENT AUTHORITY**. Custom House, King George V Lock, Security Gate 14, Woolwich Manor Way, London E16 2NJ, *Tel*: (020) 7511 5086; *Fax*: (020) 7511 0312. *Manager/company secretary*: Hamish Stewart. Responsible for management of the water area.

[229] **ROYAL DOCKS TRUST**. *Company secretary*: John Parker, 77-79 Bushey Green, Catford, London SE6 4AF, *Tel*: (020) 8461 1500.

[230] **ST KATHARINE AND SHADWELL TRUST**. PO Box 1779, London E1 9BY, *Tel*: (020) 7782 6962. Publications include a guide to artists in schools; and *A new perspective - a photographic essay on East London* (reflects on the influence of Bengali culture on Tower Hamlets).

[231] **THAMES GATEWAY LONDON PARTNERSHIP**. Unit 4, Stratford Office Village, Broadway, London E15 4NE, *Tel*: (020) 8221 2880.

* LOCAL PRESS *

Docklands Digest. PO Box 21760, London E14 9HP, *Tel*: (020) 7364 0300.
Docklands Magazine. 341-343 Roman Rd, London E3 5QR, *Tel*: (020) 8981 0416.
Dockland News. Custom House, King George V Lock, Woolwich Manor Way, London E16 2NJ, *Tel*: (020) 7473 2488.
Docklands Recorder. 182 High St North, London E6, *Tel*: (020) 8472 1421.
The Islander. Isle of Dogs Community newspaper, published by the Islander Trust, in conjunction with the Association of Island Communities. 21 Pointers Close, Isle of Dogs, London E14 3AP,*Tel*: (020) 7987 8631. *Editor*: David Tudor.
The Wharf. Mirror Group Newspapers, 22nd Floor, 1 Canada Square, London E14 5AP, *Tel*: (020) 7510 6306. Free newspaper.

NEWHAM

* LONDON BOROUGH OF NEWHAM *

[232] **NEWHAM LOCAL STUDIES LIBRARY**: at Stratford Library, Water Lane, London E15, *Tel*: (020) 8557 8856; *Archives and local history advisor*: Richard Durack; *Assistant*: Sarah Harding. (moving to new Stratford Broadway Library in 1999). *Hours*: Mon, Wed, Thurs 9.30-8; Tues 9.30-6.30; Fri, Sat 9.30-5.30.
The library has published a wide range of information sheets (dating from the 1980's and early 1990's); there are some80 'local history notes' on diverse historical and biographical subjects (see previous editions of this directory); there are three bibliographies 'Local studies sources' ('Black Saturday', the first day of the Blitz, 7th September 1940; books on Newham History; Royal Docks redevelopment).
Nine 'family history notes' cover: Local directories; Directories of London and Essex; Census returns; Parish registers; Newspapers; Electoral registers; Periodicals for family historians; Books for beginners; Poor law records.

* MUSEUMS AND VISITOR ATTRACTIONS *

[233] **NEWHAM MUSEUM SERVICE**. Museum Service Manager, Leisure Services, 292 Barking Rd, East Ham, London E6 3BA, *Tel*: (020) 8472 1430, ext. 21708. There are three establishments:

[234] **EAST HAM NATURE RESERVE**. Norman Rd, London E6 5AN, *Tel*: (020) 8470 4525. *Hours*: Tues-Fri 10-5; Sat, Sun 2-5 (during winter: 10-4; 1-4). London's largest chuchyard beside a Norman church; home to foxes, owls, kestrels, pheasants, crickets and 20 different kinds of butterflies.

[235] **MANOR PARK MUSEUM**. Manor Park Library, Romford Rd, London E12 5JY, *Tel*: (020) 8514 0274. *Hours*: Tues 10-5; Thurs 1-8; Fri, Sat 10-5. Has collections relating to the London Borough of Newham, including the Essex Pictorial Survey for the 5 North East London boroughs (held in its store).

[236] **NORTH WOOLWICH OLD STATION MUSEUM**. *Manager*: Charlie Harris, Pier Rd, North Woolwich, London E16 2JJ, *Tel*: (020) 7474 7244. *Hours* Mon-Wed 1-5; during summer: Fri 2-5; Sat 10-5; Sun 2-5. Railway engines, carriages, photographs, models and memorabilia; the story of Newham's railway industry and those who worked on it. Publications include: *Return to Woolwich: the North Woolwich railway and transport around the Royal Docks*, 1987; *Off the rails*: a teacher's pack, 1993.

[237] The **THAMES BARRIER VISITORS CENTR**. 1 Unity Way, Woolwich, London SE18 5NJ, *Tel*: (020) 8305 4188. Open daily 10-5, weekdays 10.30-5.30, weekends. Describes the construction, operation and need for the unique structure of the barrier by video displays, a working model, and a spectacular audio-visual experience. A shop sells a large selection of souvenirs and books.

* HISTORICAL/COMMUNITY HISTORY ORGANISATIONS *

[238] **EASTSIDE COMMUNITY HERITAGE**. *Contact*: Rita Chadha, The Old Town Hall, 20 The Broadway, Stratford, London E15 4BQ, *Tel*: (020) 8557 8609; *Fax*: (020) 8534 8411. Previously known as the Stratford City Challenge Community History Project, est. in 199. A Millennium Festival Fund grant has enabled the project to establish an East London People's archive. It is involved with exhibitions., publishing, research and community development. Publications include: *The way we were: memories of East Ham and West Ham; On the Broadway: a history of St John's Church; A working class war; Newham Women*; and *Earlham Grove shul - one hundred years of West Ham Synagogue and community*. A newsletter is issued.

[239] **NEWHAM HISTORY SOCIETY**. *Secretary and newsletter editor*: Mark Galloway, 52 Eastbourne Rd, East Ham, London E6 4AT, *Tel*: (020) 8471 1171; *Assistant secretary*: Stephen Pewsey, 59 Wroths Path, Loughton, Essex IG10 1SH, *Tel*: (020) 8508 5582. *President*: Derek Calder; *Chairman*: Dr S.L. Squires. Est. in 1971 to 'study and promote all aspects of the history of East and West Ham, East London and Essex'. It is affiliated to the Essex Archaeological and Historical Congress and participates in Essex-wide events which promote local history, such as the Essex History Fair. Current membership is 234. There is an annual newsletter and a series of occasional papers.

Frank Sainsbury served as secretary of the society for some 26 years, retiring in 1997; he was a founder of the society, and was borough librarian of West Ham, and later deputy librarian of the London Borough of Newham. He wrote a short book *West Ham: 800 years* in 1965; and *Six Men from Tolpuddle* (the trial of the 'Tolpuddle martyrs'), 1985. His article on the Silvertown explosion, 1917, appeared in Occasional Papers No 2, 1988.

Newsletter articles:

No 5, 1992: Memories of shops and shopping; Kier Hardie; Recollections of East Ham; Memories of day trips to Southend-on-Sea; West Ham evacuees in Oxfordshire; Shopping in 1876.

No 6, 1993: Goin' to the flicks; Prehistoric trackway found in Beckton; Christmas feasts and customs in Old Essex; A Canning Town girl's story; Memories of evacuation; The first day of the Blitz.

No 7, 1994: The first days of the Blitz; East and West Ham in 1939; A Medieval Royal murder; Medieval skeletons found in Stratford; West Ham Schools' Football Association 1905-1912.

No 8, 1995: Recollections of evacuation and three Newham schools; Recollections of Brampton Road school; East Ham village in 1872; Memories of a Plaistow childhood.

No 9, 1996: Historic buildings at risk in Newham: Memories of Plaistow in the 1930's; West Ham Schools football; The story of V2 attacks; Teenage memories of the war; Zeppelin raids over Essex between 1914-18.

No 10, 1997: Buildings at risk; Plaistow and the Essex countryside; Memories of a V2; Working conditions in Victorian offices; A forgotten East Ham V.C.; Zeppelin raids over Essex; Stratford Langthorne Abbey; West Ham Park.

Stephen Pewsey is a prolific author of books on Newham and Essex: from Phillimore: *Stratford: a pictorial history*, 1993; from Sutton: *Stratford, West Ham and the Royal Docks in old photographs*, 1996; and two volumes *Newham in old picture postcards*, published by the European Library (Zalthomme, Netherlands).

Mark Galloway is the author of *East Ham in old photographs*, from Sutton, 1996.

Howard Bloch, former Newham Library local studies librarian (69 Frinton Rd, London E3 3HE) has compiled collections of old photographs for Tempus: *Canning Town*; and *Newham Dockland*; has edited *Canning Town Voices*, also from Tempus, and wrote the history of Earlham Grove Synagogue (Eastside).

The Tempus list also includes: *Forest Gate*, from Dorcas Sanders and Nick Harris; and *Around Plaistow*, by George Taylor (a photographer).

[240] **NEWHAM PARENTS' CENTRE/PARENTS CENTRE PUBLICATIONS**. *Contact*: Vivian Archer, 743/7 Barking Rd, Plaistow, London E13 9FR,*Tel*: (020) 8472 2001; (020) 8552 9993; (020) 8479 5616. The publications programme has ceased, but the project has been responsible for: *The London blitz: a fireman's tale* by Cyril Demarne, 1981; *A marsh and a gasworks: one hundred years of life in West Ham*, 1986; and *A West Ham life*, 1984, by William George Perry.

* SOME OTHER COUNCIL CONTACTS *

Information: Stratford Reference Library, *Tel*: (020) 8557 8968; East Ham Reference Library, *Tel*: (020) 8552 7852; One Stop Shop at Newham Town Hall, East Ham, *Tel*: (020) 8472 1430; also at the Beckton Globe, 1 Kingsford Way, London E6, *Tel*: (020) 8557 6600. A *Newham Community Directory* is produced at the Chief Executive's Department (last edition: 1998).
Park Rangers: at Balsam Park, Greengate St, Plaistow, London E13 0AS, *Tel*: (020) 8472 1430, ext. 23622. Five leaflets in preparation: Beckton, Three Mills, Little Ilford to Wanstead Flats, The Alps (Beckton) to the Thames, Central Park Tree Trail.
Regeneration and Partnerships: *Contact*: Sandra Hunt, Newham Town Hall, East Ham, London, *Tel*: (020) 8472 1430.

The Docklands English Partnership office is at: Compressor House, Royal Docks Project Office, Royal Albert Docks, London E16 2QD, *Tel*: (020) 7540 5500. Projects manager: David Carr.

* SOME NON-COUNCIL CONTACTS *

Business:
EAST LONDON PARTNERSHIP. Superintendents House, Abbey Mills Pumping Station, Abbey Lane, London E15 2RW, *Tel*: (020) 8257 2257.

Residents Associations:
NEWHAM TENANTS AND RESIDENTS FEDERATION. 29 Barking Rd, East Ham, London E6 1PW, *Tel*: (020) 8552 5111.

Voluntary organisations:
NEWHAM VOLUNTAYR AGENCIES COUNCIL. St John's Church and Centre, Albert Rd, North Woolwich, London E16 2JB, *Tel*: (020) 7511 3553.

* LOCAL PRESS *

Newham News, monthly council paper, Town Hall, East Ham, London, *Tel*: (020) 8557 8759.
Newham Recorder. 182 High St North, London E6, *Tel*: (020) 8472 1421.
Stratford and Newham Express. 138 Cambridge Heath Rd, Bethnal Green, London E1, *Tel*: (020) 7790 8822.
Yellow Advertiser: 137 George Lane, London E18, *Tel*: (020) 8989 6688; (020) 8530 3641/8388.

TOWER HAMLETS

* LONDON BOROUGH OF TOWER HAMLETS *

[241] **TOWER HAMLETS LOCAL HISTORY COLLECTION AND ARCHIVES**: at Bancroft Rd Library, London E1 4DQ, *Tel*: (020) 8980 436. *Librarian*: Chris Lloyd; *Archivist*: Malcolm Barr-Hamilton. *Assistant*: David Rich. *Hours*: Mon, Tues, Thurs 9-8; Fri 9-6; Sat 9-5.
Two research handlists have been issued: (No 1: Personal names indexes; No 2: Registers of places of worship).
Recent publications:
1992: HANSHAW, Patrick. *Nothing is for ever*: growing up in Wapping during the post war years. 182pp, illus. Second part *All my yesterdays*, published in 1996, 171pp, illus.
1995: FINCH, Harold. *The Tower Hamlets connection*: a biographical guide. 176pp, illus; includes biographical and autobiographical references, bibliography, and lists of mayors, councillors, Mps.
1998: RIDGE, Tom. *Central Stepney history walk*.

Publications planned include: new edition of Colm Kerrigan's *A History of Tower Hamlets*, 1983; and a *Millennium Chronology*.
The Library sells a range of publications from societies and small publishers, and those of its own currently in print.
Chris Lloyd has compiled three volumes of old photographs,with Rosemary Taylor, for Sutton: *The changing East End; The East End at work* (due October 1999); and *Stepney, Poplar and Bethnal Green*.
In Living Memory (photographs by Stephen Beckett), 1989 and *Tower Hamlets past and present*, 1985 are still in print. Some important out of print titles include: *Bricks and mortar*: the buildings of Tower Hamlets, 1975; *The Green*: a history of the heart of Bethnal Green and the legend of the blind beggar, by A.J. Robinson, and D.H.R. Chesshyre, 1978; and *Tower Hamlets in photographs 1914-1939* (text by Bernard Nurse), 1980.

Non-book material: Includes an interesting poster Roman Road Market, by Jon George; Stanford 1862 maps, and coloured maps, 1809, 1819, 1829, 1839, 1847; a small number of postcards are also available.

* TOURISM/INFORMATION *

[242] TOWER HAMLETS INFORMATION SERVICE. *Contacts*: L. Martinez, K. Pairpoint, 18 Lamb St, London E1 6FA, *Tel*: (020) 7364 4970/4971; (020) 7375 2549; *Fax*: (020) 7375 2539. *Hours*: Mon-Fri 9.30-4.30; Wed 9.30-1; Sun 11-2.30. Provides both tourist, community and council information.
The Council has a Corporate Information Strategy Forum which is looking at the holding and dissemination of information throughout the borough, and has compiled an inventory of all existing databases. The information centre currently distributes a number of information leaflets funded by Bethnal Green City Challenge: *The American connection; Art and artists; East End markets; History through art* (the 25 cast iron roundels by Keith Bowler set into the pavements of Spitalfields; *Women of courage.*
Folding leaflets have also been produced in the past by the Tower Hamlets Environment Trust (eg: East End Music Hall; Parks and Farms in Tower Hamlets; A walk through Spitalfields); and the East End Tourism Trust (The Jewish East End; Pubs of the East End; Restaurants of the East End - all on Spitalfields/Whitechapel; The Young East End, etc).

A new programme of promotional leaflets (on tourist attractions, markets, galleries, etc) is to be published by **[243] ALTERNATIVE ARTS.** 202b Brushfield St, London E1, *Tel*: (020) 7375 0441/0484.

* MUSEUMS *

[244] RAGGED SCHOOL MUSEUM. 46-50 Copperfield Rd, London E3 4RR, *Tel*: (020) 8980 6405; *Fax*: (020) 8983 3481. *Curator*: Richard Dunn. *Hours*: Wed, Thurs 10-5; and first Sunday of each month 2-5. The museum opened in 1990 in three Victorian canal-side warehouses used previously by Dr Barnardo to house the largest ragged school in London. A classroom has been recreated in the museum. There are also displays on local history, industry and life, and a programme of temporary exhibitions and activities. The History Club meets monthly during the winter. There is a shop and a cafe. The museum has published 4 books: *Ben's Limehouse*, by Ben Thomas (2nd edition: 1998); *Common ground: portraits of Tower Hamlets*, photographs by Rehan Hamil (on 20 residents and their 'special' place in the borough), 1998; *Dr Barnardo and the Copperfield Road Ragged School*, 1993 by Tom Ridge; *Ragged schools, ragged children*, by Claire Seymour, 1995.
The museum was winner of the 1995 Museum of the Year Award for best educational initiative.

[245] ROYAL LONDON HOSPITAL ARCHIVES AND MUSEUM. St Augustine with St Philip's Church, Newark St, London £1 2AA, *Tel*: (020) 7377 7608. *Archivist*: Jonathan Evans. *Hours*: Mon-Fri 10-4.30. Opened in November 1989 to provide a permanent home for records of health care in Tower Hamlets and Newham, including the extensive archives of the Royal London Hospital. A range of books are available; histories include: *The Dental School of the London Hospital Medical Collete, 1911-1991*, by S. Francis Fish, 1991; *Emblems, tokens and tickets of the London Hospital and the London Hospital Medical College*, by Denis Gibbs, 1985; *Learning to care: a history of nursing and midwifery education at the Royal London Hospital, 1740-1983*, by Edith R. Parker and Sheila M. Collins, 1998; *L.H.M.C. 1785-1985: the story of England's first medical school*, by Sir John Ellis; *London Pride: the story of a voluntary hospital*, by A.F. Clark-Kennedy, Hutchinson, 1979; *The Royal London Hospital: a brief history*, by Sheila M. Collins, 1995. Biography/autobiography includes: *Edith Cavell: her life and her art*, by Claire H.G. Daunton, 1990; *Patients come first: nursing at 'the London' between the two World Wars*, by Margaret Broadley, 1980.
Postcard compilations include: *Looking at The London: a photographic record 1900-1920*, by Claire H.G. Daunton, 1988; and two collections of hospital and nursing in old picture postcards, by Cynthia O.Neill (Meadow Books, Oxford). There is also a wide range of postcards and greetings cards.

[246] THAMES POLICE MUSEUM. Wapping Police Station, 98 Wapping High St, London E1 9NE, *Tel*: (020) 7275 4885.

[247] THREE MILLS. Bromley-by-Bow. Stand amidst a mass of river channels; the House Mill is the oldest and largest tidal mill of its kind in the country, built in 1776 it ground grain for the local gin distillery industry. Much of the internal machinery survives and guided tours are organised by the River Lea Tidal Mill Trust, May to October, Sunday 2-4; *Tel*: (020) 8472 2829; the Lower Lea Project Education Centre is next door in the Miller's House, *Tel*: (020) 8983 1121. Leading film and TV production companies also have studios here, and there are occasional guided tours.

[248] WHITECHAPEL BELL FOUNDRY. 34 Whitechapel Rd, London E1, *Tel*: (020) 7247 2599. There is a small museum in the front office, and shop. *Hours*: Mon-Fri 9-5.

* COMMUNITY AND SPECIALIST PUBLISHERS *

[249] **EASTSIDE WORDCENTRE**. Eastside Bookshop, 178 Whitechapel Rd, London E1 1BJ, *Tel*: (020) 7247 0216; *Fax*: (020) 7247 2882. Previously known as the Tower Hamlets Arts Project, its publications have covered autobiography, local writing and community history. Autobiographies have included: *Scenes from a Stepney youth*, 1988, by Charles Poulsen; Stepney boxer Stephen Hicks' *Sparring for luck*, 1982; and *Over seven seas and thirteen rivers*, 1987, edited by Carole Adams (life stories of the Bengali Laska seamen who sailed in the Merchant Fleet of the Empire and began the Bengali communities of London's East End). Also historical accounts such as *Beyond recall* (history of Mile End Hospital) by Fraser Cleminson, 1983. *Auschwitz and East London*, 1983 considers East London racism; and a useful reference source is *East End on film*, a catalogue of East London film and video, 1985.
There is a useful catalogue of local books currently available at the bookshop.

[250] **PETER MARCAN PUBLICATIONS**. PO Box 3158, London SE1 4RA, *Tel*: (020) 7357 0368. I was working/living in Tower Hamlets between 1974 and 1989, an assistant librarian until 1984. My contribution to East End bibliography consists of catalogues, reprints and pictorial albums:
1979: *An East End directory*: a guide to the East End of London (LBTH), with special references to the published literature of the last twenty years (with two supplements for 1979-82, and 1983-4). 147pp, illus, maps.
1984: WALKER, Henry. *East London: sketches of Christian work and workers*. 192pp, illus, maps. Issue of book first published by Religious Tract Society in 1896. (East End Reprint Series No 1).
1986: PHILLIPS, Tony. *A London Docklands Guide*, 64pp, illus, maps.
1986: MARCAN, Peter. *Artists and the East End*: a survey and catalogue of work by 20th century artists representing the East End of London. 62pp, illus.
1986: MARCAN, Peter, editor: *Down in the East End*: an illustrated anthology of descriptive and imaginative prose extracts from the late 19th century to the present day. 89pp, illus. (East End Reprint Series No 2).
1987: *One dinner a week, and Travels in the East*: re-issue of book first published by the London Cottage Mission in 1884 (their stew dinners at Limehouse are described in 'One Dinner a Week'). 141pp (East End Reprint Series No 3).
1987: *A Mid Victorian East End Album*. 64pp, illus. (East End Reprint Series No 4).
1990: *A London Docklands Album*. 72pp, illus.
1992: *An East London Album*. 102pp (East End Reprint Series No 5).
1996: Revised, redesigned second impression of *A London Docklands Album*.

[251] **STEPNEY BOOKS PUBLICATIONS**. Jenny Smith, 19 Tomlins Grove, Bow, London E3 4NX, *Tel*: (020) 8790 6420. Specialises in East London history and autobiography/biography. Recent publications:
1994: LEECH, Kenneth. *Brick Lane 1978*, with photographs by Paul Trevor. Reprint of account first published in 1980 on anti-racist reactions to National Front activity in Brick Lane.
1994: JOHNSON, Malcolm. *Outside the gate*. An illustrated history of St Botolph's, Aldgate, its work with the homeless, its part in founding the Gay and Lesbian Christian Movement.
1996: FINCH, Harold. *The Tower Hamlets connection* (see above under Library).
The project started some 20 years ago; Charles Poulson's *Victoria Park*: a study in the history of East London was published in 1987. Biographical/autobiographical books have included: *Edith and Stepney* (Edith Ramsey, educationalist and social worker in Stepney), by Bertha Sokoloff, 1987; *In letters of gold* (East End suffragettes), by Rosemary Taylor, 1993; and *My Poplar Eastenders*, by Carrie Lumsden, 1991.

* HISTORICAL SOCIETIES *

[252] **EAST LONDON HISTORY SOCIETY**. *Secretary*: Doreen Kendall, 20 Puteaux House, Cranbrook Estate, London E2 0RF, *Tel*: (020) 8981 7680. *Membership secretary*: John Harrris, 13 Three Crowns Rd, Colchester CO4 5AD. *Journal editor*: Phillip Mernick, 42 Campbell Rd, Bow, London E3 4DT, *Tel*: (020) 8980 5672. *President*: Mr A. French. Est. in 1952, currently some 200 members 'to further the interest of history of the East End of London (London boroughs of Tower Hamlets, Hackney and Newham). Monthly talks, newsletters and annual journal (may be discontinued). The summer 1998 newsletter has an index to issues 1-18 of the journal, articles arranged by area covered.
Newsletter editor (and former Chair): Rosemary Taylor (29 Stern Close, Barking, Essex IG11 0XW, *Tel*: (020) 8924 2599). Co-compiler with Chris Lloyd of collections from Sutton; has compiled a CD-ROM *One hundred years of Tower Hamlets* for the LBTH Humanities Education Centre, and has another on Brick Lane planned. She has published herself two booklets: *Blackwall: The Brunswick and whitebait dinners* (1989); and *Dr Hannah Billig: the angel of Cable Street*, 1996.

The society has published one book (an especially beautiful and interesting one): *Pictorial History of Victoria Park*, by Phillip Mernick and Doreen Kendall, 1996. 72pp, may illus. (postcards, photographs, engravings), with a chronology. It is dedicated to Alan Searle (died October 1990), an influential member of the society from 1976.

Contents listings of East London Record:

No 16, 1993: 'Beyond the high-bopb' (Poplar High St) (Charles Chisnall); Juvenile street sellers and traders (John Ramsland); A century serving the deaf (Tony Clifford); Memories of Malmesbury Rd Schools 1919-1925 (Vi Short); The Volunteer Militia Companies (Clifford Gulley).

No 17, 1994/5: Old Canning Town (Ivy Alexander); A short history of the youth service in Tower Hamlets (Harold Finch); Hackney School football in the 30's (Les Jolly); Status seekers in a grand house: 21 Stepney Green (C.J. Lloyd); An East London business (builders) (E.J. Smith); The burial grounds of Blackchurch Lane, Whitechapel (Bruce Watson).

No 18, 1996: Childhood days in Hackney and Abbey Lane (George Berry); George Webster Ltd - horse contractors and carmen (Sue Winter); Agricultural holdings, East and West Ham (W. Bram Tyler); East London schooldays (Fred Wright); The Victory Parade of 1946 (Doreen Kendall); Bane's Street, Whitechapel, lost and found (Derrick Morris); 'Down the ground' (Bow Cemetery) (Bradley Snooks).

No 19, 1997: George Lansbury and the Bow and Bromley by-election of 1912 (John Shepherd); Arthur Morrison (Stan Newings); Drinking in Mile End 1750 (licensed houses: 120 premises along Whitechapel, 40 in Mile End) (Derrick Morris); The Guild of Handicraft at Essex House in Bow (Rosemary Taylor); Terror at Wenlock Brewery, 10th September 1940 (Stephen Sadler); Tunnel Vision, 1897-1997 (history of Blackwall Tunnel) (John Harris).

NB: The Record has an important bibliographical dimension: it lists new books, booklets, theses, articles and new additions to Tower Hamlets Archives.

[253] **FRIENDS OF TOWER HAMLETS CEMETERY PARK.** *Contact*: Stuart Rayment, 1 Lockhart St, Mile End, London E3 4BL, *Tel*: (020) 8983 0504. The cemetery consists of some 29 acres of woodland and dates back to the late 1830's. It has been disused since the 1970's. The Friends were est. in 1990. There is a newsletter *Stone Stories*, and a booklet by Rosemary Taylor *Every stone tells a story*.

[254] **HISTORY OF WAPPING TRUST.** *Chair*: Madge Darby, 11 Wapping Pierhead, London E1, *Tel*: (020) 7488 1763. Some other contacts: Ray Newton, 60 Gordon House, Glamis Rd, London E1 9ED, *Tel*: (020) 7488 3057; Ann Teeman, 12 Clave St, London E1 9XQ, *Tel*: (020) 7488 1763. Est. in 1984, the trust has published various projects of Madge Darby: a history *Waeppa's people*, published in 1988; several booklets: *Captain Bligh in Wapping*, 1990; *Judge Jeffreys and the Ivy Case*, 1990; *The Hermitage Shelter minutes*, December 1940, pubished in 1990; and *William Peckover of Wapping: gunner of the bounty*, 1989. She has edited the four-volume Wapping letters and diaries of Walter Jones: *'Tender Grace'*, Vol I: Diary of a honeymoon, 1886, and diary of a holiday, 1887; Vol II: Diary of the year as mayor of Stepney, 1991; Vol III: published by Connor & Butler, 1993; Vol IV: Diary of visit to the battlefields of France and Belgium, 1995. Lincoln S. Jones is the author of a booklet *Colonel Thomas Rainsborough*: Wapping's most famous soldier, 1991. More general interest publications are: *A riverside journey: Tower Bridge to Blackwall Pier in picture postcards*, c. 1990 to 1930's, compiled by Steve Kentfield; and *South of Commercial Road*, forthcoming in 1999, old and new photographs (new by John Tarby), text by Ray Newton. There are several sets of postcards, including 6 reproductions of paintings by Mackenzie Moulten, former diver with the Wapping Thames Police Station's Underwater Search Unit (now a full-time painter in Spain).

[255] **ISLAND HISTORY TRUST.** Dockland Settlement, 197 East Ferry Rd, London E14 3BA, *Tel*: (020) 7987 6041. (near to Mudchute DLR station). Set up in 1980 to collect archival material on social and economic life on the Isle of Dogs. There is now a collection of some 5,000 photographs 1870-1970; all are captioned, and there is a comprehensive index of subjects and named individuals. Collection open on Tuesdays, Wednesdays, and first Sunday of each month, 1.30-4.30. An annual calendar is issued and there are occasional publications: a booklet *The Anglican church on the Isle of Dogs* was published in 1984; and *The Island at War: memories of war-time life on the Isle of Dogs*, was published in about 1989; more recently *Memories of childhood on the Isle of Dogs, 1870-1970*, published in 1994.

[256] **SHADWELL NEIGHBOURHOOD HISTORY TRUST.** *Contact*: Cliff Askey, 14 Peabody Buildings, Block A, Brodlove Lane, Shadwell, London E1 9DT, *Tel*: (020) 7690 6186. Issues an information sheet 'Save our Shadwell', making the case for the area's geographical identity.

[257] **SPRINGBOARD.** *Contacts*: Aumie, Michael Shapiro, 32 Foscote Rd, London NW4 3SD, *Tel*: (020) 8202 7147. Set up in 1979 to develop educational programmes for the disadvantaged, elderly, lonely and housebound in the Jewish community. A 20 year anniversary accoung of the organisation is to be published in 1999. There have been a number of photographic albums: *The Jewish East End*, 1994; *Jewish Eastenders, Jewish Londoners*, 1993; *Memories of the Jewish East End*, 1985; and *More memories of the Jewish East End*, 1987; *When we were young*.

[258] **STEPNEY HISTORICAL TRUST**. *Contact*: Julia Rae, c/o London Dockers Social and Athletic Club, 6-18 Boulcott St, off Commercial Rd, London E1 0HR, *Tel*: (020) 7790 3785; *or Tel*: (020) 7790 4542. Issues a quarterly newsletter. Julia Rae published her booklet *Captain James Cook* in 1997.

Brian Nicholson at the above address is the contact for the [259] **EAST LONDON FEDERATION OF HISTORICAL ASSOCIATIONS.**

* SPITALFIELDS *

[260] **DENNIS SEVERS' HOUSE**. 18 Folgate St, Spitalfields, London E1 6BX, *Tel*: (020) 7247 4013. Dennis Severs has been the owner of this 1724 house since 1979 which he opens on the first Sunday of every month 2-5. It has been arranged as a 'time-warp', telling the story of five generations of a Huguenot silk weaving family. The rooms are arranged so that it appears that the family has just left the room, while the servants have not had time to clear up. He warns in his leaflet: 'unsuitable for children, blue-badge guides, the average businessman or tourist and the relics of old-style compound intelligence: that is seeing, dating and identifying things which here seem out of place and out of date as something which might win the Turner prize'. The house is also the setting for Mr Severs' 'theatrical tours'. (must be booked at least three weeks in advance, price £30). His motto is 'aut visum aut non' (you either see it, or you don't).

[261] **THE FRIENDS OF CHRIST CHURCH SPITALFIELDS**. *Campaign director*: Carolyn Fuest, The Old Vestry Room, Christ Church, Commercial St, London E1 6LY, *Tel*: (020) 7247 0165; *Fax*: (020) 7247 8196. Set up in the 1970's to restore Nicholas Hawksmoor's masterpiece, built 1714-1729. By 1957 the building was in disrepair and not in use for worship; worship returned in 1987. Current projects include the reconstruction of Hawksmoor's south steps, reinstatement of panneling and side galleries, conversion of unused crypt, and repair of the 1735 Robert Bridge organ. There is a newsletter *Columns*. No. 10, December 1998 contains a historical article 'The charities for the relief of poverty in the parish of Spitalfields'.

[262] **SPITALFIELDS HERITAGE CENTRE**. *Contact*: Susie Symes, 19 Princelet St, London E1 6QH, *Tel*: (020) 7247 5352. Long-term aims is to establish a resource centre and museum for the study of immigration in the area. At present there are exhibitions, lectures, tours, concerts, and a Friends organisation has been set up.
For an historical account, see *A giant among giants: a history of Rabbi Shmael Melnick and the Princelet Street Synagogue*, by Samuel C. Melnick, published by the Pentland Press.

[263] **SPITALFIELDS HISTORIC BUILDINGS TRUST**. *Contact*: Andrew Byrne, 19 Princelet St, London E1 6QH, *Tel*: (020) 7247 0971. Publishes an annual newsletter. In 1989 published an important illustrated account *The saving of Spitalfields*, by Mark Girouard, D. Cruikschank, R. Samuel and others. Andrew Byrne is also the author of *Bedford Square: an architectural history*, and *London Georgian houses*.

* ENVIRONMENTAL ORGANISATIONS *

[264] **TOWER HAMLETS ENVIRONMENT TRUST**. 150 Brick Land, London E1 6RU, *Tel*: (020) 7377 0481; *Fax*: (020) 7247 0539. *Email*: info@envirotrust.org. Set up in 1979 to improve the environment in London's East End; it has been involved with many community projects. The Mile End Park Community Liaison Team is based at the above address; Mile End Park is to be transformed into a new local facility, incorporating many sports and play, art, and ecological features. A newsletter on the new park is issued.

[265] **VICTORIA PARK SOCIETY**. *Contact*: Ms Joannie Andrews, 92 Gore Rd, London E9 7HW, *Tel*: (020) 8985 2175. Est. in the 1970's as a campaigning group against a road through the park. The society takes action when 'threats' arise.

* SOME OTHER COUNCIL CONTACTS *

Agenda 21: Sarah Collins, 41-47 Bow Rd, London E3 2BS, *Tel*: (020) 7364 5317.
Arts: *Arts officer*: Brian Oakby, Mulberry Place, 5 Clove Crescent, London E14 2BG, *Tel*: (020) 7364 5000, est. 4897. An Arts directory is produced.
Film location service: Sarah Wren, above address, *Tel*: (020) 7364 5000.
Conservation team: Mark Hutton, team leader, 41-47 Bow Rd, London E3 2BS, *Tel*: (020) 7364 5372.
Information: see Tower Hamlets Information Service.
Reference Library: at Bethnal Green Library, Cambridge Heath Rd, London E2, *Tel*: (020) 8980 6274. A database of local organisations is being developed.

* SOME NON-COUNCIL CONTACTS *

Business:
BUSINESS LINK LONDON EAST. Boardmar House, 64 Broadway, Stratford, London E15, *Tel*: (020) 8432 0400. Also at this address: **EAST LONDON CHAMBER OF COMMERCE AND INDUSTRY**, *Tel*: (020) 8432 0551; and **LONDON EAST TRAINING AND ENTERPRISE COUNCIL**, *Tel*: (020) 8432 0000.

CITYSIDE REGENERATION LTD. 107 Commercial St, London E1, *Tel*: (020) 7377 5277. Aims to stimulate tourism and economic activity in the city areas of Tower Hamlets. Programme of leaflets may be developed in 1999.

EAST LONDON PARTNERSHIP. Superintendents House, Abbey Mills Pumping Station, Abbey Lane, London E15 2RW, *Tel*: (020) 8257 2257.

An important arts marketing organisation for East London artists and designers is:
MAZORCA PROJECTS, Charity House, 14/15 Perseverance Works, 38 Kingsland Rd, London E2 8DD, *Tel*: (020) 7729 3800. It organises 'Hidden art' studio openings with detailed listings brochure; *hotline tel*: (020) 7729 3301; *Fax*: (020) 7729 3377; *Email*: info@hiddenart.co.uk; *website*: www.hidenart.co.uk. There is also a detailed listings brochure *Public art in the East End of London* (including the City): sculptures, mosaics, murals as well as historic buildings and other structures.

Spitalfields Organisations:
SPITALFIELDS ARTS PROJECT. 109 Commercial St, London E1, *Tel*: (020) 7377 2816.
SPITALFIELDS DEVELOPMENT GROUP. 65 Brushfield St, London E1, *Tel*: (020) 7377 1496.
SPITALFIELDS FESTIVAL. 75 Brushfield St, London E1, *Tel*: (020) 7377 0287.
SPITALFIELDS MARKET COMMUNITY TRUST. Atlee House, Toynbee Hall, 28 Commercial St, London E1 6LR,*Tel*: (020) 7247 6689. Funds local voluntary organisations.
SPITALFIELDS SMALL BUSINESS ASSOCIATION. 11 Deal St, London E1, *Tel*: (020) 7247 1892.
SPITALFIELDS SPACE MANAGEMENT. 65 Brushfield St, London E1, *Tel*: (020) 7377 1496.
SPITALFIELDS TOWN MANAGEMENT TEAM, is at the Tower Hamlets Environment Trust, 150 Brick Lane, London E1 6RU, *Tel*: (020) 7377 0481.

Spitalfields: a battle for land, by Charlie Foreman documents the fight for land in the locality and was published by Hilary Shipman Books, 1989 (19 Framfield Rd, London N5 1YU), *Tel*: (020) 7226 0246).

Voluntary organisations:
COMMUNITY ORGANISATIONS FORUM. The Davenant Centre, Whitehapel Rd, London E1, *Tel*: (020) 7426 9970. The last edition of the C.O.F. directory of voluntary organisations in Tower. Hamlets was published in 1997/8 (some 700 organisations). A monthly newsletter is issued.

* LOCAL PRESS *

Bethnal Green Scene, monthly community newspaper published by Oxford House, Derbyshire St, London E2, *Tel*: (020) 7739 9001, ext. 313.
East End life, weekly council newspaper, edited by Helen Watson, Mulberry Place, 5 Clove Crescent, London E14, *Tel*: (020) 7364 4128.
East London Advertiser. 138 Cambridge Heath Rd, London E1, *Tel*: (020) 7702 7777.

SEE ALSO: Docklands Section.

SOUTH LONDON BOROUGHS:

Central London boroughs south of the Thames:
Greenwich, Lambeth, Lewisham, Southwark, Wandsworth;
Boroughs further east and south:
Bexley, Bromley, Croydon, Merton, Sutton

GREENWICH

* LONDON BOROUGH OF GREENWICH *

[266] **GREENWICH LOCAL HISTORY LIBRARY**. Woodlands, 90 Mycenae Rd, London SE3 7SE, *Tel*: (020) 8858 4631; *Fax*: (020) 8293 4721. *Senior staff*: Julian Watson, Caroline Warhurst, Frances Ward; also: Jenny O'Keefe, Gwyn Roberts. *Hours*: Mon, Tues, Fri 9-5.30; Thurs 9-8; Sat 9-5. A duplicated *Guide to sources* (archival) is available.
Family history in Greenwich: a guide to sources has been updated/revised by Caroline Warhurst, and is due for publication in 1999.
Julian Watson has published several books with Greenwich Libraries: *Free for all*: a celebration of 100 years of the Woolwich Free Ferry, with Wendy Gregory, in 1989; *In the meantime*, with Kit Gregory, 1988 is a collection of photographs of vanished riverside Greenwich and *Woolwich Reviewed*, 1986 contrasts old and modern photographs. He has also written many articles.
In addition to books by Julian Watson, the following published by Greenwich Libraries are still available: *The buildings of Greenwich*, by Alan Glencross (a former borough librarian), 1974; and *The Romans in the Greenwich district*, 1974; *Thames on our doorstep*, 1979; and *A Tudor building at Well Hall*, 1978, all by Reginald R. Rigden.
The library does not have a flourishing publications programme as such, but in 1996 published *Sugar, spices and human cargo: an early black history of Greenwich*, by Joan Anim-Addo, 72pp, illus, bibliog. It extends its coverage to 1800. There is a small series of reproductions of prints. A wide range of publications is sold, and a title stock list is produced: publications from societies, authors, Age Exchange, and from the Greenwich Professional Development Centre. Commercially published collections of old photographs available include: from Sutton Publishing: *Greenwich and Woolwich*, 1990 by Ken Clarke (a journalist); and *London Borough of Greenwich*, 1997 by Jacky Franklyn and N. Nutkins (staff at Greenwich Community College); *The Royal Arsenal, Woolwich*, 1995 by Roy Masters (his father was a superintendent at the Arsenal); and *Woolwich*, 1994 by Brian Evans (author East London pictorial histories from Phillimore). From Tempus: *Greenwich*, by Barbara Ludlow, 1994 a former education officer with the Greenwich local studies library; also compiler of a booklet *What's in a name* highlighting councillors recorded in the names of public buildings in Greenwich). From Historical Publications: *Greenwich and Blackheath Past*, 1994, by Felix Barker (now deceased).
Publications still in print from the Greenwich Professional Development Centre are: *Charlton House; Crowley House and the Crowley Ironworks; Explosions at the Woolwich Arsenal; History of Abbey Wood; History of the Woolwich Ferry; History of Woolwich Market; Queen Victoria's last visit to Woolwich*; and *The village, Old Charlton*.
Books published by their authors, and currently available, include: *Boyhood memories of Eltham, 1928-1933*, published 1995; and *Boyhood memories of Plumstead, 1920-1928*, published 1994, both by Bert A. French (Clare Corner Publications, 1 Clare Corner, London SE9 2AE). The Discover... series by Darrell Spurgeon is listed in the section on specialist publishers. *Old Eltham*, by Gus White (45 Kellerton Rd, London SE13 5RB).

* TOURISM *

[267] **GREENWICH TOURISM**. *Contact*: Rosa D'Alessandro, Leisure Services, 151 Powis St, Woolwich, London SE18 6JL, *Tel*: (020) 8854 8888, ext. 2552; *Fax*: (020) 8317 2822. Responsible for the TIC and the overall development of tourism through marketing, training, publicity, etc., and the management of Cutty Sark Gardens. A leaflet *Greenwich: where time begins* summarises the principle sights, and more detailed information is included in the very attractive booklet *Greenwich: the place to celebrate the past and welcome the future* (text by Denise Silvester-Carr). It includes information on accommodation, conference and banqueting venues, restaurants and pubs.

[268a] **GREENWICH TOURIST INFORMATION CENTRE**. *Manager*: Mary Fairburn. 46 Greenwich Church St, London SE10 9BL, *Tel*: (020) 8858 6376; *Fax*: (020) 8853 4607. *Hours*: Winter: Mon-Thurs 11-4; Fri-Sun 10-5; Summer: daily 10-5. Provides tourist and local information on all topics; accommodation bookings, travel tickets nationally, souvenirs, etc. The Historic Greenwich shuttle bus operates daily in the summer, from April to October, between Greenwich BR station and all the principle sites. Centre will probably move to Pepys Building at the old Royal Naval College.
Guided walks also start from the information centre; they are led by qualified guides who are local people and members of the [268b] **GREENWICH TOUR GUIDES ASSOCIATION**, address as above. *Tel*: (020) 8858 6169. Many thematised walks are available: literary Greenwich, Historic taverns, Georgian Greenwich, architecture, ghosts, docklands, Deptford, etc. Also a lecture service available to organisations and schools. There is also a programme of walks to encourage the over 50's to be physically active.

[269] **WORLD HERITAGE SITE MANAGER**.: Geoffrey Belcher, Greenwich Development Agency, John Humphries House, Stockwell St, London SE10 9JN, *Tel*: (020) 8309 8138. Responsible for the co-ordinating and implementation of the UNESCO scheme at Greenwich.

* MILLENNIUM CELEBRATIONS IN GREENWICH *

[270] **NEW MILLENNIUM EXPERIENCE COMPANY**. 110 Buckingham Palace Rd, London SW1, *Tel*: (020) 7808·8200. Responsible for the building of the Greenwich Dome, and the nationwide festival.

[271] **N.M.E.C. VISITOR CENTRE** (on the dome). *Manager*: Andrew Parry, Pepys Building, Royal Naval College, London SE10 9NN, *Tel*: (020) 8305 3456. At this address until about October 1999. Then, the Greenwich Tourist Information Office may move to this location.

[272] **MILLENNIUM OFFICE**. London Borough of Greenwich. *Contact*: Caroline White, 11 King William Walk, London SE10 9JH, *Tel*: (020) 8305 1999. 'Cultural Plan' (events programme) office is also at this address, *Contact*: Alan Dix, *Tel*: (020) 8853 1847; *Email*: adix@greenwich.gov.uk. A magazine *2000+* is produced.

[273] **THE GREENWICH AND LEWISHAM MILLENNIUM COMMUNITY PLAY**. A vast outdoor play to celebrate the Millennium and Greenwich, organised, written and performed by local people is envisaged. *Contact*: John Turnball, 1 Montpelier Rd, Blackheath, London SE3 0RL, *Tel*: (020) 8852 8293; *Fax*: (020) 8488 8930.

Greenwich Peninsula News is a quarterly magazine on developments, published by English Partnership. *Contact*: Glenn Davey, 110 Buckingham Palace Rd, London SW1, *Tel*: (020) 7730 9399.

* MUSEUMS AND GALLERIES *

[274] **FAN MUSEUM**. 12 Crooms Hill, Greenwich, London SE10 8ER, *Tel*: (020) 8858 7879; *Fax*: (020) 8293 1889. *Hours*: Tues-Sat 11-4.30; Sun 12-4.30. The world's only fan museum housed in two restored 1720's houses. Orangery and Japanese garden.

[275] **GREENWICH BOROUGH MUSEUM**. 232 Plumstead High St, London SE18 1JT, *Tel*: (020) 8855 3240; *Fax*: (020) 8316 5754. *Curator*: Beverley Burford. *Assistant*: Chris Foord. *Hours*: Mon 2-7; Tues 10-1, 2-5; Thurs-Sat 10-1, 2-5. Opened in 1919, it owed much of its development in the early years to the enthusiasm of local societies. Collections cover local and natural history and include many local fossils, wildlife specimens, findings from local archaeology, etc. There is a changing programme of temporary exhibitions, covering diverse topics from cavemen to comic characters. There is a loan service to schools, and a Saturday Club for children. New items for the collections are always sought, as well as ideas for future exhibitions.

[276] **NATIONAL MARITIME MUSEUM**. Romney Rd, Greenwich, London SE10 9NF, *Tel*: (020) 8858 4422. *Hours*: daily 10-5. There is a Friends organisation, with office and members' room at the museum, *Tel*: (020) 8312 6678/6638.

[277] **THE OPEN MUSEUM**, at the National Maritime Museum, *Tel*: (020) 8312 6747. Runs a series of courses and seminars on naval and local history. In 1999 there was a course (19 January to 9 March) *Always with us*: a history of the poor in Greenwich 1603-1965; between 28 April and 16 June there was a course on London's docklands.

[278] **WARWICK LEADLEY GALLERY**. 5 Nelson Rd, London SE10, *Tel*: (020) 8858 0317. Anthony Cross, the manager, has worked for many years with Greenwich maps and prints. He has made a particular study of Nelson and his iconography.

[279] **WOODLANDS ART GALLERY**. *Administrator*: Simon Waters. 90 Mycenae Rd, Blackheath, London SE3 7SE, *Tel*: (020) 8858 5847. *Hours*: Mon-Sat 11-5; Sun 2-5. Programme of temporary exhibitions in four rooms. There is a Friends organisation, contact: Tessa Cross.

* HISTORIC PROPERTIES AND VISITOR ATTRACTIONS *

[280] **RANGERS HOUSE**. *Curator*: Nino Strachey. Chesterfield Walk, Blackheath, London SE10 8QX, *Tel*: (020) 8853 0035. *Hours*: April-October 10-6; November-March, Wed-Sun 10-4. Built about 1700 and famous today for the Suffolk Collection of full-length Jacobean portraits; also an architectural study collection containing features from 18th and 19th

century London houses. An English Heritage property. The Long Gallery can be hired. There is a Friends organisation, contact: Mrs E. Wilson, c/o Rangers House.

CHARLTON :
[281] **CHARLTON HOUSE**. Charlton Rd, London SE7 8RE, *Tel*: (020) 8856 3951; *Fax*: (020) 8856 4162. Built between 1607 and 1612 by Sir Adam Newton. An outstanding example of Jacobean domestic architecture. Now a community centre and a venue for private functions.

ELTHAM :
Eltham historic sites:
[282] **AVERY HILL WINTER GARDEN**. Avery Hill Park, Avery Hill Rd, Eltham, London SE9 2UG, *Tel*: (020) 8331 8088. Domed, Victorian Winter Garden with plants from all over the world. *Hours*: Mon-Sat 10-12, 1-4.

[283] **ELTHAM LODGE**. Classical mansion, built in 1664 by Hugh May. Has been the clubhouse of the Royal Blackheath Golf Club since 1923. Visits only by prior arrangement only.

[284] **ELTHAM PALACE AND THE COURTAULD HOUSE**. Court Yard, Eltham, London SE9, *Tel*: (020) 8294 2548. *Hours*: April-September, Thurs, Fri, Sat: 10-6; October-March, Thurs, Fri, Sun: 10-4. Great hall built in reign of Edward IV (1475-1483); linked to it is the house built in 1933 by Stephen Lewis Courtauld, brother of textile magnate Samuel Courtauld; interior has many decorative styles. An English Heritage property.

[285] **SEVERNDROOG CASTLE**. Castle Wood, Shooters Hill, Eltham, London SE9. A triangular 'folly' built in 1784 by wife of Sir William James to commemorate her husband's taking of the fortress of Severndroog on the Malabar Coast, India.

[286] **TUDOR BARN**. Well Hill Pleasance, well Hall Rd, Eltham, London SE9 6SZ, *Tel*: (020) 8850 5145. Restored 15th century building in use as a restaurant. Medieval moat and scented garden.

GREENWICH :
[287] **CUTTY SARK**. Cutty Sark Gardens, King William Walk, Greenwich, London SE10 9HT, *Tel*: (020) 8858 3445. *Hours*: Mon-Sat 10-6 (5 in winter), Sun: 12-6 (5 in winter).

[288] **GIPSY MOTH IV**. Cutty Sark Gardens, King William Walk, Greenwich, London SE10 9HT, *Tel*: (020) 8858 3445. Sir Francis Chichester's boat in which he made the first solo circumnavigation of the world 1966/67.

[289] **OLD ROYAL OBSERVATORY**. Greenwich Park, London SE10 8QY, *Tel*: (020) 8858 4422. *Hours*: daily 10-5.

[290] **QUEEN'S HOUSE**. Romney Rd, Greenwich, London SE10 9NF, *Tel*: (020) 8858 4422. *Hours*: daily 10-5. Designed by Inigo Jones in 1616; given by Charles I to his French wife Henrietta Maria in 1635. Exhibition on history of house in basement. House is currently closed for installation of new Millennium exhibition 'The story of time'.

[291] **ROYAL NAVAL COLLEGE**. King William Walk, Greenwich, London SE10 9NN, *Tel*: (020) 8858 2154. Built on the site of old Tudor palace, by Wren and others. Originally home of Greenwich Hospital, charity founded in 1694 for care of old and disabled sailors; hospital closed in 1869 and four years after the Royal Naval College was transferred from Portsmouth. Now occupied by University of Greenwich. Famous for its James Thornhill painted hall, and its chapel, used for classical music concerts.

WOOLWICH :
[292] **MUSEUM OF ARTILLERY IN THE ROTUNDA**. Repository Rd, Woolwich, London SE18 4BJ, *Tel*: (020) 8316 5402. *Hours*: Mon-Fri 1-4. Building was originally a large bell-tent erected in St James' Park in 1814, designed by John Nash. Museum shows the development of artillery from the middle ages to the 20th century.

[293] **RUSSIAN SUBMARINE**. Thames Barrier, Woolwich, London SE18 5NL, *Tel*: (020) 8855 7560; *Fax*: (020) 8854 8090. *Hours*: daily, 10-6. 92 metres long, this U475 class submarine was in use from 1967 until 1994.

[294] **THAMES BARRIER VISITOR CENTRE**. Unity way, Woolwich, London SE18 5NJ, *Tel*: (020) 8854 1373. *Hours*: Mon-Fri 10-5; Sun 10.30-5.30. Multi-media display on the world's largest moveable flood barrier, managed by the new Environmental Agency.

---

* HISTORICAL/AMENITY SOCIETIES *

[295] **ASHBURNHAM TRIANGLE ASSOCIATION** (area of land between South Street, Greenwich High Road, and Blackheath Road). *Contact*: Derrick Fordham, 66 Ashburnham Grove, London SE10 8UJ, *Tel*: (020) 8692 7251. An account of the area's development written by Diana Rimel was published in 1994. *Chair*: David Green, 43 Guildford Close, London SE10.

[296] **BLACKHEATH PRESERVATION TRUST**. *Contact*: Neil Rhind, Chapman House, 10 Blackheath Village, London SE3 9LE, *Tel*: (020) 8318 5692; *Fax*: (020) 8463 0609; or 3 The Lane, London SE3 9SL, *Tel*: (020) 8852 3009; *Email*: rhinds@lineone.net. In addition to managing the Trust which rescues and restores historic buildings, Neil Rhind is the author of a series of definitive, profusely illustrated local historical works on Blackheath and environs: *Volume I: the village and vale*, 1976 (out of print); *Volume II: Wricklemarsh and the Cator Estate; Kidbroke, Westcombe and the Angerstein Encroachment*, 1983; and its companion volume *The Heath*, 1987 (all published by Bookshop Blackheath). *Volume III: Blackheath in Lee Parish, from Lloyds Place to Dartmouth Row, from The Point to Crooms Hill* is still in preparation, and not yet published. *Blackheath people and house names* is a database (available on floppy disk) of 54,000 people and their addresses recorded as living in the district between 1690 and 1940; supplementary lists include: Blackheath Proprietary School alumni 1831-1907; and members of the Blackheath Golf Club 1766-1923.

[297] **BLACKHEATH SOCIETY**. *Secretary*: Gina Raggett, Chapman House, 10 Blackheath Village, London SE3 9LE, *Tel*: (020) 8297 1937; *Fax*: (020) 8463 0609. *Acting chairman*: Tony Aldous, *Tel*: (020) 8318 1745. *President*: John Grigg. Est. in 1937 'to protect and foster the amenities of Blackheath'. Currently has a membership of some 930 households. Issues a quarterly newsletter and an annual report.

[298] **CHARLTON SOCIETY**. *Chairman*: Colonel Guy Hatch, CBE, 180 Charlton Rd, London SE7 7DW, *Tel*: (020) 8856 4007. *Secretary*: Mr Roden Richardson, 79 Lansdowne Lane, London SE7, *Tel*: (020) 8858 3001. *Membership secretary*: Rita Yardley, 41 Swallowfield Rd, London SE7. Est. in about 1969 for the conservation and improvement of Charlton. A newsletter is issued. A Local History Group Journal was issued between 1983 and 1986, and a series of 5 walks were also issued in the 1980's. J.G. Smith (12 St Edwards Close, East Grinstead, East Sussex, *Tel*: (01342) 322117) is the author of a three volume *History of Charlton*, published by himself in 1970, 1975 and 1984 (now out of print).

[299] **ELTHAM SOCIETY**. *Secretary*: Mrs Marianne Atterton, Beaucourt, 90 Glenlea Rd, Eltham Park, London SE9 1DZ, *Tel*: (020) 8850 2243. Est. in 1965, currently with some 600 members 'to preserve the past, conserve the present and protect the future'. The society sponsors a Heritage Award and a Brighter Eltham Award to recognise and support local initiatives. It organises an annual Eltham in art exhibition. Research is undertaken into local history which is reported to members at lecture meetings, in the quarterly newsletter and in publications, mainly booklets and leaflets. There are also visits and social events. The society's most substantial publication has been the first volume of *Eltham in the making*, from Roman times to 1939 published in 1990, 128pp. More recent publications have included: *The Bexley Heath railway in Eltham 1895-1995*, by Gus White, 1996; and *Memories of New Eltham*, 1998.
The booklet *Edith Nesbit in Eltham* by Margaret Taylor, 1974 is to be revised/reissued. The Society also sells John Kennett's history of the Thomas Philipots almshouse charity. John Kennett is an Eltham local historian (26 Strongbow Rd, London SE9 1DT). He wrote a booklet *Trams in Eltham 1910-1952* in 1972 and Phillimore published his *Eltham: a pictorial history* in 1995.

[300] **GREENWICH COMMUNITY COLLEGE PRESS**. *Contact*: Toc Bhogal, Media Resources Officer, Greenwich Community College (now part of Woolwich College), Corelli Rd, London SE3 8EP, *Tel*: (20) 8319 8088; *Fax*: (020) 8319 8040. Publications include: *Remember Greenwich* by Iris Bryce, 1995 (author grew up in East Greenwich in inter-war years; she worked at Siemen's factory in Woolwich); *Voices of Ferrier*: an oral history of a council estate edited by Seamus O'Coilean, 1995.

[301] **GREENWICH HISTORICAL SOCIETY**. *Secretary*: Charles Marchant, 20 Avalon Rd, Orpington, Kent BR6 9AY, *Tel*: (01689) 838103. *Membership secretary/treasurer*: John Swindell, 82 Kinveachy Gardens, Charlton, London SE7 8EJ. Est. in 1991, it supersedes the Greenwich and Lewisham Antiquarian Society founded in 1905; currently has some 110 members (but membership is increasing). Meetings, lectures, visits, research. In 1961, the G & LAS published *Churches of the hundred of Blackheath*, 76pp, with bibliographies It covers churches in the old boroughs of Deptford, Greenwich, Lewisham and Woolwich (still in print).

Contents listing for the Journal of the GHS:

Vol 1, No 1: Aspects of Greenwich Park; Sydenham Common; Music hall in Greenwich and Lewisham II; Recent books of local interest; St John's Station.

Vol 1, No 2: Nicholas Lanier: a Greenwich notable (1588-1612), Part 1 (Susan E. James); The nineteenth century census (Veronica Moore); The Mayor of Kidbrooke in 1539 and 1608 (Michael Egan); The riverside between Deptford and Greenwich (Alan Pearsall); The end of Deptford Power Station (Alan Pearsall); Obituary: Sir Robert Somerville, William Bonwitt; Queen Elizabeth's Oak.

Vol 1, No 3: Nicholas Lanier, Part 2 (Susan E. James); Lost churches of Greenwich and Blackheath (Alan Curtis); The observant friary at Greenwich: a topographical note (Michael Egan); Obituary: Sir Leslie Monson; Recent books of local interest (Julian Watson).

Vol 1, No 4: Collectors and tenants in mid 16th century Kidbrooke (M.J. Egan); A letterbook of 1711 by Captain Sir William Gifford (David B. Ellison); The Cator Estate: 200 years of development, Part I (Alan Curtis).

Vol 1, No 5: Poor law in Greenwich (Frances Ward); Households of Blackheath Park in 1851 (Mildred Collins); The Cator Estate, Part II (Alan Curtis).

Vol 2, No 1: William IV and the coffins of St Mary's (William Clarke); Greenwich in 1905 and the formation of the Greenwich Antiquarian Society; A Greenwich-built locomotive in Holland (Alan Pearsall); The National Maritime Museum - a brief history (Ursula Stuart Mason).

[302] **GREENWICH INDUSTRIAL HISTORY SOCIETY**. *Secretary/newsletter editor*: Mary Mills, 24 Humber Rd, London SE3, *Tel*: (020) 8858 9482. A specialist on gas industry history. Her book *Greenwich Marsh: the 300 years before the dome* is due for publication soon. *Chair*: Jack Vaughan, 35 Eaglesfield Rd, London SE18, *Tel*: (020) 8855 65121 (specialist interest: Woolwich Arsenal). *Vice-chair*: Barbara Ludlow, 45 Coombe Avenue, London SE3 7PZ. The society was launched in 1998. There are meetings, and informative newsletters (with an events listings for other societies). Issue 4, October 1998 has material on the redevelopment of the Woolwich Arsenal site.

The interests of the society are potentially wide-ranging ... 'anchors, propellers, sacking, lampblack, inlaid linoleum, cement, artificial stone, fireworks, the Great Globe, and more and more and more, even time itself, and big, big, BIG guns' (from publicity leaflet).

[303] **GREENWICH SOCIETY**. *Secretary*: Ray Smith, 14 Trenchard St, Greenwich, London SE10 9PA, *Tel*: (020) 8853 1603; *Fax*: (020) 8293 0702. *Chair*: Ursula Bowyer, 111 Maze Hill, Greenwich, London SE10 8XQ, *Tel*: (020) 8858 0492. *Vice-chair*: Richard F. Moy (proprietor of Spread Eagle - antiques, bookshop, restaurant in Greenwich), 37 Hyde Vale, Greenwich, London SE10 8QQ, *Tel (work)*: (020) 8305 1666. Est. in 1965, currently with some 700 household members. There are committees for traffic and transport, planning and development and open spaces public relations and membership, and events. A quarterly newsletter is issued and a leaflet *Greenwich Peninsula Walk*, written by Diana Rimel, illustrated by Peter Kent has been issued recently.

[304] **SHOOTERS HILL LOCAL HISTORY GROUP**. *Contact*: Keith Littlewood, 30 Ightham Rd, Erith, Kent DA8 1LX. A small group of some 25 members: research into Shooters Hill and environs; talks. Publishes an occasional journal *Aspects of Shooters Hill*:

No 1, 1984: The road over Shooters Hill (Albert Smith); The early postal history of Shooters Hill (Peter Bathe); There was a tavern...on Shooters Hill (Jack Vaughan); Severndroog Castle: a commemoration (Jack Vaughan).

No 2, 1989: The stones of Shooters Hill (Jack Vaughan); Eglinton School (Ann Leggett); Buses over Shooters Hill (Chris Johnson); From Tower House to Brinklow Crescent (Susan Parker and Andrew Bullivant).

No 3, 1999: not yet published, but articles scheduled for publication are: Highway robbery (Chris Ford); The Royal Herbert Hospital (Andrew Bullivant); Shrewsbury House, its history and its surroundings (Douglas Johnson); Shooters Hill's open air school (Chris Johnson); The saving of Shooters Hill (Chris Johnson); East London river crossings (Doug Johnson); Trams around Shooters Hill (Tony Johnson).

[305] **WESTCOMBE SOCIETY**. *Acting chairman*: Andrew Riley, 20 Humber Rd, London SE3, *Tel*: (020) 8830 4085.

[306] **WOOLWICH AND DISTRICT ANTIQUARIAN SOCIETY**. *Secretary*: Mr J.W. Marrett, 4 Hill End, Shooters Hill, London SE18 3NH, *Tel*: (020) 8856 9561. *President*: Mr J. Moss, St Michael's Vicarage, 21 Borgard Rd, Woolwich, London SE18 5LD, *Tel*: (020) 8855 8495. *Newsletter editor*: Mr A.L. Fawcett, 86 St Mary St, Woolwich, London SE18 5AJ, *Tel*: (020) 8855 5796. *Proceedings editor*: Mr T. Robin, 42 Lovelace Green, Eltham, London SE9, *Tel*: (020) 8856 8081. The society was established in 1895 and currently has over 200 members. It aims to study and record matters of historic and prehistoric interest in the locality and help preserve all buildings and landmarks of historic and antiquarian interest, and the amenities of the district. Meetings and visits. Proceedings have been published every 3-5 years since 1958.

Vol XL, 1993: Memorials on Woolwich Common; Royal Herbert Hospital; The 'links' and Plumstead Common; St Nicholas Church; Short history of the Royal Artillery; Plumstead Common riots; King's Warren School; Colonel John Travers R.A.
Vol XLI, 1995: A selection of memories of bygone days, by members of the society.
In 1970 the society published the 430 page volume *The Woolwich story, 1890-1965*, by Edward Frances Ernest Jefferson (now out of print).

Other Woolwich contacts:
Rob Ribbins, Woolwich Town Centre Manager, 23 Woolwich New Rd, London SE18 6EU, *Tel*: (020) 8312 5251.

[307] **WOOLWICH FERRY SERVICE** (Woolwich Free Ferry), London SE18, *Tel (Mon-Fri)*: (020) 8854 8888. Evenings and weekends: *Tel*: (020) 8312 5577.
In 1989 Greenwich Libraries published *Free for all*: a celebration of 100 years of the Woolwich Free Ferry, by Julian Watson and Wendy Gregory.

[308] **Royal Arsenal Site** (at present restricted access pending redevelopment).
Project office for the new Royal Artillery Museum: Royal Arsenal West, Warren Lane, London SE18, *Tel*: (020) 8855 7755; *Fax*: (020) 8855 7100. This new museum will incorporate collections in the rotunda and the Royal Military Academy and will occupy the former Royal Laboratory Model Room and the New Laboratory Square complex.
Specialist publications on the Arsenal include: *The Royal Arsenal Woolwich*, by Wesley Harry, Ministry of Defence, 1987; *Royal Arsenal Woolwich*, RCHM, 1994; and *Royal Arsenal Woolwich: an archaeological study*, by Mills Whipp Partnership, 1995. In 1997 Greenwich Council published a major inventory: *Royal Arsenal Catalogue*: a catalogue of archives and artefacts relating to the Royal Arsenal, Woolwich; and in the same year the Greenwich Borough Museum published *Aspects of the Arsenal*, edited by Beverley Burford and Julian Watson. With 132pp, it has specialist chapters on subjects raging from buildings and architecture to industrial relations. Both publications are sold at the Local Studies Library.
A leaflet *Woolwich architectural heritage trails* by Carol Kenna was published by Greenwich Tourism and the Greenwich Mural Workshop in 1994.
Darrell Spurgeon's *Discover Woolwich and its environs* (2nd edition: 1996) contains much succinct information, with clear maps.

* PARKS/ENVIRONMENT *

[309] **FRIENDS OF GREENWICH PARK**. *Contact*: Faith and William Clarke, 37 Park Vista, Greenwich, London SE10 9LZ. *Chairman*: Sir Alan Bailey. Brings together all interested in the park, its history, flora and fauna and maintenance. There is an annual lecture. There is a seasonal newsletter. No 18, spring 1998 has a *Millennium Guide* supplement, and No 16, Summer 1997 contains an interview with Jennifer Page, chief executive of the New Millennium Experience Company.
There are also three guides, compiled by Annie Burton: *A guide to trees in the park* (with a chronology); *A child's guide to trees in the park*; and *A guide to herbs in the herb garden*. The Friends have recently launched a £13,000 appeal for a new fountain, to be designed by Kate Malane, for the herb garden.
Greenwich Park office is at Blackheath Gate, *Tel*: (020) 8858 2608. The visitor centre, open during the summer months is at St Mary's Gate (King William Garden), and will be an information point for events and activities organised in the park during the Millennium celebrations.

[310a] **GREENWICH ENVIRONMENT FORUM**. *Contact*: Anna Townend, 22 Coleraine Rd, London SE3 7PQ, *Tel*: (020) 8858 3844; *Fax*: (020) 7928 6001. Est. in 1985 for 'community consultation and action on the environment'. Newsletter issued. Anna Townend is also the contact for [310b] **GREENLANDS IN TRUST (GLIT)**.

[310c] **GREENWICH SUSTAINABLE MILLENNIUM NETWORK**. *Contact*: David Sharman, 55 Mayhill Rd, Charlton, London SE7 7JG, *Tel*: (020) 8305 2196.

[311] **GREENWICH WATERFRONT DEVELOPMENT PARTNERSHIP**. 44 Greenwich Church St, London SE10 9BL, *Tel*: (020) 8853 4629; *Fax*: (020) 8305 2422.
23 Woolwich New Rd, London SE18 6EU, *Tel*: (020) 8312 5251; *Fax*: (020) 8312 5252. The chairman is Councillor Len Duvall. The partnership consists of representatives from Greenwich Council, Greenwich business and community forums, from the Single Regeneration Budget 'delivery' agencies (Creekside Renewal Partnership, Greenwich Development Agency, and the Woolwich Development Agency), and from the three local area agencies (East Greenwich Management Agency, Greenwich Town Centre Agency, and Woolwich Town Centre Agency). The partnership's annual report gives a vivid picture of current redevelopment.

[312] **PLUMSTEAD COMMON ENVIRONMENT GROUP**. *Contact*: Ms J. Cowdell, 8 Blendon Terrace, Plumstead Common, London SE18 7RR, *Tel*: (020) 8854 5167.

[313] **WOODLANDS FARM TRUST**. (Membership section): 331 Shooters Hill, Welling, Kent DA16 3RP, *Tel/Fax*: (020) 8319 8900. *Email*: wfarmtrust@gp.apc.org. Located on the south-eastern slopes of Shooters Hill on the Bexley/ Greenwich border, this 89 acre site is of considerable heritage value: formerly ancient woodland, the farm was created between 1799 and 1842. It closed in the late 1980's, but its future was secured by the Trust. There are many initiatives planned: arts, crafts, visitor facilities, environmental, educational, agricultural and horticultural activities.

* SOME OTHER COUNCIL CONTACTS *

Agenda 21/nature conservation: Keith Tallantire, Planning Department, Peggy Middleton House, 50 Woolwich New Rd, London SE18 6HQ, *Tel*: (020) 8312 5536.

Arts development: *Contacts*: Chris Lea, arts development officer; Alan Dix, cultural consultant, Millennium office, 11 King William Walk, London SE10 9JH, *Tel*: (020) 8853 1847. NB: this office operative only up to end of 2000. Bi-monthly/quarterly brochure issued. *Black arts officer*: Angela Rolle.

Conservation areas/listed buildings: Steve Crow, Jon Hardy (within the policy and projects unit of the planning department), address as above, exts. 5034, 5217. Some 5 leaflets have been issued to date on the 19 conservation areas.

Reference library (main collection): at Woolwich Library, Calderwood St, London SE18, *Tel*: (020) 8316 6663.

* SOME NON-COUNCIL CONTACTS *

Some contacts for the arts:
GREENWICH AND DOCKLANDS INTERNATIONAL FESTIVAL. 6 College Approach, London SE10, *Tel*: (020) 8305 1818; *Fax*: (020) 8305 1188.
GREENWICH PRINTMAKERS ASSOCIATION. Art Gallery, 1a Greenwich Market, London SE10, *Tel*: (020) 8858 1569.
GREENWICH CITIZENS GALLERY. 151 Powis St, Woolwich, London SE18 6JL, *Tel*: (020) 8316 2752. *Contact*: Beverley Burford.

Business:
A Greenwich business directory is produced by the council's economic development unit (contact: Tom Travers, *Tel*: (020) 8317 5581, with the **BEXLEY AND GREENWICH CHAMBER OF COMMERCE**, Morden Wharf Rd, London SE10, *Tel*: (020) 8293 3456.

Voluntary organisations:
GREENWICH VOLUNTARY ACTION COUNCIL. St Mary's Church, Greenlaw St, London SE18, *Tel*: (020) 8316 6644.
GREENWICH WATERFRONT COMMUNITY FORUM. Christchurch Way, London SE10, *Tel*: (020) 8854 8884.

Local Press:
Greenwich Time, council newspaper, produced about every fortnight, edited by Jim Mallory, Woolwich Town Hall, London, *Tel*: (020) 8854 8888, ext. 5042/3.
The Guide (monthly magazine). 13 Blackheath Village, London SE3, *Tel*: (020) 8297 0809.
Kentish Times (for Eltham area). 161 The Broadway, Bexley Heath, Kent DA6 7ES, *Tel*: (020) 8301 6663.
Meridian Line (monthly magazine). 10 College Approach, London SE10, *Tel*: (020) 8305 2999.
Mercury Group (includes Greenwich). 116 Deptford High St, London SE8 4NX, *Tel*: (020) 8692 1122.
Newshopper Group. Mega House, Great View Drive, Petts Wood, Orpington, Kent BR5 1BT.
Thamesmead People (Greenwich/Bexley). 5 Harts Lock Drive, London SE2, *Tel*: (020) 8473 0128.

LAMBETH

* LONDON BOROUGH OF LAMBETH *

[314] **LAMBETH ARCHIVES**. The Minet Library, 52 Knatchbull Rd, London SE5 9QY, *Tel*: (020) 7926 6076; *Fax*: (020) 7926 6080. *Hours*: Mon 9-7.30; Tues, Thurs 9.30-5.30; Wed closed; Fri 9.30-1; Sat 9.30-1, 2-4.30. *Phone to make appointment. Archive managers*: Jon Newman, Sue McKenzie (job-share); *Archives officer*: Graham Gower (see below, under Streatham Society).

Librarian Beryl Barrow has now retired. She is the author of *Lambeth 1950-1970* (Britain in old photographs series, Sutton Publishing).

There is a series of information guides: No 1: Records of interest to family historians; No 2: Record agents list; No 3: Sources for business history; No 4: Maps and plans; No 5: Handlist of local newspapers; No 6: Publications price list; No 7: List of periodicals held; No 8: Local history, family history and amenity societies; No 9: House history; No 10: Resources for teachers; No 11: The environment in Lambeth Archives (i.e. storage problems, etc). No 12: Entertainment in Lambeth.

Lambeth Archives organise an annual Open Day, in the autumn, in collaboration with Lambeth Local History Forum: bookstalls, and stands, talks, exhibitions.

Lambeth Archives do not have a publishing programme as such, but in 1997 they issued three photocopied booklets: Family history at Lambeth Archives: a guide to local resources; House history at Lambeth Archives: a guide to resources and advice on techniques; and A short walk in the Minet Estate, a historical walk with maps and illustrations.

Several important London Borough of Lambeth publications are still in print: *Lambeth's open spaces: an historical account*, by Marie Draper, 1979; *St Luke, West Norwood 1825-1975*, by M. Lambert and K. Holdaway, 1974.

In addition to its own publications, those from societies, Sutton Publishing and Historical Publications, the following are also currently available:

Alice from Tooting, Plowright Press (PO Box 66, Warwick CV34 4XE), 1997 (reminiscences by Alice Mullen); *On Lambeth Marsh: the South Bank and Waterloo*, by Graham Gibberd (a retired architect), published by Jane Gibberd (20 Lower Marsh, London SE1 7RJ, *Tel*: (020) 7633 9562; they run their second-hand and remaindered book business from here); *Round about a pound a week*, by Maud Pember Reeves, published by Virago Press (working-class living conditions in Vauxhall, 1909-13); *The Windrush legacy*: memories of Britain's post-war Caribbean immigrants (based on oral history interviews, with an introduction by Professor Stuart Hall) from the Black Cultural Archives, 1998(378 Coldharbour Lane, London SW9 8LE, *Tel*: (020) 7738 4591).

Non-book material:

Lambeth Archives have issued three maps (A2 sheets on high quality cream card): Lambeth parish, northern part, 1831; Clapham Common and surrounding area, 1827; Streatham Parish, 1852.

Alan Godfrey reprints are also sold.

There are facsimile theatre posters, including: Astley's Amphitheatre, Bower Saloon, Victoria Theatre. Postcards series include: Lambeth potteries, and Edwardian views of Brixton, Clapham and Streatham.

[315] **LAMBETH ENVIRONMENT FORUM.** *Hon. secretary*: Tim Mather, 233a Railton Rd, Herne Hill, London SE24 0LX. *Chair*: Derek Hoare, 2 Holmewood Gardens, London SW2 3RS, *Tel*: (020) 8674 0063. A partnership between local people and Lambeth Council, arising from the 1992 Rio Earth Summit. It promotes environmental initiatives and encourages sustainable policies, lifestyles and activities within the Council and the borough at large. There are 7 workgroups: education and awareness, energy, waste and recycling; parks, open spaces and nature conservation; pollution and health; sustainable economic development; transport; built environment. A number of Friends of parks organisations in Lambeth have been set up recently, and they can be contacted through Derek Hoare: organisations for Brockwell Park, Clapham Common, Kennington Park, Larkhall Park, Myatts Fields, Spring Gardens (Vauxhall Cross), Streatham Common, Vauxhall Park.

[316] **LAMBETH LOCAL HISTORY FORUM.** *Contacts*: John Cresswell, 142 Harborough Rd, London SW16 2XW, *Tel*: (020) 8677 2537. Brian Bloice, 220 Woodmansterne Rd, London SW16 5UA, *Tel*: (020) 8764 8314. Publishes a list of Lambeth societies, and helps organise the Lambeth Archives Open Day at end of September.

* MUSEUMS/ARCHIVES *

[317] **BLACK CULTURAL ARCHIVES/MUSEUM.** 378 Coldharbour Lane, Brixton, London SW9 8LF, *Tel*: (020) 7738 4591; *Fax*: (020) 7738 7168. Museum open Mon-Sat 10-6; archives 10-4, by appointment.

[318] **FLORENCE NIGHTINGALE MUSEUM.** 2 Lambeth Palace Rd, London SE1 7EW, *Tel*: (020) 7620 0374. *Hours*: Tues-Sun 10-5. On the site of St Thomas' Hospital, the museum recreates her life and achievements, with a life-size recreated ward scene as centre-piece.

[319] **MUSEUM OF GARDEN HISTORY.** The Tradescant Trust, Lambeth Palace Rd, London SE1 7LB, *Tel*: (020) 7261 1891. *Hours*: Mon-Fri 10.30-4; Sun 10.30-5. Celebrates the work of the two John Tradescants, plant collectors. Part of the St Mary's churchyard is a replica 17th century garden.

* AMENITY, ENVIRONMENTAL AND HISTORICAL ORGANISATIONS *

[320] **BRIXTON SOCIETY**. *Hon. secretary*: Alan Piper, 82 Mayall Rd, London SE24 0PJ, *Tel/Fax*: (020) 7207 0347. *Email*: apiperbrix@aol.com. *Membership secretary (and publications orders)*: Bill Linskey, 32 Stockwell Green, London SW9 9HZ, *Tel*: (020) 7274 3855; *Email*: wjdcl@globalnet.co.uk.
Est. in 1974 as the amenity society covering the central part of the London borough of Lambeth, including most of Stockwell and Tulse Hill. Local history activities include guided walks, occasional talks and a growing range of publications. Also involved with planning matters, conservation and community projects. Quarterly newsletter issued (three indexes: 1983-87; 1987-92; 1993-98).

Recent publications:
1994: *Brixton memories*: collected oral, local history. 52pp, illus.
1996: PIPER, Alan. *A history of Brixton*, 104pp, illus.
Brixton: the story of a name was reprinted in 1998; *Effra: Lambeth's underground river* was reprinted in 1994.
Brixton Town trails, compiled by the late Ken Dixon is to be revised.
Booklets in the 'Brixton abridged' series include: *Trams in Brixton, 1870-1951*, 6pp; *Stockwell Congregational School*, 4pp; *"Most agreeable suburb": Brixton in the 1840's*, 2pp. *Brixton memories of Dora Tack*, 4pp; *"Sketches of Living London: the Brixton Road, 10 September 1896"*, 2pp; *A Jamaican childhood*, 6pp.
Some 22 Edwardian postcards have been issued, and some 2 are added to the range each year. Alan Piper is currently compiling brief accounts of five Brixton almshouses. Occasional items on local history are contributed to *Brixton On-line*, the community website on the Internet: http://www.brixton.co.uk.

[321] **CLAPHAM ANTIQUARIAN SOCIETY**. *Secretary*: Nicholas Long, 58 Crescent Lane, London SW4 9PU, *Tel*: (020) 7622 7420. Est. in 1923, the society is currently not very active. Nicholas Long holds the papers of the former archivist Eric Smith (now deceased). Under his Clapham Press imprint he has published two books by Eric Smith: *Macaulay School: the story of a church school, 1648-1987*, and *Clapham saints and sinners* (a Clapham who's was who, based on articles from the society's news sheet).

[322] **CLAPHAM SOCIETY**. *Hon. secretary*: David Perkin, 14 Englewood Rd, London SW12 9NZ, *Tel/Fax*: (020) 8673 2570. *Membership secretary*: Mrs Joyce Luck, 15 Cavendish Rd, London SW12 0BH, *Tel*: (020) 8673 2616. Est. in 1968; the amenity society for Clapham and those parts of Battersea near to Clapham Common. Monthly meetings; newsletter issued monthly. Subcommittees deal with planning and transportation, the Common and open spaces. In 1995 the society published *The story of Clapham Common*, 48pp, illus, maps. A revised and much expanded edition of *The buildings of Clapham* (published 1978) is planned for 1999.

[323] **COIN STREET COMMUNITY BUILDERS**. 99 Upper Ground, London SE1 9PP, *Tel*: (020) 7620 0544; *Fax*: (020) 7620 1608. Since 1984 have created and managed Bernie Spain Garden, Gabriel's Wharf, Oxo Tower Wharf, and the riverside walkway, as well as providing 160 new homes. The Coin Street Festival, The Bargehouse, Bargehouse St, London SE1, *Tel*: (020) 7928 0960, *directors*: Adrian Evans, Bettany Hughes, is an annual event: three months of free summer outdoor entertainment by international artistes.

[324] **FRIENDS OF CLAPHAM COMMON**. *Chairman*: Paul Newman, *Tel*: (020) 7223 4734. Mail address: c/o K.S. Gebhardt, Ground Floor, St James' Wing, St George's Hospital, Blackshaw Rd, London SW17 0QT. Est. in 1998 in response to local concerns over the use and management of the Common. The Friends aim to protect it from schemes which threaten its integrity, to improve it as a refuge from the bustle of surrounding life, and to develop a better home for wildlife.

[325] **FRIENDS OF WEST NORWOOD CEMETERY**. *Hon. Secretary*: Jill Dudman, 119 Broxholm Rd, London SE27 0BJ, *Tel*: (020) 8670 5456. *Membership secretary*: FWNC, 63 Bradley Rd, London SE19 3NT, *Tel*: (020) 8653 2741. Est. in 1990 to promote interest in and conservation of this major Victorian metropolitan cemetery, with its 64 listed monuments, built in 1837, designed by Sir William Tite. General tours are held on the first Sunday of each month; there are also special theme tours in the summer and indoor lecture meetings in the winter. Three newsletters are issued each year; there are 12 postcards; illustrated booklets have been published: *West Norwood Cemetery - the Dickens connection*, by Paul Graham, 1995; *West Norwood Cemetery's sportsmen*, 1995; *West Norwood Cemetery's musicians*, 1998; and *West Norwood Cemetery's music hall*, 1998, all by FOWNC chairman Bob Flanagan. His booklet *West Norwood's South Bank theatricals* is in preparation, and there is to be a book on palaeontologist Gideon Mantell by Ken Woodhams, and a new cemetery guide book. Jill Dudman is the author of *Lambeth, Kennington and Clapham*, and *Brixton and Norwood*, Britain in old photographs series from Sutton Publishing.

[326] **HERNE HILL SOCIETY**. *Hon. officials*: *Secretary*: Sheila Northover, 24 Brantwood Rd, Herne Hill, London SE24 0DJ, *Tel*: (020) 7274 2638. *Newsletter editors*: Annie and Dave Gelly, 16 Poplar Walk, Herne Hill, London SE24 0BU. *Contact for local history*: Adrian Hill, 4 Stradella Rd, London SE24 9HA, *Tel*: (020) 7274 4838. Est. about 1983, it has some 350 members and is concerned with planning issues and local history. There is a full programme of social and community events. A quarterly newsletter is issued.

The society has published booklets by former Hon. Secretary Patricia Jenkyns: *A glance at the history of Herne Hill*, 1986; *The story of Sir Henry Bessemer*, 1984; and *The making of John Ruskin*, 1986. It also sells *John Ruskin's Camberwell*, by James S. Dearden published in 1990 by the Brentham Press for the Guild of St George. There are also notelets (from old postcards), notelets and posters drawn by Alison Roache, and postcards showing photographs by Ian Leslie.

[327] **HIGH TREES COMMUNITY DEVELOPMENT TRUST** (Lambeth), c/o 4 Sheppard House, High Trees, London SW2 3PR, *Tel*: (020) 8674 8299.

[328] **LAMBETH WALK PARTNERSHIP**. *Contact*: Peter Williams, 127 Lambeth Walk, London SE11 6EH, *Tel*: (020) 7926 8120; *Fax*: (020) 7926 8121; *Email*: par-lambeth-walk@midnet.com. The partnership is between the London Borough of Lambeth, Peabody Trust, London and Quadrant Housing Trust, and the community. *Vauxhall Regeneration News* is the newsletter of the partnership and the Vauxhall Regeneration Company.

[329] **LAMBETHANS SOCIETY**. *Secretary*: Mrs Doreen Heath, 47 Tulsemere Rd, West Norwood, London SE27 9EH, *Tel*: (020) 8670 8924. *Chairman*: Alan Piper, 82 Mayall Rd, London SE24 0PJ, *Tel/Fax*: (020) 7733 6354. Has a programme of meetings and guided walks. Covers the whole of the borough. Publications include: *Local place names: derivation and imagination*, by Brian Vale, second edition, 1993; and *Early industry in Lambeth*, by Alan Piper, 1995. Also 9 black/white views. Est. some 45 years ago as the borough's civic society.

[330] **MINET CONSERVATION ASSOCIATION**. *Chair*: Mel Brown, 10 Templar St, London SE5 9JB, *Tel*: 020) 7737 6696.

[331] **NORWOOD SOCIETY**. *Chairman*: Philip Goddard, 133 Church Rd, London SE19 2PR, *Tel*: (020) 8653 6228. *Secretary*: David Kenyon, 29 Woodsyre, Sydenham Hill, London SE26 6SS, *Tel*: (020) 8670 7073. *Local history contact*: Keith Holdaway, 223 Leigham Court Rd, London SW16 2SD, *Tel*: (020) 8761 1751. Est. in 1965 'to preserve, protect and improve features of historic and public interest in the Norwood area' (parts of the London boroughs of Lambeth, Southwark, Croydon and Bromley). There is a quarterly journal the *Norwood Review* (editor: Nicholas Reed, *Tel*: (020) 8659 5776).

A recent publication has been: *Emile Zola: photographer in Norwood, 1898-1899*, published in 1997.

Other publications still available are: *Down at Beulah*, by John Warwick, 1986 (Royal Beulah spa and gardens); *Keep on the grass*, by Geoffrey Manning, 1986 (open spaces circular walk); *Norwood past*, 1986 (items from the Norwood Review); *The Phoenix suburb*, 2nd edition, 1982, by Alan Warwick; *On the trail of Norwood*, by John Yaxley, 1986 (walk along Church Rd and the Triangle); *The story of Norwood*, by J.B. and H.A. Wilson, 2nd edition, first published by Lambeth Libraries, to be reissued in 1999.

[332] **OLD LAMBETH WALK DEVELOPMENT TRUST**. 81 Lambeth Walk, London SE11 6DX, *Tel*: (020) 7735 7235.

[333] **OVAL CRICKET GROUND REDEVELOPMENT**. *Contacts*: John Edwards, Friends of the Oval Campaign, c/o Kennington Park Estate Community Centre, 8 Harleyford St, London SE11 5TR, *Tel*: (020) 7735 9663; Paul Sheldon, Chief Executive, Surrey County Cricket Club, The Oval, Kennington, London SE11 5SS, *Tel*: (020) 7582 6660.

[334] **OVAL REGENERATION PROGRAMME**. *Contact*: c/o Lambeth Co-operative Development Agency, 11 Mowil St, London SW9, *Tel*: (020) 7582 0003.

[335] **STOCKWELL PARK CONSERVATION SOCIETY**. *Hon. Secretary*: Louise Peachey, 6 Lorn Rd, London SW9 0AD, *Tel*: (020) 7333 3357. Est. in 1986 to monitor planning applications in the area around Stockwell Park Road (Stockwell Park as such no longer exists).

[336] **THE STREATHAM SOCIETY**. *Current Hon. Secretary* (he is planning to leave London in 1999): John Cresswell, 142 Harborough Rd, London SW16 2XW, *Tel*: (020) 8677 2537. *Internet*: http://www.wwwebspace.uk/~streascc. *Organising secretary of the Local History Research Group*: Brian Bloice, 220 Woodmansterne Rd, London SW16 5UA, *Tel*: (020) 8764 8314; *Email*: brianbloice.compuserve.com. He has a special interest in historic buildings and their architects and is a local history tutor at Wandsworth Adult College, Morley College and Lambeth Community College.

The group publishes a list of members interests and areas of research. Est. in 1974, the society has since then enjoyed a steadily rising membership and is consulted nationally and internationally, and is committed both to the past, present and future of Streatham. There are plans to establish a local museum. Meetings, visits and musical and theatrical events are organised. There is a bi-monthly newsletter *Pump* and a programme of publishing booklets of autobiography and historical research. John Cresswell is planning a new publication on entertainment in Streatham.

1993: FEAST, Douglas. *After the fire*. On the fire at St Leonard's church. 28pp, illus.

1998: BRYANT, Kenneth. *Streatham's 41*. 2nd edition, greatly revised. 94pp, maps, illus. On the V-1 Flying Bomb Offensive as experienced in Streatham.

Histories of churches and schools in Streatham have also been published recently:

1993: BRINE, Gerald. *A history of the church and parish of the English Martyrs, Streatham* (Mitcham Lane, SW16). 71pp, illus.

1995: COOMBS, Joyce *and* WALKER, Judy. *The church on the hill: St Peter's, Streatham*. (113 Leigham Court Rd, London SW16 2NX). 65pp, illus.

1995: McHENRY, Alexander. *St Thomas Church, Telford Park: a short history* (Telford Avenue, London SW16). 27pp.

1997: VAN HASSELT, Alexandra. *History of Streatham Hill & Clapham High School for Girls* (42 Abbotswood Rd, London SW16 1AW).

Publications still in print include: *Lambeth's theatrical heritage*, by J. Cresswell, 1991; *Brief history of Streatham*, 2nd edition, 1990 by Graham Gower; and *Streatham: pictures from the past*, 1983 compiled by Keith Holdaway, Graham Gower and John Cresswell.

Graham Gower (19 Lexton Gardens, Clapham Park, London SW12 0AY, *Tel*: (020) 8674 8473) also publishes booklets on Streatham with John Brown's Local History Publications imprint (316 Green Lane, Streatham, London SW16 3AS, *Tel*: (020) 8677 9562): *Historic Furzedown; A history of suburban Streatham; Streatham Farms;* and *The tile and brickmakers of Streatham*.

John Brown, himself, has written and published: *The Coulthursts of Streatham Lodge; Dead Centre of Streatham* (on St Leonard's churchyard); *Roe Bridge, Mitcham Lane; The Streatham grave robbers; Streatham races; Zeppelins over Streatham*. He has also issued two reprints: *Bygone Streatham*, written, illustrated and published by J. Harvey Bloom, 1926; and *Streatham old and new*, by H.B., (early twentieth century publication) (topographical, historical perambulations).

[337] **VAUXHALL ST PETER'S HERITAGE CENTRE**. Kennington Lane, London SE11 6HY, *Tel*: (020) 7793 0263; *Fax*: (020) 7820 0038. *Administrator/director*: Giles Semper. Aims to promote interest in the historic South Bank of the Thames with exhibitions, talks and walks. The church was built 1863/4, architect: John Loughborough Pearson, and deserves to be much better known. The centre is also a base for the Vauxhall Employers Group, and the local community Vauxhall Festival, *Tel*: (020) 7820 0038 (answerphone).

The Friends of the Centre organisation currently has some 50 members.

VISION FOR VAUXHALL, *Chair*: Mary Ackland-Hood, 9 Sentiman Rd, London SW8 1LD, a forum group of concerned, interested individuals, also meets here monthly.

The current administrator contact for the **VAUXHALL REGENERATION COMPANY** is: Roger Keeling, Enterprise PLC, 52 Portland St, London W1V 4LP, *Tel*: (020) 7287 5858.

[338] **VAUXHALL SOCIETY**. *Hon. secretary*: Jim Nicholson, 20 Albert Square, London SW8 1BS, *Tel*: (020) 7735 3473. *Chairman*: Chris Cossey, 320 Kennington Rd, London SE11, *Tel*: (020) 7735 7314. Est. in 1969, the society has some 200 members; it aims 'to stimulate public interest and care for the character, history, and future of the area and to maintain and improve the quality of life for all who live there'. It covers the northern part of Lambeth, with adjacent areas of Wandsworth and Southwark. There is a quarterly newsletter and in 1992 a 200 page *Selection of key newsletters with index to local history articles* was issued. In 1991 two historical accounts were published with the St Peter's Heritage Centre: *St Peter's Church, Vauxhall, a history*, by David Beevers, 24pp; and *Vauxhall Gardens, 1661-1859*, by Jim Nicholson, 15pp.

* SOME OTHER COUNCIL CONTACTS *

Conservation officer: Edmund Bird, Town Planning Division, Acre House, 10 Acre Lane, Brixton, London SW2 5LL, *Tel*: (020) 7926 1215.

Reference library: Tate Library, Brixton Oval, London SW2 1JQ, *Tel*: (020) 7926 1067.

* SOME NON-COUNCIL CONTACTS *

Business information:
SOUTHSIDE BUSINESS NETWORK. 444 Brixton Rd, London SW9, *Tel*: (020) 7924 0122; *Fax*: (020) 7733 7070.

Residents associations:
LAMBETH FEDERATION OF HOUSING CO-OPERATIVES. 260 Coldharbour Lane, London SW9, *Tel*: (020) 7333 7370. For residents and tenants associations contact: Stewart Dickson, Hambrook House, Porden Rd, London SW2 1RJ, *Tel*: (020) 7926 3576.

Voluntary organisations:
LAMBETH VOLUNTARY ACTION COUNCIL. 95 Acre Lane, London SW2, *Tel*: (020) 7737 1419.

* LOCAL PRESS *

New Lambeth, council paper published every two months, edited by Andrew Tainton, Town Hall, Brixton Hill, London SW2 1RW, *Tel*: (020) 7926 2240.
Streatham, Clapham and Dulwich Guardian (free newspaper), 33-44 London Rd, Morden SM4 5BR, *Tel*: (020) 8646 6336.
Streatham, Clapham and Dulwich Mercury, South London Press Group, 2-4 Leigham Court Rd, London SW16 2PD, *Tel*: (020) 8769 4444.

LEWISHAM

* LONDON BOROUGH OF LEWISHAM *

[339] **LEWISHAM LOCAL STUDIES AND ARCHIVES**. Lewisham Library, 199-200 Lewisham High St, London SE13 6LG, *Tel*: (020) 8297 0682; *Fax*: (020) 8297 1169; *Email*: localstudies@lewisham.gov.uk. *Hours*: Mon 10-5; Tues, Thurs 9-8; Sat 9-5; closed Wed. *Archivist*: Jean Wait. *Assistant*: John Coulter.
John Coulter is the author of many books: *Lewisham: history and guide* (includes a walk along the High Street, Lewisham Hill and Dartmouth Row), from Sutton, 1994. Three collections of old photographs of Lewisham and Deptford also from Sutton; and in the Archive Photographs series from Tempus a collection *Lewisham*, with Barry Olley, and a collection *Sydenham and Forest Hill* with John Seaman; and from Historical Publications *Sydenham and Forest Hill past*. A new title from Sutton *London of 100 years ago* will concentrate on contemporary written accounts.
The department publishes a small amount: in 1998, a booklet *Sources for family history*, 20pp; and four guided walks of the late 1980's and early 1990's: *From the Marquis of Grandby to the Obelisk* (New Cross to Lewisham); *From the tiger to the clock tower (Lee High Road)*; *A walk down the High Street (Lewisham)*; *Greenwich and Deptford History Trail* (with the London Borough of Greenwich).
Another trail *From the Swan to the slip* (from Lee High Road to Eliot Vale, Blackheath) was produced by Jeremy Carden (who also publishes old prints as postcards) for Diana Rimel.
There are also several publications from the council of interest: *Commemorative plaques in Lewisham*, a booklet published in 1995, and *Lewisham 2000*, a pictorial history of the redevelopment of the Town Centre, with historical maps and illustrations. Other publications still in print are: *Looking back at Lewisham*, a short history of the borough, by Jane Kimber, 1992; *Rock around Lewisham* by Mel Wright, 1990 (Lewisham's associations with rock and popular music, 1950-1990); and *Yours is the cause: a brief account of suffragettes in Lewisham, Greenwich and Woolwich*, by Iris Dove, 1988, published jointly by Lewisham Library Service and Greenwich Libraries.
Postcards:
There is a set of 8 postcards of Lewisham at war; and five sets (8 in each) showing miscellaneous Lewisham views: Blackheath, Catford, Deptford, Forest Hill and Lewisham.
The department also sells a variety of items from other sources: the publications from the Deptford Forum Publishing, for example (see entry in section on publishers), from Sutton and Chalford. Publications from individuals and organisations include: *Deptford women remembering*, by Deepways Reminiscence and Creative Writing Group, published by the Co-oPepys Community Arts Project in 1993 as part of the European Older Womens Project.
Discover Deptford and Lewisham, by Darrell Spurgeon (on buildings in Deptford, New Cross, Brockley, Lewisham and Ladywell; personal, enthusiastic, free of jargon).
The churchyard of St Mary the Virgin, Lewisham, by Ken White, 2nd edition, 1998. (12 Fermor Rd, London SE23 2HN). Covers history, trees, gravestones.
Hither Green: the forgotten hamlet, including the Corbett Estate, by Godfrey Smith (100 The Woodlands, London SE13 6TX), published in 1997; 15 chapters including a list of early residents 1715-1841.
The Lewisham and District Camera Club, a history 1947-1959, by Ken White, 1992 (see above).

The Lewisham Unitarians 1897-1997: a commemorative booklet compiled from congregational records. A history of the church at its three sites, by Gordon Dennington.

A part of Deptford: past and present: the parish of Our Lady of the assumption 1842-1992 by Father John Kenne. (The Roman Catholic church in Deptford High Street).

Public houses of Lee and Lewisham, by Ken White (see above). A rather extraordinary work, with the author's own calligraphic text and drawings, 1992, 346pp; in seven chronological parts.

Red alert: the story of south East London at war, 1939-1945, by Lewis Blake (revised and enlarged edition incorporating material from 'Bromley in the Front Line') (62 Park Hill Rd, Shortlands, Bromley, Kent).

St Mary's C. of E. Primary School, Lewisham 1883-1993, compiled by Joan Read (29 Ewhurst Rd, London SE4 1AG).

Both Joan Read and Ken White are prolific authors, who publish their own work. Joan Read has been writing on Lewisham since the 1970's: general titles such as *Lewisham flashbacks*, 1991; *Joan Read's Lewisham Local History Notebook*, 1992; *Read about Lewisham* (a narrative text involving the author and her two young friends 'Danny and Brad'), 1976; *Lewisham street names*, 1990; more specialised titles such as: *Sydenham Wells*, 1977; *Forest Hill*, 1979; *The manor of Hatcham: aspects of its development*, 1979.

She is a former Lewisham Local Studies Librarian; she wrote the history of Lewisham Town Hall in 1971 and contributed text to the borough guide books. Between 1983 and 1987 she wrote a series of weekly articles for the South London Press.

Ken White's work is more eccentric: he uses his own calligraphic manuscripts as print. In addition to the three titles above, his books include: *The Croydon canal and its neighbours*, 1989; *Deptford riverside*, 1996; *Pissaro up to date in Lewisham*, 1992; and *Watering places in Lewisham*, 1998 (covers topics such as drinking fountains, horse troughs, ponds, pumps, wells, etc).

* AMENITY AND HISTORICAL SOCIETIES *

[340] **BROCKLEY SOCIETY**. *Chairman*: Joseph Cullen, 17b Tressillian Crescent, London SE14, *Tel*: (020) 8694 1476. Est. in 1974. The society has a local history group which has published several sets of postcards and researches items for the newsletter. *Contact*: Mrs G. Heywood, 14 Darling Rd, London SE4 1YQ, *Tel*: (020) 8692 6977.

[341] **DEPTFORD HISTORY GROUP/DEPTFORD TOUR GUIDES ASSOCIATION**. *Contact*: John Warren, 5 Edmund House, 75 St Donats Rd, London SE14 6TL, *Tel*: (020) 8691 7543.

[342] **GROVE PARK COMMUNITY GROUP**. Est. in 1972 as a broad-based community association. Since 1981 has had office/centre at: The Ringway Centre, 268 Baring Rd, Grove Park, London SE12 0DS. John King has written two booklets: *Grove Park: a history of a community*, 1983; and *Grove Park in the Great War*, 1983.

[343] **LADYWELL VILLAGE SOCIETY**. *Contacts*: Sue Gore, 11 Cliffview Rd, Lewisham, London SE13 7DB, *Tel*: (020) 8692 4154; Ron Cowper, 135 Hither Green Lane, London SE13 6QT, *Tel*: (020) 8852 5709. Est. in 1984. Booklets: *Well of our Lady* and *Ladywell Spa* have been published.

[344] **LEE MANOR SOCIETY**. *Chairman*: Charles Batchelor, 14 Southbrook Rd, London SE12 8LQ, *Tel*: (020) 8318 3182. *Secretary*: Roy Cromb, 69 Effingham Rd, London SE12, *Tel*: (020) 8333 2926. *Treasurer*: Jean Martin, 68 Handen Rd, London SE12. Est. in 1975 to promote an interest in the conservation of the Lee Manor Conservation Area, mainly Victorian dwellings, in the east of the borough of Lewisham; also includes the Manor House, a country mansion dating from the 1770's; from 1796 until 1899 the home of the Baring family, founders of Baring Brothers, still a prominent merchant bank in the City of London; now a library and the gardens a public park. The society is currently restoring an ice house there. The society regards all residents as members; a monthly meeting open to all attracts up to a dozen officials and active members. There is an illustrated brochure on the history of the society and area, and also a full colour map and guide.

[345] **LEWISHAM ENVIRONMENT TRUST**. *Secretary*: Phil Ashford, Town Hall Chambers, Rushey Green, Catford, London SE6 4RY, *Tel*: (020) 8314 8533. *Chairman*: Raymond Hall, *Tel*: (020) 8318 9233. Est. in 1986, a voluntary organisation to improve, care for and protect the local natural and built environment. Phil Ashford is also Lewisham's conservation officer. Leaflets are available on conservation areas, listed buildings, trees.

There is also a [346] **LEWISHAM FORUM FOR AMENITY AND CONSERVATION SOCIETIES**. *Contact*: Gina Raggett, Blackheath Society, Chapman House, 10 Blackheath Village, London SE3 9LE, *Tel*: (020) 8297 1937.

[347] **LEWISHAM LOCAL HISTORY SOCIETY**. *Chairman*: John King, 44 Le May Avenue, London SE12 9SU, *Tel*: (020) 8857 1819. *Membership secretary*: Mr W.H. Seamer, 2c Lawrie Park, Sydenham, London SE26 6DN. *Publications officer*: Cliff Robertson, 55 Milborough Crescent, London, SE12 0RR, *Tel*: (020) 8851 3936. *Journal editor*: Tom Shepherd, 2

Bennett Park, Blackheath Village, London SE3 9RB, *Tel*: (020) 8852 0219. Est. in 1961, there is a full programme of talks; also excursions and walks and an annual 4-day tour. Bimonthly newsletter and a journal replacing the former transactions.

Recent publications: GEORGE, Ken. *Two sixpennies please: Lewisham's early cinemas*, 1996, 94pp, illus. (first edition: 1987). Surveys the history of the borough's 29 silent cinemas. Ken George (166 Verdant Lane, London SE6 1LJ, *Tel*: (020) 8698 9228) has also published himself: *The big five: Lewisham's super cinemas*, 1997, 76pp, illus. Covers: The Capitol (Forest Hill), Splendid (Downham), State (Sydenham), Gaumont (Lewisham), and Odeon (Deptford). *The Cannon, Catford*, 1993, 13pp, illus. 80th anniversary history of the borough's last surviving cinema.

MACARTNEY, Sylvia, and WEST, John. *The Lewisham silk mills and the history of an ancient site*, 1998, 113pp, illus. Published in association with G.L.I.A.S.(first edition: 1979). The story of armour, small arms, silk, and gold and silver wire drawing.

RIMEL, Diana. *Thomas Dinwiddy: a forgotten architect*, 1994, 22pp, illus. Life of the architect of Grove Park Hospital, Laurie Grove Baths and other local buildings.

The society also has two series of leaflets: *Borough profiles* feature: Dr Charles Burney, Leland Henry Duncan, Henry Tobbats Stainton (entomologist), Thomas Tilling, Charles James Folkard (children's book illustrator), John Evelyn. The *Borough Byways* walks series feature: Deptford and New Cross; Hither Green; A field path in Lee; Hocus Pocus (Ladywell); Romans and railways (Lewisham); Walking on the Common (Sydenham); Forest Hill; Ladywell; Manor Lane; Around Bell Green; Southern boundary of Lewisham; Ravensbourne Walk: Ladywell to Bellingham. There is also a leaflet on Halifax Street (Sydenham).

Articles in the Lewisham History Journal:

1993: Does Lewisham need a museum? (John King); The Benedictine Priory of Lewisham: land of St Peter's of Ghent (Jennifer Mills); Early medical practice in Lewisham (Dr R. Meyrick); The Horniman family: its achievements in business, museums and the theatre (Muriel Shaw).

1994: Farewell to Manor House (Alfred Wood); The Carews of the Hundred of Blackheath (Joan A. Carew Richardson); History of S.E. London post (Peter Bathe); The summer of the doodlebugs (Ray Munday); Past times in Sydenham (Joan Read).

1995: Our clock tower (Jim Park, Jean Wait); Lewisham remembers 1945 (Jonathan Derrick); A brief history of the gas industry in S.E. London (Brian Sturt); Lewisham's West Indian connections: a tale of three 17th century expansionists (John Anim-Addo).

1996: The Deptford Ragged School (George Maslin); Henry William Forster MP (Frederick Whyler); Forest Hall Baths (Malcolm Taylor).

1997: The Deptford Estate in the mid-18th century (Alan Fraser); A view of Deptford in the mid 18th century (Alan Fraser); Sherlock Holmes in Lee and Lewisham (Jonathan Oates).

1998: The 1497 Cornish uprisings and the Battle of Blackheath (Ann T. Jenkin); John Kenyon of Lewisham (Clare Taylor); The changing face of Rotherhithe (Stuart Rankin).

[348] **MANOR HOUSE GARDENS USER GROUP**. *Chair*: Carolyn Bosworth (a wine consultant), 74 Taunton Rd, London SE12 8PB, *Tel*: (020) 8318 3078. Est. in 1993, the group secured a heritage lottery grant of £727,000 for environmental improvements (article with photograph in South London Press, Dec 5th 1997).

[349] **PENNYFIELDS COMMUNITY ASSOCIATION**. *Contact*: Bryan Leslie, 14 Allenby Rd, London SE23 2RQ.

[350] **SYDENHAM SOCIETY**. *Chair*: Pat Trembath, 97 Longton Grove, London SE26 6QQ, *Tel*: (020) 8659 4903. Est. in 1972, current membership over 850. Committees cover amenities, conservation, roads and transport. There is a quarterly newsletter with some historical articles.

[351] **TELEGRAPH HILL SOCIETY**. *Chairman*: Malcolm Bacchus, 92 Jerningham Rd, London SE14, *Tel*: (020) 7635 9421. *Membership secretary*: Jayne Bates, 39 Erlanger Rd, Telegraph Hill, London SE14 5TF, *Tel*: (020) 7639 9448. Concerned with: transport, roads and pavements, planning, parks and amenities, and local history. Publications include a guided walk, reproduction of a 1892 street map, and a 1914 OS map, and a series of postcards. There is a bi-monthly newsletter.

* SOME OTHER COUNCIL CONTACTS *

Agenda 21: Clare Bruce-Smith, Laurence House, 1 Catford Rd, London SE6 4SW, *Tel*: (020) 8314 8003. A business directory (last edition: 1998) is published by the **Business Information Centre**, *Tel*: (020) 8314 8111, at the Department of Leisure, Economy and Environment, Laurence House, 1 Catford Rd, London SE6 4SW.

Conservation officer: Phil Ashford, Town Hall Chambers, Rushey Green, Catford, London SE6 4RY, *Tel*: (020) 8314 8533.

Lewisham Library is at 199-201 Lewisham High St, London SE13 6LG, *Tel*: (020) 8297 9677. Based here are: **Borough Information Centre**, *Tel*: (020) 8314 7070; **Lewisham Local Studies Centre** (see above); **Reference Library**, *Tel*: (020) 8297 9430; **Tourist Information**, *Tel*: (020) 8297 8317. Details on some 2000 organisations are held on the community information database.

Nature conservation, etc. *Contact*: Bernard Bligh, Laurence House, 1 Catford Rd, London SE6 4BA, *Tel*: (020) 8314 8143.

Parks: For details on Lewisham's 9 parks users groups, contact Martin Hyde, Development officer, *Tel*: (020) 8314 8028; there are groups for Beckenham Place Park, Blackheath, Forster Memorial Park, Hillyfields, Manor House Gardens, Manor Park, Mayo Park, Sydenham Wells, Telegraph Hill. Brookmill and Friendly Gardens planned.

* SOME NON-COUNCIL CONTACTS *

Voluntary organisations:
VOLUNTARY ACTION LEWISHAM, 120 Rushey Green, London SE6, *Tel*: (020) 8695 6000.

* LOCAL PRESS *

Lewisham Life is published bi-monthly, edited by Adrian Wardle, from Town Hall, Catford, London SE6, *Tel*: (020) 8314 6081.

Mercury Group newspapers (Bexley, Greenwich, Lewisham, Streatham), 116 Deptford High St, London SE8 4NX, *Tel*: (020) 8692 1122.

Newshopper, free newspaper (owned by Newsquest), Mega House, Crest View Drive, Petts Wood, Orpington, Kent BR5 1BT.

SOUTHWARK

* LONDON BOROUGH OF SOUTHWARK *

[352] SOUTHWARK LOCAL STUDIES LIBRARY. 211 Borough High St, London SE1 1JA, *Tel*: (020) 7403 3507; *Fax*: (020) 7403 8633. *Hours*: Mon, Thurs 9.30-8; Tues, Fri 9.30-5; Sat 9.30-1. A publicity leaflet is issued; and there are two information sheets: *List of researchers and local societies*; and *Sources for family history*. Census, parish register and directory searches can be undertaken for a fee.

The first Southwark Local History Fair, organised by the Library, was held at Chumleigh Gardens in 1998.

Archivist: Stephen Humphrey (see advert). Books include two collections of old photographs on Southwark, Bermondsey and Rotherhithe, and one on Camberwell, Dulwich and Peckham (Sutton); *The story of Rotherhithe*, 1997; and the *Guide to the Archives in Southwark Local Studies Library*, 1992. He has also reprinted himself Fenner Brockway's 1949 book *Bermondsey story: The life of Alfred Salter*.

Librarian: Len Reilly. Books include: booklet guide to sources: *Family history of Southwark*, 1996; and *Southwark: an illustrated history*, 1998 (9 chapters, 92pp, with many illus. (including watercolours)).

Recent publications from the library:
In addition to the above items there have been new, substantially expanded editions, with new illustrations, of books in the Neighbourhood Histories series: Mary Boast, former librarian, has revised her accounts of the 'Borough' (1998). Camberwell (1996), Dulwich (1990), and Walworth (1993). Rotherhithe was rewritten in 1997 by Stephen Humphrey, and John Beasley has revised his account of Peckham.

The first edition of the *Story of Bermondsey* was published in 1984; and the first edition of *The Story of Bankside* in 1985, both by Mary Boast.

There have also been new editions of *Charles Dickens and Southwark*, 1994, by Graham Prettejohns, Brenda Mann, and Larry Ilott; and of *The Mayflower and pilgrim story*: chapters from Rotherhithe and Southwark, 1995, also by Mary Boast.

Southwark at war: a book of memories, compiled and edited by Rob Davis and Pam Schweitzer was published in 1996.

In addition to booklets from societies listed in this chapter, specialist books published by authors and organisations are also stocked.

Stuart Rankin's shipbuilding series is listed under Rotherhithe & Bermondsey Local History Group. John Beasley's Peckham series under the Peckham Society.

Other recent titles, currently sold, include:

Bermondsey and Rotherhithe perceived, 1998 (2nd edition of A Bermondsey & Rotherhithe Album), (Peter Marcan Publications).

A century of the OBC, by Mark Say, 1997, published by Deptford Forum Publishing, on behalf of the Oxford and Bermondsey Club.

An illustrated history of Borough Market, by Dominic Webster, Jackie Power, Teresa Hoskyns and Raymond Brown, published by the Borough Market Trust (8 Southwark St, London SE1, *Tel*: (020) 7407 1002). Jackie Power is a Trustee of the Borough Market, and a former chair of Southwark's Conservation Areas Advisory Group.

Making a splash: a history of Dulwich Baths, by Polly Bird (1 Downswood Court, West Bank, Abbots Park, Chester CH1 4BF). Author was a governor of Grove Vale School for 10 yeas and writes on education, business and women's issues for commercial publishers.

Visions of Southwark, 1997 (Peter Marcan Publications).

Postcards: Sets of five postcards each have been issued on: 'The Borough'; Newington; Peckham; People and places; Poverty and pleasure; Riverside; Rotherhithe; Surrey Docks; Women; Women working.

A booklet of 12 sepia views of the vicinity of Camberwell Green *Around the Green*, was issued in 1991.

Old prints: Although now out of print Southwark Libraries *Scenes from the past* series should be noted: three collections of loose reproductions, with useful notes, published in 1974.

In 1998 the Education Department produced three spiral bound historic walks: The *Bankside Trail*, the *Bermondsey Trail* and the *Southwark Trail*, written by Chris Culpin. There is also a teacher's 'pack' on Victorian Southwark.

Also run by Southwark Council is:

[353] **SOUTH LONDON GALLERY**. Peckham Rd, London SE5 8UF, *Tel*: (020) 7703 6120. *Director*: David Thorpe. *Part-time (Mon, Fri) curator of permanent collections*: Chris Jordan. The Southwark topographical collection is of special interest and features work mainly from the earlier decades of the 20th century; an artist/title/location catalogue has been created: Southwark Local Studies Library has a card index. some 2,000 items are held. The modern prints collection (some 700 works) was built up in the 1960's. The historical collection and the beginnings of the gallery are described in *Art for the people: culture in the slums of late Victorian Britain*, edited by Giles Waterfield, Dulwich Picture Gallery, 1994. The gallery's current policy is to stage contemporary art shows from outside sources.

* TOURISM/HERITAGE ORGANISATIONS *

[354] **SOUTHWARK HERITAGE ASSOCIATION**. *Contacts*: *Former chairman*: Peter Challon, 21 Bousfield Rd, London SE14 5TP, *Tel/Fax*: (020) 7207 0509. *Newsletter editor*: Robert Godley, Planart Ltd, (printers), 9 Morocco St, London SE1 3HB, *Tel*: (020) 7407 5811. (Publishers of a 'glossy' tourist guide *Southwark: a guide to the historic area known as the 'Borough'*, and of a forthcoming guide to the London Borough of Greenwich). Newsletter Spring 1997 describes its aims: 'to create partnerships with local residents, businesses and attractions, and to act as an umbrella organisation with other groups in order to promote and advance the regeneration of the Borough'. In 1998 its events included a Chaucer inspired medieval pilgrimage from Southwark to Canterbury, an evening on entertainment in late medieval and Elizabethan London at the Clink Museum, and a tour 'Unknown Southwark'. Newsletter New Year 1999 reports on its involvement with schemes such as Southwark Young Pilgrims, Southwark Mysteries, the new Tourist Information Centre (see below), the new London Bridge Museum, Pool of London Partnership initiatives (including a poetry competition) and the Mayor of Southwark's booklet of 'Utterances for Carers and the Cared for'

The SHA was established in the late 1980's as a small pressure group to promote tourism. Early publications included: *London's historic riverside*, a booklet featuring landmark and historic buildings, museums and galleries and restaurants; and a folding leaflet *Mayflower: American heritage in Southwark and the City* (both initiated by Heather Pickering).

Another SHA initiative is the Tourist Information Centre, set up in 1984, previously at Hay's Galleria. It has now moved to a new site near London Bridge, and is known as the [355] **SOUTHWARK INFORMATION CENTRE**, 6 Tooley St, London SE1, *Tel*: (020) 7403 8299; managed by Albion Heritage Services (Paul and Heike Herbert) in partnership with Southwark Council.

Southwark Council responded to these initiatives by setting up the [356] **SOUTHWARK TOURISM UNIT**. *Contact*: Gwen Owen, Town Hall, Peckham Rd, London SE5 8UB, *Tel*: (020) 7525 1570; *Fax*: (020) 7525 1568. She has been responsible for three attractive publications: the booklet *Southwark tales: a guide to literary associations and places to visit in Southwark*; and two folding leaflets with pictorial maps: *Southwark riverside* and *In and around Dulwich*. A new edition of Southwark Tales is planned for 1999 plus themed guides, and a Millennium Walk from Westminster to Tower Bridges.

[357] **MAYFLOWER 1620 LTD.** *Contact*: Veronica Alden, 216 Upland Rd, East Dulwich, London SE22 0DJ, *Tel*: (020) 8299 0470. Set up to train unemployed people in Southwark as tourist guides (see article in the Focus on a Firm series, South London Press, October 24th 1997). A recent scheme involving Southwark school students as tourist guides Southwark Young Pilgrims is described in the Southwark Heritage Newsletter Autumn, 1997.

[358] **BRAMAH TEA AND COFFEE MUSEUM.** Maguire St, London SE1, *Tel*: (020) 7370 0222. *Proprietor*: Edward Bramah. *Hours*: Daily 10-6.30. Large collection of teapots, coffee machines, pictures, etc, (recent press feature in South London News, March 5th, 1999).

* MUSEUMS/HISTORIC PROPERTIES/VISITOR ATTRACTIONS *

[359] **BRUNEL'S ENGINE HOUSE.** Railway Avenue, Rotherhithe, London SE16. The museum is managed by Brunel Exhibition Rotherhithe, a voluntary society; *Contact*: Peter Salter, 12 Kinburn St, Rotherhithe, London SE16 1DN, *Tel*: (020) 7252 0059. Open on the first Sunday of every month, 12-4.00. A bi-annual newsletter is issued and in 1992 a substantial historical account was published: *Brunel's tunnel ... and where it led*, by Andrew Mathewson and Derek Laval, edited by Corinne Orde.
The engine house is part of the works for the Thames Tunnel, built by Mark Isambard Brunel 1825-43, the first under-water tunnel in the world. A 1885 Rennie engine is on display and there are changing exhibitions of local interest. Those interested in voluntary work on Sundays at the museum should contact Robert Hulse, *Tel*: (020) 7231 3314.

[360] **THE CLINK PRISON MUSEUM.** *Contact*: Ray Rankin (proprietor); Rosemary Smith (education officer), 1 Clink St, London SE1 9DG, *Tel*: (020) 7403 6515; (020) 7378 1558; *Fax*: (020) 7403 5813. *Hours*: 7 days a week 10-6. Also available for corporate entertainment and private parties. There is an illustrated booklet, *A short history of the Clink Prison*, by E.J. Burford.

[361] **THE CUMING MUSEUM.** 155-157 Walworth Rd, London SE17 1RS, *Tel*: (020) 7701 1342; *Fax*: (020) 7703 7415. *Curator*: Sophie Perkins; *Museum officer*: Keith Bonnick. *Hours* Tues-Sat 10-5. The museum of Southwark's history and the home of the world-wide collections of the Cuming family. Between 1780 and 1900 Richard and Henry Syer Cuming collected over 100,000 objects. Today the collections consist of archaeology British and foreign, social history, prints, coins, ceramics, ancient Egyptian and Etruscan objects. The museum's collection of local objects and displays illustrate Southwark's growth and development from the Romans to the present.
Talks on Southwark's history are held here.

[362] **FRIENDS OF KINGSWOOD HOUSE.** *Contact*: Jane Wenlock, c/o Kingswood House Centre, Seeley Drive, Kingswood Estate, Dulwich, London SE21, *Tel*: (020) 8761 7239. Set up in June 1998, currently with some 30 members, to promote the preservation, upkeep and historical importance of this large mansion, originally Kingswood Lodge, built in the 18th century and enlarged by subsequent owners who have included Lawson Johnson, founder of Bovril, and Lord Vestey, pioneer of the chilled meat trade. The house is now owned by the Southwark Council, and in use as a library, community centre and venue for meetings, receptions, etc. Four sheets of historical and background information are available from Yvonne Witter at the above address. A history was published by the Dulwich Society in 1985 (reissued in 1999).

[363] **FRIENDS OF SOUTHWARK CATHEDRAL.** Southwark Cathedral, Montague Close, London SE1 9DA. 'For people who value Southwark Cathedral and wish to contribute regularly towards its mission, maintenance and the enhancement of its beauty'. Friends receive a regular newsletter and invitations to a busy and varied programme of social events at or near the cathedral, and to take part in an annual visit to another cathedral. Southwark Cathedral publishes a colour guidebook, and in 1993 produced *Stained glass in Southwark Cathedral*, by Kenneth London.

[364] **THE GOLDEN HINDE.** Saint Mary Overie Dock, Cathedral St, London SE1 9DG, *Tel*: (020) 7403 0123. Bookings and information: (0541) 505041; *Email*: info@goldenhinde.co.uk. *Fax*: (01722) 333 343. A full size reconstruction of the 16th century warship in which Sir Francis Drake circumnavigated the world between 1577 and 1580. Crew members are in period dress and there are five decks of exhibits and artefacts. It is available for: living history experiences, Tudor workshops, pirate parties, weddings, private and corporate hire and school field trips. An interesting booklet on the reconstruction of the ship (by the Hinks shipyard at Appledore in the early 1970's) is published.

[365] **KIRKALDY TESTING MUSEUM.** 99 Southwark St, London SE1 0JE. *Contact*: Peter J. Skilton, 35 Selkirk Drive, Erith, Kent DA8 3QR, *Tel*: (01322) 332195. The museum was established in 1987 to show the history of materials testing and particularly the great influence that David Kirkaldy made in the field. The main item on display is the original Kirkaldy testing machine, built by Greenwood and Batley of Leeds in 1864. The building was empty from 1974 to 1982 when the Industrial

Buildings Preservation Trust acquired the freehold from the Crown Commissions and started on the refurbishment of the building. A Friends organisation was set up to provide voluntary help in maintaining and operating the museum.

[366] **LONDON DUNGEON**. 28 Tooley St, London SE1, *Tel*: (020) 7403 7221. *Hours*: Summer 10-5; winter 10-4.30.

[367] **OLD OPERATING THEATRE, MUSEUM AND HERB GARRET**. 9a St Thomas's Street, London SE1 9RY, *Tel*: (020) 7955 4791. *Hours*: daily 10-4. Site managed and curated by Kevin Flude and Paul Herbert on behalf of the trustees of the Lord Brock Memorial Trust (he was a pioneer of heart surgery and ensured that the site was restored and preserved); now owned by Butcher Robinson and Staples Ltd). The roof garret of the 18th century St Thomas church was converted into a womens' operating theatre in 1821, closing in 1862 when St Thomas' hospital moved to Lambeth, and not rediscovered until 1957. There is a programme of events and lectures, and poetry reading are also held in the operating theatre. An illustrated guidebook and history is published.

[368] **PUMPHOUSE EDUCATIONAL MUSEUM/LAVENDER POND NATURE PARK/ ROTHERHITHE HERITAGE MUSEUM**. Lavender Rd, Rotherhithe, London SE16 1DZ, *Tel*: (020) 7231 2976. *Head of centre*: Caroline Marais. *Hours*: Mon-Fri 9.30-3.00. The educational museum collects diverse objects and artefacts for use in schools and with the elderly (substantial lottery grant received in 1998 for this reminiscence work). The Heritage Museum has tableaux and exhibition cases on Rotherhithe history, and includes Thames foreshore objects (many clay pipes) found by Ron Goode.

[369] **ROSE THEATRE TRUST**. *Contact*: Dr Clare Graham, c/o HSE (Room 007a GSW), Rose Court, 2 Southwark Bridge, London SE1 9HS, *Tel* (020) 7207 6280; *Fax*: (020) 7207 6223; *Email*: admin-rose@theatre.org. A press release, 28th January 1999 states that the site of the theatre and its remains in the basement of the HQ of the Health & Safety Executive are to be opened to the public in early April 1999. A sound and light show, by theatre designer William Dudley, will tell the story of the Rose and of Bankside. This is the first stage of a massive fund-raising campaign for the site's preservation and development.

[370] **TRUSTEES OF BOROUGH MARKET**. *Director*: Philip Obeney, 8 Southwark St, London SE1 1TL, *Tel*: (020) 7407 1002; *Fax*: (020) 7403 9162.

[371] **WINSTON CHURCHILL'S BRITAIN AT WAR MUSEUM**. 64-66 Tooley St, London SE1, *Tel*: (020) 7403 3171. *Hours*: Summer 10-5.30; winter 10-4.30.

* AMENITY AND HISTORICAL SOCIETIES *

[372] **BERMONDSEY STREET ASSOCIATION**. The 'village office', the contact address for the association has recently opened at: the Watch House, 199 Bermondsey St, London SE1 3UV, *Tel*: (020) 7403 1753. For membership, contact: Clive Hicks, c/o Engineering Design Consultants, 106-108 Bermondsey St, London SE1 3TX, *Tel*: (020) 7357 7223. Another contact: former Chairman, Michael Davis, The Glasshouse, Melior Place, London SE1 3QP; *Newsletter editor*: Denise Rogers, headteacher at Snowfields School, Kirby Grove, London SE1, *Tel*: (020) 7525 9065. The winter 1998 newsletter provides background on the BSA's work in the 1990's, as well as current concerns, including the redevelopment of Bermondsey Square.

[373] **BOROUGH HIGH STREET AMENITY FOUNDATION**. *Secretary*: John Barrett, 35 St Thomas St, London SE1 9SN. A small charity which will consider making small grants for the preservation and conservation of buildings in Borough High Street.

[374] **CAMBERWELL SOCIETY**. *Secretary*: Joanna Macpherson, 8 Lyndhurst Grove, London SE15 5AH, *Tel*: (020) 7701 3052. *Chair*: Hania Hardinge, 3 Love Walk, London SE5 8AD, *Tel*: (020) 7701 9144. *President*: Conrad Dehn, 38 Camberwell Grove, London SE5 8BN, *Tel*: (020) 7701 4758. *Camberwell Quarterly editor*: Tony Wilson, 160 Benhill Rd, London SE5 7LZ, *Tel*: (020) 7703 0398.
Est. in 1970, with currently some 850 members. Sub-committees for: planning, traffic and transport, tube (underground service to Camberwell), parks and open spaces. The society has successfully lobbied against the threatened demolition of Addington Square, Denmark Hill Railway Station, and St Giles Tower, and is pro-active in regeneration schemes. It also raises funds for local charities. *Camberwell Quarterly* contains much news on local issues, events, personalities, history and book reviews. Issue No 80 has a Camberwell bibliography and issue No 120 surveys major buildings. There is a series of prints and cards.
Camberwell Arts Week is held annually in June; *Tel contact*: (020) 7708 0309.

[375] **DULWICH ESTATE GOVERNORS**. Old College, Gallery Rd, London SE21, *Tel*: (020) 8299 1000; *Fax*: (020) 8693 2456.

[376] **THE DULWICH SOCIETY**. *Secretary*: Patrick Spencer, 7 Pond Cottages, London SE21 7LE, *Tel*: (020) 8693 2043. *Chairman*: William Higman, 170 Burbage Rd, London SE21 7AG, *Tel*: (020) 7274 6921. *Membership secretaries*: Robin and Wilf Taylor, 30 Walkerscroft Mead, Dulwich, London SE21 8LJ, *Tel*: (020) 8670 0890. *President*: Captain Denys Wyatt. The society was est. in 1965 and has some 1000 members. There are groups concerned with traffic and transport, planning, gardens (arranges visits to local gardens), wildlife, trees and local history. A newsletter is issued four times a year; *Newsletter editor*: Brian McConnell, *Tel*: (020) 8693 4423.
The chairman of the small local history group is Patrick Darby, 10 Raleigh Court, Lymer Avenue, London SE19 1LS, *Tel*: (020) 8670 3426. His father William Darby wrote *Dulwich discovered*, 1966, and *Dulwich: a place in history*, 1961. Patrick is the author of *A gazetteer of Dulwich roads and place-names*, 34pp, published by the society in 1997, and in 1999 he will publish himself a History of houses on north side of Dulwich Common, some 100pp. He maintains a card index of Dulwich people up to 1808 (some 4000 cards), and has a manuscript book *Dulwich Data Links*, a catalogue of deeds from 967. He has also published maps of Dulwich for the dates 1626, 1808, 1876 and 1906.

Another important contact for Dulwich history is Brian Green, 133 Burbage Rd, Dulwich, London SE21 7AF, *Tel*: (020) 7274 1996. He runs the Art Stationers and Village Toy Shop at 31 Dulwich Village (est. in 1867), and under his imprint Village Books has published two small books *Dulwich Village*, 1983; and *Around Dulwich*, 2nd edn, 1989. Baron published his *Victorian and Edwardian Dulwich*, 3rd edn, 1995; and the Dulwich Society is the publisher of his *Dulwich, the home front 1939-1945*, published 1995 and *A Dulwich corner*, published 1994 (on Pond Cottages, the Tollgate and the old windmill). Lastly his historical account: *To read and sew: James Allen's Girls School, 1741-1991* was published by the governors of the school in 1991 (East Dulwich Grove, SE22). There is a copy of his 1988 thesis *History of education in Dulwich 1619-1882* in the Southwark Local studies Library.
God's gift: a living history of Dulwich College, by Sheila Hodges was published by Heinemann in 1981; *Dulwich: a collection of writings about the village and the college*, by the college in 1969.

[377] **FRIENDS OF DULWICH PICTURE GALLERY**. *Membership secretary*: David Parry, 6 Alleyn Rd, London SE21 8AL, *Tel*: (020) 8670 3992. *Chairman*: Desna Allan, 78 Honor Oak Rd, London SE23 3RR, *Tel/Fax*: (020) 8699 7073. *Secretary*: c/o Dulwich Picture Gallery, College Rd, London SE21 7AD, *Tel*: (020) 8693 5254.
Note: The gallery has now closed for refurbishment and new building, and will re-open in May 2000. The Friends play an important function in all aspects of the work of the gallery and organise the programme of evening concerts and talks, and the Saturday morning concerts. (During refurbishment concerts will be held at the Old Library, Dulwich College). Friends enjoy a discount on gallery catalogues, study lectures, outings to places of artistic and historic interest, including overseas visits, and regular mailings including the gallery magazine *Private view*.
The complete illustrated catalogue of the gallery is published by the Unicorn Press (21 Afghan Rd, London SW11 2QD).
Other Dulwich picture gallery publications include: *Art for the people* (on the South London Gallery) by Giles Waterfield, 1994; *Charles Barry, junior and the Dulwich College Estate* by Jan Piggot, 1986; and *Soane and after: the architecture of Dulwich picture gallery*, by Giles Waterfield, 1987.

[378] **FRIENDS OF HOLY TRINITY ROTHERHITHE**. c/o Holy Trinity Vicarage, Bryan Rd, London SE16 1HJ. Set up in 1996 to raise funds for church maintenance, including the renovation of the important Hane Feibusch mural (he is a major 20th century religious mural painter) and the refurbishment of the Lady Chapel. The original church, built in 1838, was destroyed during World War II, and rebuilt in 1960. Friends receive a regular newsletter.

[379] **FRIENDS OF NUNHEAD CEMETERY**. *Chairman*: Ron Woollacott, 185 Gordon Rd, London SE5 3RT (a former Royal Mail administrator, now works full-time as local historian, and topographical artist; some of his Peckham line drawings and further biographical details appear in the compiler's 'Visions of Southwark'. He published his informative illustrated booklet *A historical tour of Nunhead and Peckham Rye* in 1995). *Other contacts*: Jeffery M. Hart, 2 Croslet Vale, Blackheath Hill, London SE10 8DH, *Tel*: (020) 8691 0216. Rex Batten (a retired literature school teacher), 179 Landells Rd, London SE22, *Tel*: (020) 8693 6191. FONC was est. in 1981, currently with some 1,700 members, to promote for the public benefit, the preservation, care and improvement of Nunhead Cemetery as a place of historical and ecological interest, and as a burial ground. The cemetery dates back to 1844; entrance and lodges designed by James Bunstone Bunning, Anglican chapel at top of main avenue by Thomas Little. Volunteer workers undertake an important conservation programme, and with a recent million pound lottery grant much restoration work will be carried out. There is an annual open day in May and guided walks take place on the last Sunday of each month. The illustrated guide book, 1988, is especially informative, with specialist articles on natural history, buildings, graves and monuments, with a guided walk by Jeff Hart. A less scholarly, but equally interesting book is *Nunhead remembered*: a collection of stories, anecdotes and observations, mainly from Nunhead cemetery, edited by

Rex Batten. There are the two books of biographical information by Ron Woollacott: *Nunhead notables*, 1984 and *More Nunhead notables*, 1995; and booklets on natural history topics: *The butterflies of Nunhead Cemetery*, by Richard Jones (current president of the Amateur Entomologists' Society; 13 Bellwood Rd, London SE15 3DE) was issued in 1997; booklets on two cemetery curiosities have also been published: *The Leysdown tragedy*: an account of the deaths and funeral of 8 Walworth scouts in 1912 (buried in the cemetery), by Reg Batten, 1992; and *The Scottish martyrs*, by Wally Macfarlane (the story of the political reformers of 1793 commemorated by an obelisk. The author died in 1997: he was especially active in the trade union movement, in radical politics, and in his own community on the Rye Hill estate (article in Southwark News, February 27th, 1997).

[380] **FRIENDS OF ST GILES' CHURCH CAMBERWELL**. 81 Camberwell Church St, London SE5 8RB. Set up by the Vicar and Parochial Church Council to raise money to meet the costs of repairs and maintenance.
The medieval church building, destroyed by fire in 1841, was replaced by the present-day George Gilbert Scott Victorian gothic building. A short guide and history by Mary Boast was published in 1987; and a booklet on the East Window by Les Alden in 1992.

Globe Theatre, Bankside
[381] **FRIENDS OF SHAKESPEARE'S GLOBE**. 1 Bear Gardens, London SE1, *Tel*: (020) 7928 5665.
The Globe's planned education centre will be sited at Bear Gardens, *Tel*: (020) 7902 1433.

[382] **SHAKESPEARE'S GLOBE VISITORS CENTRE**. New Globe Walk, London SE1 9DT, *Tel*: (020) 7902 1500; *Fax*: (020) 7902 1515.

[383] **LONDON BRIDGE EXHIBITION OFFICE**. *Exhibition manager*: Kim Ryder, 1-7 Shand St, London SE1 2ES, *Tel*: (020) 7407 3169; *Fax*: (020) 7407 3189. CIT/ Markborough are the developers of the site just to the west of Tower Bridge, adjacent to Potters Fields.

[384] **PECKHAM SOCIETY**. *Secretary*: Christine Bannan, 67 Gordon Rd, London SE15 2AF, *Tel*: (020) 7732 9243 (author of booklet *Church and chapel in Peckham*). *Chairman*: Peter Frost, 178 Peckham Rye, London SE22 9QA, *Tel*: (020) 8693 4001. *Journal editor*: John D. Beasley, 6 Everthorpe Rd, London SE15 4DA, *Tel/Fax*: (020) 8693 9412. The society aims 'to encourage interest in and care for the environment and history of Peckham, Nunhead and surrounding area'. Talks, visits.
John Beasley writes prolifically on Peckham, Southwark generally (articles in the South London Press), and social work issues. He spent many years in Tower Hamlets as a social worker; he is also a lay Methodist preacher. Under his own imprint the South Riding Press (same address as above), he has published: *East Dulwich: an illustrated alphabetical guide*, 1998; *Origin of names in Peckham and Nunhead*, 1993; *Peckham and Nunhead churches*, 1995; *Peckham Rye Park centenary*, 1995; *Transport in Peckham and Nunhead*, 1997.
From other publishers: *The bitter cry heard and heeded*: the story of the South London Mission 1889-1989 (Central Hall, Bermondsey St, London SE1 3UJ); *Building together: the story of Peckham Methodist Church*, 1985 (Wood Rd, London SE15 2PX); *Peckham and Nunhead* (Archive Photographs series, Tempus), 1995; *The story of Peckham*, 1983, new edition currently in preparation (London Borough of Southwark); *Who was who in Peckham*, 1985 (Chener Books, booksellers, 14 Lordship Lane, London SE22 8HN).

[385] **ROTHERHITHE & BERMONDSEY LOCAL HISTORY GROUP**. *Chair*: Stuart Rankin, 4 Helier Court, Eleanor Close, Rotherhithe, London SE16 1PE. *Secretary*: Michael Daniels, 6 King's Stairs Close, Rotherhithe, London SE16 4JF. *Membership secretary*: Malcolm Meachen, 25 Shipwright Rd, Rotherhithe, London SE16; *Newsletter editor*: Peter Gurnett, 12 Amersham Grove, New Cross, London SE14. Est. in 1997 'to encourage interest in the history of Rotherhithe, Bermondsey, the surrounding areas, Docklands and the River Thames. It has an interesting programme of talks given by specialists, held at the Old Mortuary; and publishes articles and research in its biannual newsletter the *Redriffe Chronicle*.
No 1, Winter 1997/8: Hale's Rocket Factory; Bermondsey factory memories; The last sailing barge; 'The Blue' in the 20's and 30's, Part I; The Russian-built replica of Peter the Great's frigate Shtandart.
No 2, Summer 1998: Rotherhithe's forgotten tunnel; local heroes and villains, No 1: James Glaisher (1809-1903), astronomer, meteorologist and balloonist; 'The Blue' in the 20's and 30's Part II; The leather makers of Bermondsey.

Stuart Rankin, a former railwayman, has written extensively on the subject of railway architecture. He is also a maritime historian and is publishing his detailed research in a series of Rotherhithe Local History Papers:
1: *Shipbuilding in Rotherhithe: an historical introduction*, 1997.
2: *Shipbuilding in Rotherhithe: the Nelson Dockyard*, 1996.
3: *Shipbuilding in Rotherhithe: Greenland Dock and Barnard's Wharf*, 1997.
4: *Shipbuilding in Rotherhithe: from Bullhead Dock to Pageants Stairs* (in preparation; may be issued in two parts).

5: Reprint (with some additional material) of *Historical notice of the Commercial Docks in the Parish of Rotherhithe, County of Surrey*, by Nathaniel Gould, 1844.

Peter Gurnett, a former engineer with Deptford firm J. Stone & Co is a specialist in the history of Trinity House, and of Deptford.

[386] **ROTHERHITHE ST MARY'S ASSOCIATION**, *Contact*: Annabel Hands, Sands Films, 119 Rotherhithe St, London SE16, *Tel*: (020) 7231 2209. Est. in 1997, representing some 10 local organisations, to oppose, initially, the Tunnel Wharf redevelopment plan (case lost). It is concerned with planning and conservation issues in the small area around St Mary's church.

[387] **SOUTHWARK AND LAMBETH ARCHAEOLOGICAL SOCIETY**. *Secretary*: R.J. Buchanan, 79 Ashridge Crescent, Shooters Hill, London SE18 3EA, *Tel*: (020) 8854 3389. Est. in 1965 'to promote the study and knowledge of the history and archaeology of the area throughout the London boroughs of Southwark and Lambeth. It has particular links with the Cuming Museum and the Southwark and Lambeth Archaeological Excavation Committee (now within MOLAS). Lectures, visits, archaeological processing and publication. Newsletter issued.

[388] **SOUTHWARK COMMUNITY PLANNING AND EDUCATION CENTRE**. *Co-ordinator*: Emma Williamson, 48 Willowbrook Rd, London SE15 6BW, *Tel*: (020) 7732 8856. Provides a professional and independent planning and environmental service to residents and groups in Southwark: planning aid, regeneration support, environmental education, pro-active outreach, supporting community initiatives.

[389] **TIME AND TALENTS ASSOCIATION**. *Director*: Ian Owers. *Administrator*: Heather Livermore. The Old Mortuary, St Marychurch St, Rotherhithe, London SE16 4JE, *Tel*: (020) 7231 7845; *Fax*: (020) 7252 2288. A flourishing community centre established in 1887 in Bermondsey. The Rotherhithe & Bermondsey Local History Group holds its talks and meetings here and there is also a reminiscence group. Publications include a history *By peaceful means: the story of Time and Talents 1887-1987*, by Marjorie Daunt; a booklet *Rotherhithe Trail Walk*, a leaflet *History of the Old Mortuary*, and a contemporary community survey *Bermondsey and Rotherhithe: a profile of a fragmented community*, undertaken 1996/7.

A new group [390] **WEST BERMONDSEY 98** was set up in 1998 to campaign for improvements to West Bermondsey. Its members include individuals and organisations including tenants associations, the charity Charterhouse Southwark, and the BSA. (source: short article in Southwark News, September 3rd, 1998).

* PARKS *

Southwark Council maintains a particularly large and active parks department and encourages the development of friends groups. The Parks Ranger Service has its HQ at: Chumleigh Gardens, Burgess Park, London SE5 0RJ, *Tel*: (020) 7525 1050; *Fax*: (020) 7525 1051; *Email*: southwark_park_rangers@compuserve.com. The telephone number contacts for the area teams are as follows:
Burgess Park Area Team: Tel: (020) 7525 1066; *Fax*: (020) 7525 1067.
Dulwich Park Area Team: Tel/Fax: (020) 8693 5737.
Geraldine Mary Harmsworth Park Area Team: Tel/Fax: (020) 7735 3704.
Peckham Rye Park Area Team: Tel/Fax: (020) 8693 3791.
Southwark Park Area Team: Tel/Fax: (020) 7232 2091.
New developments in the parks and calendars of events (sports, arts, natural history, including tree trails, local history, etc) are published in the new colour newsletter *Parks and Open Spaces Quarterly (POSq)*, available free to all interested persons.
Leaflets have been produced on: the multi-cultural gardens Chumleigh Gardens (enclosed area within Burgess Park); the conference suite and visitor centre also there; allotments and park gardens in Southwark; Russia Dock woodland: self-guided trail. Burgess Park Walk. *A Burgess Park tree and ecology survey*, by David Solman was published in 1989.

A book on the history of Burgess Park, by Tim Charlsworth (160 Peckham Rye, London SE22 9QH) a geography teacher, and author of 'The architecture of Peckham', (Chener Books, 1988) is to be published in 1999 by Groundwork Southwark.

Friends of Parks Organisations:
[391] **DULWICH PARK FRIENDS**. PO Box 16860, London SE21 7QZ. *Chair*: Michelle Pearce, 128 Court Lane, London SE21, *Tel*: (020) 8693 1962. Works to protect and enhance the park in partnership with Southwark Council.

[392] **FRIENDS OF BERMONDSEY AND ROTHERHITHE PARKS.** *Contact*: Gary Magold, c/o Southwark Park Area Team, *Tel*: (020) 7232 2091. Set up in 1996, and currently with some 30 members; meets monthly at Parkside Tenants Association Hall, New Place Square, Southwark Park Rd, London SE16.

[393] **FRIENDS OF DULWICH UPPER WOOD.** *Contact*: Mr J. Murphy, c/o Bowley Centre, Farquhar Rd, London SE19 1SS, *Tel*: (020) 8761 6230; (020) 7394 0538 (evenings).

[394] **FRIENDS OF GERALDINE MARY HARMSWORTH PARK.** The Senior Park Ranger, 91 St George's Rd, London SE1 6ER, *Tel*: (020) 7735 3704. Recently set up, the organisation is actively seeking members. The Park Ranger's Visitor Centre (directly adjacent to the sports area within the park) is open 12.30-5.30 (4.00 in winter), every day.

[395] **FRIENDS OF LAVENDER POND.** *Contact*: Mr E.D. Simpson, c/o TRUE, PO Box 574, Timber Pond Rd, London SE16 1AG, *Tel*: (020) 7232 0498.

[396] **FRIENDS OF PECKHAM RYE PARK.** *Chair*: Philip Wragg (a chartered surveyor), 15 Colyton Rd, London SE22 0NE, *Tel*: (020) 8693 7226. *Membership secretary*: at 42 Hichisson Rd, London SE15 3AL. Campaigns for improvements to the park and common and works to ensure its protection and enhancement (to be designated a conservation area).
A booklet *Peckham Rye Park centenary*, 1995 is available from the South Riding Press.

[397] **FRIENDS OF RUSKIN PARK.** *Membership secretary*: Hilary Brindley, 102 Ferndene Rd, London SE24 0AA, *Tel*: (020) 7274 2598; *Fax*: (020) 7738 6116; *Email*: hbrindey@compuserve.com. Est. in 1997, currently with about 90 members, to protect and improve the park and liaise with Lambeth Council. Organises events such as bird and tree walks, and publishes a quarterly newsletter.

[398] **FRIENDS OF THE GREAT NORTH WOOD.** *Secretary*: David Freeman, 30 Gilkes Crescent, London SE21 7BS, *Tel*: (020) 8299 1868; *Email*: greatnwood@aol.com. *Treasurer/membership*: Paul Blencowe, 17 Elms Crescent, Clapham Park, London SW4 8QE, *Tel*: (020) 7622 6093. *Newsletter ('The wood warbler') editor*: Mathew Frith, *Tel*: (020) 7708 5283. Est. in 1992 to promote the interest in, protection, and sympathetic management of the woodlands within the area of the historic Great North Wood - some 30 woodlands and areas of open green spaces. A folding leaflet describes sites managed mainly by the London boroughs of Croydon, Lewisham and Southwark. A brief history by L. Neville was published by the London Wildlife Trust in 1987.
A guided walk leaflet *From the Nun's Head to the Screaming Alice* - a green walk along the old Crystal Palace high level railway was issued in 1995.

* REMINISCENCE GROUPS *

These meet at [399] **SOUTHWARK PENSIONERS CENTRE.** 305-307 Camberwell Rd, London SE5 9HQ, *Tel*: (020) 7708 4556.
TIME AND TALENTS CENTRE. The Old Mortuary, St Marychurch St, Rotherhithe, London SE16 4JE, *Tel*: (020) 7231 7845.

[400] **GOOD OLD DAYS ORAL HISTORY GROUP.** *Contact*: Emily Braidwood, c/o Southwark Community Planning and Education Centre, 48 Willowbrook Rd, London SE15 6BW, *Tel*: (020) 7732 8856.

* SOME OTHER COUNCIL AND NON-COUNCIL CONTACTS *

Senior archaeology officer: Sarah Gibson, Planning Dept, Chiltern House, Portland St, London SE17 2ES, *Tel*: (020) 7525 5488.
Conservation officer: Onya Dhonnchadha, address as above, *Tel*: (020) 7525 5488.
Local Agenda 21: Environmental development and education unit, Regeneration and Environment Department, Walworth Rd Town Hall, London SE17 1RY, *Tel*: (020) 7525 2070/2193/2185. Series of leaflets issued including one on the built environment.
Reference library: Newington Library, Walworth Rd, London SE17, *Tel*: (020) 7708 0516.

Arts:
Southwark Arts Register (artists, organisations) is now being produced on CD Rom (last hard copy edition: 1992). *Contact*: Roland Shannon, 31 Morecambe St, London SE17 1DX, *Tel*: (020) 7701 9323. Intergalatic Arts runs and hires studios here,

provides graphic art services, and is a base for the Browning Festival, and the Southwark Arts Forum, contact: Andy Mitchell. Newsletter 'Artery' issued.

The Southwark Council contact for the arts is: Camille Goddard, Spa Rd, Offices, London SE16, *Tel*: (020) 7525 3795.

SOUTHWARK FESTIVAL. 16 Winchester Walk, London, *Tel*: (020) 7403 7400/7474.

DULWICH FESTIVAL. 74 Calton Avenue, London SE21, *Tel*: (020) 8299 1011.

Business Information:

The **Southwark Business Directory** (current edition: 1999, with some 4,000 entries) is available from the Southwark Business Desk, Chiltern House, Portland St, London SE17 2ES, *Tel*: (020) 7525 5353.

SOUTHWARK CHAMBER OF COMMERCE. *Contact*: Nancy Hammond, Town Hall, Room 33, West House, 31 Peckham Rd, London SE5, *Tel*: (020) 7525 7347.

SOUTHSIDE CHAMBER OF COMMERCE (S. London branch of the London Chamber of Commerce), 444 Brixton Rd, London SW9 8EJ, *Tel*: (020) 7924 0122. Some 500 members in Lambeth, Southwark and Wandsworth.

Residents/Tenants associations:

SOUTHWARK GROUP OF TENANTS ORGANISATIONS. 19 Buller Close, London SE15, *Tel*: (020) 7639 6718. There are residents associations, for example, in Nunhead, Bankside, Tooley Street, Trinity and Newington.

Voluntary organisations:

SOUTHWARK COUNCIL FOR VOLUNTARY SERVICES. Employment Unit, 135 Rye Lane, London SE15, *Tel*: (020) 7732 9776.

---

* LOCAL PRESS *

In SE1, 45 Dolben St, London SE1 0UQ, *Tel*: (020) 7633 0603; *Fax*: (020) 7620 4356. *Editor*: Leigh Hatts (author of *Pub walks in North London*, Countryside Books).

South London Press. 2 Leigham Court Rd, London SW16, *Tel*: (020) 8769 4444.

Southwark Life, quarterly, full colour magazine, written and edited by Vronni Ward, *Tel*: I929) 7525 7341; and Nicole Terrieux, *Tel*: (020) 7525 7349; from Southwark Marketing & Communications Unit, Town Hall, Peckham Rd, London SE5 8UB, *Fax*: (020) 7525 7310.

Southwark News: Contact: Paul Vinnell, Tower Bridge Business Complex, Clements Rd, London SE16 4DA, *Tel*: (020) 7231 5258. Since the death of the original proprietor David Clark, the paper has been published on a fortnightly basis.

WANDSWORTH

* LONDON BOROUGH OF WANDSWORTH *

[401] **WANDSWORTH LOCAL HISTORY LIBRARY**: at Battersea Library, 265 Lavender Hill, London SW11 1JB, *Tel*: (020) 8871 7753. Local history librarian Richard Shaw retired in December 1998. *Senior assistant librarian*: Meredith Davis. *Hours*: Tues 10-1, 2-8; Wed and Fri 10-1; Sat 2-5, by appointment. Despite these drastic reductions in hours, the library has maintained a small publishing programme:

1992: LOOSE, Jacqueline. *Duels and duelling*: affairs of honour around the Wandsworth area. 28pp, illus. First published in 1982.

1992: LOCK, Gloria. *Caribbeans in Wandsworth*. 44pp.

1993: SHERWOOD, Tim. *Change at Clapham Junction*: the railways of Wandsworth and South West London, 100pp.

1994: BARBER, Susan. *Fascinating facts*, 16pp. Photographs with captions of local events.

1995: *Huguenots in Wandsworth*, by R.A. Shaw, R.D. Gwynn and P. Thomas, 30pp. First published in 1985.

1995: *Picture the past*: scenes of the Borough of Wandsworth. 55pp (third collection).

1996: GOWER, Graham. *Balham: a brief history*. 50pp. First edition published 1991.

Other books in print, and currently on sale include: *Evelyn de Morgan, oil paintings* from the De Morgan Foundation, 1996; *Heaver Estate*, from Wandsworth Borough Planners Service, 1996; *Tooting Bec Lido*, by Janet Smith, 1996 (see advert); *We served: war-time Wandsworth and Battersea*, by Anthony Shaw and John Mills, London Borough of Wandsworth, 1989.

The brown dog affair, by Peter Mason, 1997 (published by Two Sevens Publisher, 30 Winter St, London SW11 2TZ), is on the anti-vivisection movement at the turn of the century with reference to the hospital at Letchmere Park, Battersea.

Museums/visitor attractions:
[402] **WANDSWORTH MUSEUM**. *Curator*: Pat Astley-Cooper; *Assistant curator*: Susan Barber. The Courthouse, 11 Garratt Lane, London SW18 4AQ (opposite the Arndale Centre), *Tel*: (020) 8871 7074 (general enquiries); (020) 8871 7075 (education section); *Fax*: (020) 8871 4602. *Hours*: Tues-Sat 10-5; Sun 2-5. Collections include everyday objects used by residents from prehistoric times to the 20th century, paintings prints and photographs. Exhibitions and events are organised both in the museum and around the borough. The museum shop sells books, maps, prints, reproductions, souvenirs. Water-colour views held by the museum have been reproduced as colour postcards and greetings cards. There are also some postcards of old prints. There are two teaching 'packs': one on transport, 1995; one on Tudor costume (with the Museum of Fulham Palace). Also *Remembering the 1930's*, from the West London Museums Group, 1998.

[403] **YOUNG'S BREWERY**. Ram Brewery, Wandsworth High St, London SW18 4JD, *Tel*: (020) 8875 7005. A living and working museum of English brewing through the ages. Real ale has been produced here for more than 400 years. The visitors centre is open seven days a week. Full brewery tours last about 45 minutes.

* HISTORICAL AND AMENITY SOCIETIES *

[404] **BALHAM SOCIETY**. *Secretary*: Stephen P. Smith, 15 Rossiter Rd, London SW12, *Tel*: (020) 8673 6335. Organises several local history talks each year, and several walks in the summer. A local history research group is planned. Newsletter issued.

[405] **BATTERSEA POWER STATION COMMUNITY GROUP**. *Contact*: Brian Barnes, 69 Condell Rd, London SW3 4HS, *Tel*: (020) 7627 5821; *internet*: www.batterseapowerstation.com. Est. in 1983 when the station was closed, and the Central Electricity Generating Board launched a competition to find a future use for the building, to provide a forum for the local community. The building was designed in the 1930's by Sir Giles Gilbert Scott. A newsletter, the *Battersea Bulletin* is issued.

[406] **THE BATTERSEA SOCIETY**. *Contact*: Peter Deakins, 34 Albany Mansions, Albert Bridge Rd, London SW11 4PG, *Tel*: (020) 7223 5999. First formed in 1970, and revived in 1998 aiming to improve and enhance the local environment in the old borough of Battersea.

[407] **FRIENDS OF BATTERSEA PARK**. *Secretary*: Elaine Hodges, 46 Westbridge Rd, London SW11 3PW, *Tel*: (020) 7228 3771. Est. in 1988 to 'help maintain and improve the park as an oasis of tranquillity, natural beauty and recreation'. It also aims to monitor any proposed changes, organise walks and lectures and raise funds. There is an illustrated quarterly magazine. An *Illustrated history of Battersea Park* was published in 1993; available from the Pump House.
Battersea Park: Albert Bridge Rd, London SW11, *Tel*: (020) 8871 7530; open daily 8.00-dusk.

[408] **PUTNEY SOCIETY**. *Secretary*: Derek Purcell, 8 Dryburgh Mansions, London SW15 1AJ, *Tel*: (020) 8788 1373. The amenity society for Putney and Roehampton, est. in 1959. Sub-committees deal with planning, redevelopment and conservation area; road and transport; footpaths, trees and open spaces; and community affairs. In 1992 it published a new edition of *Putney and Roehampton: a brief history*, by Scott MacRobert.

[409] **TOOTING LOCAL HISTORY GROUP**. *Contact*: John Rattray, 64 Oakmead Rd, Balham, London SW12 9SJ, *Tel*: (020) 8675 4854. Not very active at present, but has several local history walks during the summer months. In 1985 Frank Staff (now deceased) published his book *Tooting rambles*, 128pp; containing chapters on the history of Tooting, Streatham and Balham and their neighbouring villages. A contact for the Tooting Common Friends organisation is: Jeremy Jessel, 85 Culverden Rd, Balham, London SW12, *Tel*: (020) 8673 0147.

[410] **WANDSWORTH HISTORICAL SOCIETY**. *Chairman*: Patrick J. Loobey, 231 Mitcham Lane, Streatham, London SW16 6PY, *Tel*: (020) 8769 1999. *Membership secretary*: Hilary Sims, 31 Hill Court, Putney Hill, London SW15 6BB, *Tel*: (020) 8789 1654. *Journal editor*: Tony Evans, 554 Garratt Lane, London SW17 0NY, *Tel*: (020) 8947 2805. *Newsletter editor*: Margaret Hunt, 22 Amerland Rd, London SW18 1PZ. *Books editor*: Dorian Gerhold, 37c Montserrat Rd, Putney, London SW15 2LD, *Tel*:(020) 8788 0546. Monthly meetings, outings and visits; archaeological excavations.
Recent publications from the society include: *Putney in 1636: Nicholas Lane's map*, by Dorian Gerhold, 1994, 52pp; *Roman Putney*, by Nicholas Fuentes and Pamela Greenwood, 1993; *Villas and mansions of Roehampton and Putney Heath*, by Dorian Gerhold, 1997, 88pp; *William Field's photographs of Putney*, by Michael Bull and Dorian Gerhold, 1997, 103pp.
Forthcoming publications from the society will be: *Cinemas of Wandsworth, Battersea, Clapham and Streatham; 150 years of Wandsworth Prison; Pubs of Putney and Roehampton; Roehampton in 1617 - the village surveyed*.

Articles in recent issues of the *Wandsworth Historian* (commenced in 1971):

No 65, Winter 1992: The place name 'Totterdown' (Graham Gower); Putney on a postcard (Michael Bull) ; The River Wandle in 1633 (Rita J. Ensing); The 1642 Bridge of boats (Nicholas Fuentes); Jean Baptista Muller; Beaduric and Battersea (Keith Bailey).

No 66, 1993: Private education in Putney during the last hundred years: a survey (Klaus Marx); A Greek Trireme at Putney; Roe Bridge, Mitcham Lane (John W. Brown); The Emperor Claudius comes to Putney (Nicholas Fuentes); Susanna Powell, a widow in Wandsworth in Jacobean times (Rita J. Ensing); Further notes on the origins of St Patrick (Roderick Staples).

No 67, Spring 1995: Waltham Abbey and Battersea (Keith Bailey); Putney property holders in 1787 (Dorian Gerhold); St Patrick of Battersea (Nicholas Fuentes); Meeting place of the Brixton Hundred (Graham Gower); Thomas Temple, Vicar of Battersea (Roger Logan); The founding of the Telegraph Inn (Dorian Gerhold); Putney or Putlei? What's in a name? (Keith Bailey).

No 68, Autumn 1997: The Beaufoys at Battersea, Part 3 (Diana Gunasena); The Porter family: Lords of Allfarthing Manor (Tony Evans); Putney's tithe barn (Dorian Gerhold); A Southfields dairyman and policeman (William Henry Skinner).

Dorian Gerhold and members of the society are the authors of two histories from Historical Publications: *Putney and Roehampton past*, 1994; and *Wandsworth past*, 1998.

Patrick Loobey has a large photographic collection (see advert), and he has fully exploited it in a wide range of publications: under his own imprint (Positive Pastimes, now discontinued): *Battersea: pastimes from postcards*, 1989; and *Putney and Roehampton: pastimes from postcards*, 1988. From S.B. Publications: *Fulham and Hammersmith: a portrait in old picture postcards*, 1993; *Wandsworth, Earlsfield and Southfields*: a portrait in old picture postcards, 1993.
From Sutton: *Balham and Tooting; Barnes, Mortlake and East Sheen; The Boroughs of Wandsworth and Battersea at war; Brentford and Chiswick; Merton, Morden and Mitcham; Streatham* (two collections); *Wimbledon*.
From Tempus: *Battersea and Clapham; The Borough of Wandsworth; Putney and Roehampton; Wandsworth*, including Southfields and Earlfields; planned for 1999: *Chelsea; Hammersmith and Fulham; Battersea and Clapham*, a further selection.

[411] **WANDSWORTH SOCIETY**. *Secretary*: Craig McCraiger, 28 Alverstone Avenue, London SW19. The amenity society for the town of Wandsworth, est. in 1971, current membership about 1,000. There are sub-groups for: planning, roads and transport, open spaces and Agenda 21 issues, rivers, regeneration (town centre Challenge Partnership). There are monthly meetings on a variety of topics. There is a quarterly newsletter and occasional papers are published.

* SOME OTHER COUNCIL CONTACTS *

Arts: Charles Catlin, Principal arts/community services officer, Town Hall, Wandsworth High St, London SW18 2PU, *Tel*: (020) 8871 7380.
Conservation: *Contact*: J. Webb, Principal Planning officer, Town Hall, *Tel*: (020) 8871 6645.
Economic Development office: Norman Frost, Town Hall, *Tel*: (020) 8871 7698.
Information: Information point at Town Hall, *Tel*: (020) 8871 6060; reference libraries at: Battersea Library, 265 Lavender Hill, London SW11 1JB, *Tel*: (020) 8871 7467; and West Hill Library, West Hill, London SW18 1RZ, *Tel*: (020) 8871 6387.
Parks: at Town Hall, *Tel*: (020) 8871 6347. The Nature Study Centre is on Wandsworth Common (behind Neal's Lodge Restaurant, next to the bowling green), *Tel*: (020) 8871 3863. A number of attractive leaflets have been produced recently: *Battersea Park nature trail; Introducing Battersea Park; Tooting Common nature trail; Wandsworth Common nature trail; Wild flowers at Morden Cemetery*; and *Wildlife habitats in Wandsworth*.

* SOME NON-COUNCIL CONTACTS *

Business:
WANDSWORTH CHAMBER OF COMMERCE. 125 Upper Richmond Rd, London SW15, *Tel*: (020) 8780 6541.

Voluntary organisations:
WANDSWORTH ASSOCIATION OF VOLUNTARY AND COMMUNITY ORGANISATIONS. *Contact*: Graeme Lyall (chairman), Wandsworth Age Concern, 202 Tooting High St, London SW17 0SF, *Tel*: (020) 8682 1100.
WANDSWORTH VOLUNTEER BUREAU. 170 Garratt Lane, London SW18, *Tel*: (020) 8870 4319.

* LOCAL PRESS *
Balham and Tooting Guardian, 34-44 London Rd, Morden SM4 0BR, *Tel*: (020) 8646 6633.
Brightside, council paper produced every 2-3 months, by press office, *Tel*: (020) 8871 6173.
Putney Chronicle. Newspaper House, Winslow Rd, London W6, *Tel*: (020) 8741 1611.

Wandsworth Borough News. 144 Wandsworth High St, London SW18, *Tel*: (020) 8874 4226.
There are three different editions, covering: Battersea & Clapham, Putney & Wandsworth, Tooting and Balham. *Battersea News* is also published from the above address.

BEXLEY

* LONDON BOROUGH OF BEXLEY *

[412] **BEXLEY LOCAL STUDIES CENTRE**. Hall Place, Bourne Rd, Bexley, Kent DA5 1PQ, *Tel*: (01322) 526574. *Local studies manager*: Stuart Bligh. *Archivist*: Oliver Wooller (working on book on the great estates of Bexley for publication in 2000). *Hours*: Mon-Sat 9-5.
Recent publications:
1993: DU BOULAY, F.R.H. *Medieval Bexley*, 59pp, illus.
1993: REILLY, Leonard (now local studies librarian with Southwark). *Family history in Bexley*, a guide to tracing your Bexley ancestors, 24pp.
1994: PRICHARD, John A. *Belvedere and Bostall: a brief history* (History of Erith, Part 5), 36pp.
Other parts (still in prints) are: I: from the earliest times to 1485, published in 1976; II: 1485-1837, published in 1977; ;III: 1837-1894, published in 1978; IV: 1894-1965, published in 1989.
1995: PACKER, James. *Bexley pubs*: the history of your local. 100pp, illus. Part 2 on vanished pubs in preparation.
1996: BARR-HAMILTON, M. and REILLY, Leonard. *From country to suburb*: the development of the Bexley area from 1800 to the present day. 96pp, illus. Authors are former Bexley Local Studies staff.
1996: HUTCHERSON, Ruth. *History of Danson*, 42pp, illus. Revised edition of booklet first published in 1985.
1996: TESTER, Peter. *Bexley Village: a short history*, revised, third edition (by Russell Gray).
1998: THOMAS, E.O. *The story of Barnehurst* (east of Bexleyheath), 76pp, illus.

Bexley Library publications are mainly booklet histories of specific areas, or else photographic collections. The following are still in print:
Archaeology of Bexley, 1985, by Peter Tester; *Bexley Deneholes*, 1992 by R.F. le Gear; *Bexley Heath phenomenon*, 1983, by J.E. Hamilton; *East Wickham and Welling*, 1991, by Peter Tester; *Footscray*, 1982, by Gertrude Nunn; *History of Erith* (parts 1-4), by John Prichard); *Homefires: a borough at war*, 1986, by Mick Scott; *Industries of Crayford*, 1990, by Jim Hamilton; *Over the road: Welling, Bexleyheath and Crayford in old photographs*, 1982, by Mick Scott; *Sidcup story*, 1988, by John Mercer.
Their most substantial publication, now out of print, has been *Blackfen: from country to suburb*, by Susan J. Ilott, published in 1977, and running to 188 pages. There is also a range of black and white and colour postcards, some prints and maps.

Publications from commercial publishers, sold at the library, include:
From Phillimore: *Bexley, Bexleyheath and Welling: a pictorial history*, by John Mercer, 1995; and *Sidcup: a pictorial history*, 1994 (John Mercer: 16 Eynswood Drive, Sidcup DA14 6JQ).
From Sutton: *Bexley in old photographs*, by Mike Scott; *London Borough of Bexley in old photographs*, by John Mercer.
Kent: a chronicle of the century, by Bob Ogley (Frogletts Publications, Brastead Court, Westerham, Kent, *Tel*: (01959) 562972) is in 4 parts and is a pictorial history. *A wood on our doorstep: Joydens Wood*, by Ian Hammerton, was self-published in 1998 (Tanglewood, 65 Norfield Rd, Willmington, Dartford, Kent DA2 7NY). There are also two school histories: *History of Hook Lane School*, 1997, by Dawn Catten and *Three Cheers for North Heath*, 1994, by Bonita Chamberlain.

* MUSEUMS AND HISTORIC PROPERTIES *

[413] **BEXLEY MUSEUM**. Hall Place, Bourne Rd, Bexley, Kent DA5 1PQ, *Tel*: (01322) 526474. *Curator*: Jessica Vale; *Assistant*: Janice Crane. *Hours*: Mon-Sat 10-4.15; during summer Mon-Sat 10-5, and Sun 2-6. Permanent displays on the geology, archaeology and natural history of the borough. Changing exhibitions on local history themes. Guided tours of Hall Place, a Tudor and Stuart country house set in public gardens, can be arranged.

[414] **CROSSNESS ENGINES TRUST**. *Contact*: Michael Dunmow, *Tel*: (020) 8303 6723. Est. in 1985 to restore the 1865 Joseph Bazalgette beam engines and pumping station at Crossness Treatment Works, Belvedere Rd, Abbey Wood SE2 9AQ. Its all-volunteer workforce welcomes support. A museum of Sanitation Engineering is also being developed, along with a visitor centre. It is a Grade I listed building with outstanding cast ironwork. For details on opening days, contact: (020) 8311 3711.

[415] **DANSON MANSION**. Danson Park, Danson Rd, Bexleyheath. A Georgian neo-Palladian villa, built in the 1760's.

[416] **ERITH MUSEUM**. At Erith Library, Walnut Tree Rd, Erith, Kent DA8 1RS, *Tel*: (01322) 336582. *Hours*: Mon, Wed 2.15-5.15; Sat 2.15-5. Displays on geology, archaeology and history of Erith and the Thameside area, including prehistoric finds, vehicle models and reconstruction of an Edwardian kitchen. School visits by arrangement outside normal hours. (Erith Museum *may* be amalgamated with the Bexley Museum over the next few years).
There is a Friends group [417] **FROBLOMS**, *Contact*: Alan Boakes, 223 Bexley Rd, Erith DA8 3DU, *Tel*: (01322) 349803.

[418] **FRIENDS OF RED HOUSE**. *Secretary*: Stuart Bligh, 17 Malcolm Rd, Woodside, London SE25 5HE, *Tel*: (020) 8655 2928. Est. in January 1998 to 'support the Red House Trust the objects of which are to secure the long-term future of the house which William Morris built for himself and his new wife Jane in Bexley Heath in 1860'. The Friends group provides practical support to Ted and Doris Hollamby for whom Red House has been home since 1951. There is a website at: http//www.rebs.demon.co.uk. *Email*: arby@rebs.demon.co.uk.

* AMENITY AND HISTORICAL SOCIETIES *

[419] **BEXLEY CIVIC SOCIETY**. *Secretary*: Jean Davis, 4 Woodlands Rd, Bexleyheath, Kent DA7 4AF, *Tel*: (020) 8313 9570. *Membership secretary*: Jennifer Thicke, 117 Martens Avenue, Bexleyheath DA7 6AB, *Tel*: (01322) 527947. Est. in 1971, currently with some 250 members. Promotes amenities in the London Borough of Bexley. There are sub-committees for planning and conservation, publicity and membership, social activities and environmental issues. Some current concerns are: preservation of Oxleas Woods, the restoration of Danson Mansion and stables, the preservation of Footscray Meadows; it is also carrying out a survey of industrial history in the borough. There is a quarterly newsletter. Affiliated to the London Forum and the Kent Federation of Amenity Societies.

[420] **BEXLEY HISTORICAL SOCIETY**. *Chairman*: Jim Packer (author of *Bexley pubs*, from Bexley Libraries). 36 Cowper Close, Welling, *Tel*: (020) 8301 2007.

[421] **CRAYFORD MANOR HOUSE HISTORICAL AND ARCHAEOLOGICAL SOCIETY**. *Secretary*: Mrs P. Warner, 17 Swanton Rd, Erith DA8 1LP, *Tel*: (01322) 433480. *Chairman*: Mr E. Thomas, 4 Mayplace Close, Bexleyheath DA7 6DT, *Tel*: (01322) 526639. *Excavations*: Mrs A. Al-Jalili, 5 Hill Crescent, Bexley. Est. in 1961 to encourage archaeological excavations and other forms of historical research; also visits, lectures. Some 100 members. Annual proceedings (booklets) are published.

[422] **ERITH AND BELVEDERE LOCAL HISTORY SOCIETY**. *Secretary*: Mrs Bonita Chamberlain, 67 Merewood Rd, Barnehurst, Kent DA7 6PF, *Tel*: (01322) 337893. Est. in 1973, with some 100 members currently. Monthly talks on local history and allied subjects. Newsletter issued twice a year.

[423] **LAMORBEY AND SIDCUP LOCAL HISTORY SOCIETY**. *Secretary*: Miss Frances Oxley, 48 Beverley Avenue, Sidcup DA15 8HE, *Tel*: (020) 8300 1511. *Chairman*: Eric Percival. Est. in 1952, currently with some 100 members. Meetings and visits. Newsletter and occasional publications. Two collections *Sidcup remembered*, and *Further recollections of old Sidcup*, are available.
Pioneers of the time: the story of Douglas Macmillan, MBE and Dame Ethel Smythe, by Denise Baldwin and Katherine Harding was published in 1996.

* SOME OTHER COUNCIL CONTACTS *

Arts: Contact : Ian Sutton, Hill View, Hillview Drive, Welling DA16 3RY, *Tel*: (020) 8303 7777, ext. 4263.
Conservation areas/listed buildings: Contacts: Martin Nicholls, John Davison, Environmental Services, Wyncham House, 207 Longlands Rd, Sidcup DA15 7JH, *Tel*: (020) 8303 7777, exts. 4786 and 4785. Issues 'character statements' on the 21 conservation areas.
Heritage/Tourism officer: Stephen Hemming, address as above, ext. 4263.
Nature conservation: Contacts: David Coleman, Ben Thomas, as above, ext. 3511. David Coleman is the Bexley contact for Local Agenda 21.
Reference Library: Central Library, Townley Rd, Bexleyheath DA6 7HJ, *Tel*: (020) 8301 5151. Tourist Information Centre here.

* SOME NON-COUNCIL CONTACTS *

Business:
BEXLEY AND GREENWICH CHAMBER OF COMMERCE. Morden Wharf Rd, London SE10, *Tel*: (020) 8293 3456.
The council has an Economic Development Unit.

Voluntary organisations:
BEXLEY VOLUNTARY SERVICE COUNCIL. 8 Brampton Rd, Bexleyheath DA7 4EZ, *Tel*: (020) 8304 0911.

* LOCAL PRESS *

The *Bexley Magazine*, is produced by the Council's information unit, *Tel*: (020) 8303 7777, ext. 2222.
Kentish Times, 161 The Broadway, Bexleyheath DA6 7ES, *Tel*: (020) 8301 6663.
News Shopper (free), Megahouse, Great View Rd, Petts Wood, Kent BR5 1BT, *Tel*: (01689) 836211.
South East London Mercury, 116 Deptford High St, London SE8 4NX, *Tel*: (020) 8710 6436.

BROMLEY

* LONDON BOROUGH OF BROMLEY *

[424] **BROMLEY LOCAL STUDIES AND ARCHIVES**. Central Library, High St, Bromley BR1 1EX, *Tel*: (020) 8460
9955, ext. 261. *Librarian*: Simon Finch; *Archivist*: Elizabeth Silverthorne. *Hours*: Mon, Wed, Fri 9.30-6; Tues, Thurs 9.30-8;
Sat 9.30-5.
No new publications have been produced in recent years; however, a revised reissue, 1999, of *A look back at Orpington* (old
photographs), compiled by John Edwards, Bill Morton, Tom Sign and Dick Turner is in preparation; as well as a new edition
of W.H. Parkinson's *Mottingham from hamlet to urban village* (first published in 1977, by a former Mottingham librarian);
and also a revised edition of Graham Reeves' *Palace of the People*.

Still in print are some booklets by Ken Wilson (a retired architect): *The Palace in Bromley* (i.e. Bromley, not Crystal Palace),
1983; *The story of Biggin Hill*, 1982 and *Sundridge Park*, 1984.
Also: *A history of Petts Wood* (3rd edition, 1990), 108pp, by Peter Waymark, published in association with the Petts Wood and
District Residents' Association. *Undaunted: the story of Bromley in the second world war*, by Graham Reeves, 109pp,
published in 1990.
The library also sells some privately published items: books on West Wickham, by Joyce Walker (Hollies Publicans, 69
Hawes Lane, West Wickham BR4 0DA): *West Wickham past into present* (with Patricia Knowlden), *West Wickham in the
Great War; West Wickham in the 2nd World War*; and *Vanished West Wickham*.
There are two recent school histories: *The best school of all: Bromley County School for Girls*, by Hazel Davey, 1992,
reprinted 1997 (24 Sackville Avenue, Hayes BR2 7JT); and *Warren Road Primary School, 1938-1998*, by Janice English.

Photographic collections: from Sutton: *Bromley, Keston and Hayes; Crystal Palace, Penge and Hayes*, both compiled by Mike
Scott; and *Chislehurst and Sidcup*, by John Mercer. From Tempus: *Beckenham and West Wickham*, compiled by Simon Finch
(Bromley Local Studies Library); and *Chislehurst to Sidcup*, by Hilary Heffernan.

* MUSEUMS AND VISITOR ATTRACTIONS *

[425] **BETHLEM ROYAL HOSPITAL ARCHIVES AND MUSEUM**. Monks Orchard Rd, Beckenham, Kent BR3 3BX,
Tel: (020) 87776 4307/4277. *Hours*: Mon-Fri 9.30-5.30. Telephone first before visiting. Shows works of talented artists who
suffered from mental disorder. The original 'Bedlam' was founded in 1247.

[426] **BROMLEY MUSEUM**. The Priory, Church Hill, Oprington BR6 0HH, *Tel*: (01689) 873826. *Curator*: Dr Alan Tyler;
Assistant: Melanie Parker. Situated next to Oprington Library. *Hours*: Mon-Fri 1-5; Sat 10-5; Sun and bank holidays 1-5,
April-October. Open Mon-Fri mornings for educational purposes only. Housed in an impressive medieval/post medieval
building set in attractive gardens. The story of the borough from prehistoric times to the 20th century. Holdings include the
anthropological and archaeological collection of Sir John Lubbock, 1st Lord Avebury. There is a changing programme of
exhibitions in the museum's Great Hall.

[427] **CHARLES DARWIN MEMORIAL MUSEUM**. Down House, Luxted Rd, Downe, Oprington, *Tel*: (020) 7973 3399. English Heritage property. Guidebook by Solene Morris and Louise Wilson published.

[428] **CHISLEHURST CAVES**. Old Hill, Chislehurst, *Tel*: (020) 8467 4264.

[429] **CROFTON ROMAN VILLA**. Orpington, *Tel*: (01689) 873826, or (020) 8462 4737.

[430] **ROMANO-BRITISH BATH HOUSE & ANGLO SAXON CEMETERY**. Poverest Rd, Orpington. Viewing by arrangement with Bromley Museum. Recent excavation work at Orpington is recorded in *The Roman villa site at Orpington*, by Brian Philip, 100 pp published in 1996 by Kent Archaeological Rescue Unit wth Bromley Libraries. An earlier report *Excavation of the Roman and Saxon site* at Orpington, by Susann Palmer was published by Bromley Libraries in 1984.

* AMENITY AND HISTORICAL SOCIETIES *

[431] **BECKENHAM CIVIC SOCIETY**. *Chairman*: David Wood, 16 Greycot Rd, Beckenham BR3 1TA, *Tel*: (020) 8650 4191. Est. in 1943, currently with some 100 members.

[432] **BROMLEY AND WEST KENT ARCHAEOLOGICAL GROUP**. *Contact*: Brian J. Philip, 5 Harvest Bank Rd, West Wickham BR4 9DL, *Tel*: (020) 8462 4737. Est. in 1960 to carry out programmes of excavation, preservation and publication in the Bromley and Bexley areas and throughout West Kent. It is an amateur group which works with the Kent Archaeological Rescue Unit, also contactable at the above address.

[433] **BROMLEY BOROUGH LOCAL HISTORY SOCIETY**. *Secretary*: Mrs Patricia Knowlden, 62 Harvest Bank Rd, West Wickham BR4 9DJ, *Tel*: (020) 8462 5002. *Chairman/membership*: Dr Anthony Allnutt, Woodside, Old Perry St, Chislehurst BR7 6PP, *Tel*: (020) 8467 3842. *Newsletter editors*: Mr P and Mrs D Rason, 1 South Drive, Orpington BR6 9NG, *Email*: Denise@rason.freeserve.co.uk. *Publications sales*: Don Frisby, 18 Pickhurst Lane, Hayes, Kent BR2 7LJ, *Tel*: (020) 8325 5865. *Vice President/public relations officer*: Dr E.R. Inman, 28 Downs Hill, Beckenham BR3 5HB, *Tel*: (020) 8650 8342; *Fax*: (020) 8325 1521. The society was est. in 1974 and currently has some 300 members. There is a Beckenham and Penge group, contact: Shirley Morris, *Tel*: (020) 8650 5888. There are monthly meetings, visits and walks. A journal *Bromley Local History Journal* was published 1976-90 (nine issues). There are plans to publish an updated version of issues No 7 and 8 (*At the turn of the century: Bromley and around*). There are occasional specialist publications: booklets *Shortlands*, and *The Story of Elmers End*, both by Len Hevey, 1991; and *Bromley Manor and Palace*, by Patricia Knowlden, published in 1997. There is a quarterly newsletter *Bromleage*, and the December 1998 issue contains a title index for February 1993 to December 1998.

Patricia Knowlden is also the author of: *The long alert 1937-1945*, published in 1988, on civil defence in West Wickham; and she edited *Bromley: a pictorial history*, published by Phillimore in 1990.
Len Hevey (now deceased) is the author of *The early history of Beckenham*, published by his daughter Fiona Carter (11 Plymouth Wharf, London E14 3EL).
Dr Eric Inman is the author (with Nancy Tonkin, now deceased) of *Beckenham*, published by Phillimore in 1993, and of *Chislehurst caves: a short history*, published by Kent Mushrooms in 1996.

[434] **CHELSFIELD VILLAGE SOCIETY**. *Contact*: Mrs J. Binns, 1 Orleystone Gardens, Orpington BR6 6HB. Issues a bi-monthly newsletter.

[435] **CHISLEHURST SOCIETY**. *Local history contact and newsletter editor*: Roy Hopper, 157 Rowley Avenue, Sidcup, *Tel*: (020) 8302 2842. Est. in 1934 initially as the Chislehurst Residents Association, becoming the Chislehurst Society in 1988. Talks, walks. Newsletter *The Cockpit* is issued twice a year.
In 1998 Clive Birch (Baron Birch publishers) reissued for the society *A history of Chislehurst*, 1899 by Webb, Miller and Beckwith. *Imperial Chislehurst* by T.A. Bushell was also issued by the same publishers (Clive Birch, King's Cote, Valley Rd, Finmere, Milton Keynes MK18 4AL).

[436] **CRYSTAL PALACE CAMPAIGN**. *Secretary*: at 33 Hogarth Court, Fountain Drive, London SE19 1UY. *Telephone contacts*: (020) 8656 5524; (020) 8244 8399 (press officer); (020) 8670 3720 (chairman). The campaign to save Crystal Palace from the developers will perhaps be regarded as one of the last classic environmental battles of this century. Its newsletter is a valuable record of events. The October 1998 issue has a column 'The things they say' (i.e. the powers that be). Mary Nightingale interviewing Deputy Chief Executive David Bartlett on TV London Today commented: 'We have never received so many calls...local residents are furious...what do you say to that?' 'we don't believe they are furious' he replied apparently.

The South London Press, March 5th, 1999 reports on Operation Paxton when police moved in to evict protesters. The Paxton 100 fund-raising appeal is limited to 100 subscribers who donate and pledge up to £500. They receive a copy of Patrick Beaver's *The Crystal Palace: a portrait of a Victorian enterprise*, published by Phillimore in 1994, with a book plate designed by Audrey Hammond. A report *The people's park* outlines the campaign's own alternatives to Bromley's plan and is available from the secretary.

[437a] **CRYSTAL PALACE FOUNDATION.** *Membership secretary*: David Pritchard; *Sales Manager*: Melvyn Harrison, c/o 84 Anerley Rd, London SE19 2AH, *Tel*: (020) 8778 2173 (home of Eric Price). Est. in 1979 'to promote the memory of the Crystal Palace and to enhance the public amenities of the site and its historic connections'. There are guided tours and talks; excavation and restoration of areas of historic interest in the park. It supports the Crystal Palace Museum, and organises research for publications and exhibitions, and arranges other events. There is a twice yearly magazine *Crystal Palace matters* and a newsletter. Several reminiscence publications have been issued: *Crystal Palace is on fire: memories of the 30th November, 1936*, by Alison Edwards and Keith Wyncoll, 2nd edition, 1992; *The perfect playground: childhood memories of the Crystal Palace*, edited by Alison Edwards, Patricia Scott and Eileen Pulfer, 1990. There are also two videos. *The Crystal Palace dinosaurs: the story of the world's first prehistoric sculptures*, by Stephen McCarthy and Mark Gilbert was published in 1994.

[437b] **CRYSTAL PALACE MUSEUM.** Anerley Hill, London SE19, *Tel*: (020) 8676 0700. *Curator*: Ken Kiss; *Chairman of the trustees*: Barrie McKay. *Hours*: Sun, bank holidays 11-5.

[438] **CRYSTAL PALACE TRIANGLE COMMUNITY ASSOCIATION (CPTCA).** *Membership secretary*: Mrs J. Moore, 9 Hamlyn Gardens, London SE19 2NX. *Chair*: Katharyn Kenny, 26d South Vale, London SE19 3BA, *Tel*: (020) 8653 7188. Est. in 1970, aiming to 'co-operate with other local and interested bodies in protecting, preserving and improving the character and amenities of the area, and to provide where possible facilities towards enriching the leisure time of all'. There is a bi-monthly newsletter and an important book *Crystal Palace - Norwood Heights*, by Audrey Hammond and Brian Dann, published in 1989 (see advert); first edition published in 1988 by the Croydon Society. An educational book by the same authors was also published at this time *Know your place*.

[439] **ENVIRONMENT BROMLEY (ENBRO)**. *Membership secretary*: at 304 Court Rd, Orpington BR6 9DA, *Tel*: (01689) 873494. Telephone contact for walks organiser: (01689) 873348. The organisation is a voluntary body 'with the purpose of conserving and interpreting the man-made and natural environment of the London Borough of Bromley and adjacent, and produces an extensive programme of walks for members'.

[440] **FARNBOROUGH VILLAGE SOCIETY.** *Contact*: Mrs D. Smith, 47 Durrant Way, Farnborough BR6 7EH.

[441] **HEART OF BROMLEY RESIDENTS ASSOCIATION.** *Contact*: Tony Banfield, 8 Pixfield St, Beckenham Lane, Bromley BR2 0DG, *Tel*: (020) 8464 3181.

[442] **HISTORICAL ASSOCIATION**, Beckenham and Bromley Branch. *Secretary*: Mr P. Ellis, 63 Groveland Rd, Beckenham BR3 3PX, *Tel*: (020) 8650 2826. *Programme secretary*: Mrs A. Wagstaff, 182 Devonshire Way, Shirley, Croydon, Surrey CR0 8BX, *Tel*: (020) 8777 7742; *Fax*: (020) 8777 1486. Editor of the *Beckenham Historian*, a monthly bulletin: John Wagstaff, address/tel, as above. Talks on varied, diverse historical subjects, visits.

[443] **ORPINGTON AND DISTRICT AMENITY SOCIETY.** *Contact*: Cllr. P. Woods, 49 Towncourt Crescent, Petts Wood, Orpington BR5 1PH.

[444] **ORPINGTON AND DISTRICT ARCHAEOLOGICAL SOCIETY.** *Membership secretary*: Michael Meekums, 27 Eynsford Close, Petts Wood, Orpington. Est. in 1975, currently with some 150 members. Excavations, processing and research; meetings and visits; quarterly newsletter *Archives*. Michael Meekums is also a contact for the Bromley branch of the Kent Archaeological Society.

[445] **ORPINGTON HISTORICAL SOCIETY.** *Contact*: Miss O. Reakes, 33 Woodhurst Avenue, Orpington, *Tel*: (01689) 826577. Comparable to the Beckenham and Bromley branch of the Historical Association, with general historical activities, rather than a local history society.

[446] **ST MARY CRAY ACTION GROUP.** *Chairman*: John Blundell, 35 Tandridge Drive, Crofton, Orpington. Amenity society, with historical interests.

[447] **WEST WICKHAM RESIDENTS ASSOCIATION**. *Contact*: John Pint, 4 Grosvenor Rd, West Wickham BR4 7PU, *Tel*: (020) 8777 0326.

* PARKS/COMMONS *

[448] **CHISLEHURST COMMONS CONSERVATORS**. *Clerk*: John Goff, The Old Fire Station, Hawkwood Lane, Chislehurst BR7 5PW, *Tel*: (020) 8467 1886.

[449] **FRIENDS OF BECKENHAM PLACE PARK**. *Secretary*: at 18 Greycot Rd, Beckenham BR3 1TA. Another contact: Hugh Lipinatt, Parks officer, London Borough of Lewisham.

[450] **FRIENDS OF KELSEY PARK (Beckenham)**. *Contact*: Gordon Hughes, 5 The Pines, 23 The Knoll, Beckenham BR3 5UE, *Tel*: (020) 8650 4173.

[451] **FRIENDS OF PRIORY GARDENS**. *Secretary:* Mrs Hazel Pender, 110 Avalon Rd, Orpington BR6 7BH, *Tel*: (01689) 831912.

[452] **GODDINGTON PARK PRESERVATION ASSOCIATION**. *Contact*: Mrs P. Dunmall, 74 Craven Rd, Orpington, *Tel*: (01689) 828693. Responds to any undesirable threats.

* SOME OTHER COUNCIL CONTACTS *

Agenda 21: Mike Ibbott, Civic Centre, Stockwell Close, Bromley BR1 3UH, *Tel*: (020) 8313 4520; *Fax*: (020) 8313 0095.
Conservation officers: Kevin Morris, Rynd Smith, Heritage & Urban Design Group, *Tel*: (020) 8313 4664. There is a wide range of fact sheets and leaflets providing practical guidelines. There are 42 conservation areas, and a voluntary body; an Advisory Panel for Conservation Areas meets monthly to make comments on planning applications.
The conservation officers are also the contacts for the newly formed **BROMLEY'S HISTORIC BUILDING OWNERS' GROUP**. It aims to increase support and understanding for the historic environment of Bromley, and to provide a forum for the exchange of ideas and experiences of working with historic structures.

The *Countryside Management Service* is at the Civic Centre, *Tel*: (020) 8313 4665. The Voluntary Countryside Ranger Group undertakes practical conservation work, *Tel*: (0689) 862815. Trees and landscaping, *Tel*: (020) 8313 4516. Parks and conservation manager: Colin Buttery, *Tel*: (020) 8313 4434.

Publications:
Newsletter: Much useful information and articles on the built and natural environment feature in *The Rabbit* (incorporating the Acanthus, the historic building newsletter) produced by the Heritage and Urban Design Group.
There is also a seasonal guide *Bromley walks, talks and events*.
Heritage walks: Produced by Heritage and Urban Design, Civic Centre, *Tel*: (020) 8313 4515. These attractive booklets, with small colour photographs and maps feature historic buildings in the following areas: Beckenham, Bromley, Chislehurst, Farnborough, Orpington, Penge, St Mary Cray, West Wickham. Planned: Anerley, Upper Norwood and Hayes.
Nature trails currently available: Hayes Common, Ravensourne, Scadbury Park. There are also 'circular walks' for: Berry's Green, Bromley, Chelsfield, The Cray riverway, Cudham, Farnborough, Green St Green, Leaves Green, Nash, St Mary Cray, St Paul's Cray. Other publications include: *Hedgerows in Bromley*: a survey of their value for wildlife, landscape and history, 1995; and a report on Bromley's woodland future: *Indicative forestry and woodland strategy*, 1994.

Reference library: Central Library, High St, Bromley BR1 1EX, *Tel*: (020) 8460 9955, ext. 251; *Fax*: (020) 8313 0475. The reference library is just commencing a computerised community information service. A wide range of lists (including one on environmental and natural history, and one on historical organisations in the borough) is available from: Room W58, Bromley Civic Centre, Stockwell Close, Bromley BR1 3UH, *Tel*: (020) 8313 4433.
A business information centre is run at the reference library.

* SOME NON-COUNCIL CONTACTS *

Arts:
BROMLEY ARTS COUNCIL. *Contact*: D.J. Curtis, 24 Sundridge Avenue, Bromley BR1 2PX.

Business:
BROMLEY BUSINESS PARTNERSHIP. Northside House, 69 Tweedy Rd, Bromley BR1 3WA, *Tel*: (020) 8315 6740.

Residents associations:
BROMLEY RESIDENTS FEDERATION. *Contact*: Mrs Green, 84 Barnfield Wood Rd, Beckenham BR3 6SU, *Tel*: (020) 8658 1579.

Voluntary organisations:
BROMLEY CENTRE FOR VOLUNTARY SERVICE. 28a Beckenham Rd, Beckenham, *Tel*: (020) 8663 3373.

* LOCAL PRESS *

Bromley and Biggin Hill News, Winterton House, High St, Westerham TN16 1AT, *Tel*: (01959) 564766.
Kentish Times, 40 Harmer St, Gravesend DA12 2AY, *Tel*: (01474) 363363.
News Shopper (free), Mega House, Crest View Drive, Petts Wood BR5 1BT, *Tel*: (01689) 894821.

CROYDON

* LONDON BOROUGH OF CROYDON *

[453] **CROYDON LOCAL STUDIES LIBRARY AND ARCHIVES.** *Librarian*: Steve Roud (compiler with Jacqueline Simpson of the Oxford Dictionary of English Folklore). *Archivist*: Steve Griffiths. Central Library, Croydon Clocktower, Katharine St, Croydon, Surrey CR9 1ET, *Tel*: (020) 8760 5400. *Hours*: Mon 9-7; Tues 9-6; Thurs 9.30-6; Fri 9-6; Sat 9-5. The library does not publish, nor does it sell publications (sales of books are handled by the shop within the Croydon Clocktower Centre).

[454] **UPPER NORWOOD JOINT LIBRARY.** *Contact*: Jerry Savage, Upper Norwood Library, Westow Hill, London SE19, *Tel*: (020) 8670 2551. Funded jointly by Croydon and Lambeth boroughs. Local studies collection covers Norwood and Crystal Palace.

[455] **CROYDON MUSEUM AND HERITAGE SERVICE.** *Collections and interpretation manager*: Ann Carter; *Heritage and Millennium officer*: Adrienne Bloch; Croydon Clocktower, Katharine St, Croydon, Surrey CR9 1ET, *Tel*: (020) 8760 5400, ext. 1143; (020) 8253 1026. *Email*: museum@croydon.gov.uk. The museum service looks after three galleries within Croydon Clocktower, a cultural centre. *Hours*: Mon-Sat 11-5; Sun 12-5. *Lifetimes: the interactive museum*: tells the story of Croydon people from 1830 to the present using objects and touch screen computers. Leaflets have been issued on *Black lifetimes*; and *South Asian lifetimes*.
Riesco Gallery: Over 200 pieces from 2500 BC to the 19th century: one of the finest collections of Chinese pottery and porcelain in the country. There is an education pack *Pottery through the dynasties* by Joanna Burch. Raymond Riesco was an insurance broker in the City and lived at Heathfield, South Croydon. He died in 1964 and his Chinese ceramics collection was bequeathed to Croydon borough.
Temporary exhibition gallery: varied programme of exhibitions.
Museum service provides education services for schools and colleges and cares for the Croydon Art Collection, over 2,000 paintings, prints and drawings.

The Heritage Service administers a heritage grants scheme: a plaques scheme was initiated in 1996 commemorating local people, places and events. Information sheets are issued on :Page & Overton's brewery; Croydon Cattle Market; Gillett and Johnston foundry; Park Hill water tower; The old forge; Addington Village Road; Croydon Airport terminal building.
It is also responsible for *Addington Palace*, former home of the Archbishop of Canterbury, with grounds designed by Capability Brown; managed by Westmead Business Group on behalf of the borough, it is open to the public on six days every year. Also responsible for Shirley Windmill, one of only four surviving windmills in Greater London.

* TOURISM *

[456] **CROYDON TOURIST INFORMATION CENTRE.** *Manager*: Liz Hollowood, Central Library, address as above, *Tel*: (020) 8253 1009. Provides information on Croydon, London and South East England generally. Publishes a mini guide, a visitors 'pack', and an accommodation guide.

* FEDERATIONS OF GROUPS *

[457] **ASSOCIATION OF CROYDON CONSERVATION SOCIETIES**. *Chairman*: Malcolm Jennings, 106 Langdale Rd, Thornton Heath, Surrey CR7 7PQ, *Tel*: (020) 8684 4000. For societies and groups concerned with the natural environment.

[458] **CROYDON LOCAL STUDIES FORUM**. *Contact*: Peter Walker, 208 Turnpike Link, Croydon CR0 5NZ, *Tel*: (020) 8680 3815. Est. in 1992 to bring together local history organisations and their activities It has organised several local history fairs. There is a regular leaflet 'Events of local interest', and a guide to local groups and societies: 'Studying Croydon's heritage'.

* AMENITY AND HISTORICAL SOCIETIES *

[459] **BOURNE SOCIETY** (S. Croydon and East Surrey region). *Chairman*: Roger Packham, 40 Raglan Precinct, Town End, Caterham CR3 5UG, *Tel*: (01883) 349287. Est. in 1956 to extend knowledge of the local history of the areas of: Caterham, Chaldon, Chelsham, Chipstead, Farleigh, Godstone, Kenley, Purley, Sanderstead, Warlingham, Whyteleafe and Woldingham. There are meetings, outings and events. A quarterly news bulletin is published and there are also village histories of: Purley, Caterham, Sanderstead. A book on Warlingham by Dorothy Tutt is in preparation. *Sales officer*: John Tyerman, 60 Onslow Garden, Sanderstead CR2.
A collection of old photographs from Tempus: *South Croydon, Selsdon and Sanderstead* was compiled by Ralph Rimmer.

[460] **CROYDON ORAL HISTORY SOCIETY**. *Contact*: May Johnson, Flat 2, 30 Howard Rd, London SE25 5BY, *Tel*: (020) 8654 6454. Est. in 1989 to document the history of everyday life in the borough by meams of tape-recording residents' memories. All recordings are stored at the Croydon Local Studies Library. Members of the society have now moved away and it may well be wound up soon. Publications in the *Croydon Talking series* are: General; Schooldays; South Norwood; Shops and shopping; Surrey Street; War memories.

[461] **CROYDON SOCIETY**. *Contact*: May Johnson, Flat 2, 30 Howard Rd, London SE25 5BY, *Tel*: (020) 8654 6454. Est. in 1975, currently with over 400 members, covering the borough of Croydon. Concerned with: transport, protection of conservation areas, listed buildings and those of merit, planning and new buildings, preservation of open spaces. There are talks and walks throughout the year. A news bulletin *Focus* is issued three times a year. The society has published booklets on: *Croydon conservation areas; Croydon churches; Croydon workhouse; Croydon at work; Croydon's built heritage.*

[462] **CROYDON NATURAL HISTORY AND SCIENTIFIC SOCIETY**. Registered office (and address for all general correspondence): 96a Brighton Rd, South Croydon CR2 6AD. The society was founded in 1870 as the Croydon Microscopical Club. It aims to encourage the study of: archaeology, botany, entomology, geology, industrial studies, local history, meteorology and ornithology. There are lectures, talks, exhibitions, field excursions and surveys. *President of society, local history section secretary, editor and sales officer*: Brian Lancaster, 68 Woodcote Grove Rd, Coulsdon, Surrey CR5 2AD, *Tel*: (020) 8668 6909. *Bulletin editor*: J.B. Greig, 62 Boundary Rd, Carshalton SM5 4AD, *Tel*: (020) 8669 1501. *Conservation officer*: Dr J. McLauchlin, 33 Norman Avenue, s. Croydon CR2 0HQ, *Tel*: (020) 8668 1431. *Museum curator*: K.E. Woodhams, 60 Penwortham Rd, S. Croydon CR2 0QS, *Tel*: (020) 8668 3353.
There has been a series of illustrated books on Croydon's history, written or edited by John Gent since the 1970's; recent titles are:
1993: *Croydon between the wars*: photographs from the period 1919 to 1939. 2nd edition (first edition: 1987).
1994: *Croydon in the 1940's and 1950's.*
1995: *Croydon old and new*, new edition (previous edition: 1978).
1999 (forthcoming): *Croydon from above.*
In the 1980's there were new editions of *Croydon: the story of a hundred years* (the town between 1870 and 1970),6th edn, 1988; *Edwardian Croydon illustrated*, 2nd edn, 1990; and *Victorian Croydon illustrated*, 2nd edn, 1987.
Ron Cox's *At the going down of the sun*: the war memorials of Croydon was published in 1993.
Brian Lancaster's *Croydon Church townscape* was published in 1997.
Contents of recent proceedings include:
1993, Vol 18 Part 3: Non-conformity in Croydon, by Jeremy Morris.
1994, Vol 18 Part 4: A museum for Croydon; Plate rails; Old Waddon, by Ken Woodhams, Peter Burgess, Lilian Thornhill respectively.
1996, Vol 18 Part 5: Flora of the Wandle, by Dr Jane McLauchlin and Gwynneth Fookes.
1999 (forthcoming): 'Dirty old town to model town' (provisional title), on the Croydon Local Board of Health, by Brian Lancaster.

[463] **FRIENDS OF SHIRLEY WINDMILL**. *Chairman*: Ray Wheeler, 88 Palace View, Shirley, Croydon CR0 8QN, *Tel*: (020) 8777 5271. *Secretary*: Ian Jeeves, 11 Westway Gardens, Shirley, Croydon CR0 8RA, *Tel*: (020) 8654 0899. The mill replaced an earlier one destroyed by fire in 1854; it has undergone restoration over the years and the mill and adjoining land were acquired by Croydon Corporation in 1951. A 1996 Heritage Lottery grant has enabled further restoration and opening to the public: on National Mills Day (second Sunday in May), and on first Sunday, 10-5 in June-October. A leaflet guide is issued, and there is also a newsletter *The Fantail*. a teachers' pack is available from Croydon's Heritage office.

[464] **FRIENDS OF SOUTH NORWOOD COUNTRY PARK**. *Contact*: Mrs M. Johnson, Flat 2, 30 Howard Rd, London SE25 5BY, *Tel*: (020) 8654 6454. Newsletter issued.
Organises walks. May Johnson is also a contact for the South Norwood Residents Association.

[465] **FRIENDS OF THE OLD PALACE**. *Secretary*: Mrs A. Rainforth, c/o The Old Palace School, Croydon CR0 1AX. Est. in 1965 'to promote and foster the interests of the Old Palace, its restoration and maintenance and of the Old Palace School. Guided tours are organised during four weeks of the year, during school holidays, tours last about two hours and include tea in the Normal undercroft. There is a twice yearly newsletter.
A booklet *Croydon palaces* (on Old Palace and Addington Palace), was published by Deptford Forum Publishing on behalf of Croydon Heritage in 1997 and relates the associations of the archbishops of Canterbury with both properties. Old Palace in Central Croydon was finally sold in 1781 and the mansion and estate at Addington then purchased. Archbishop Frederick Temple sold Addington Palace in 1898.

[466] **THE WHITGIFT FOUNDATION**, *Archivist*: Frederick H.G. Percy, Whitgift School, Haling Park, South Croydon CR2 6YT, *Tel*: (020) 8688 9222. Clerk to the governors, North End, Croydon, *Tel*: (020) 8688 1733. The foundation comprises: the Whitgift Hospital, or almshouse, erected in 1599; Whitgift House, South Croydon; and Whitgift, Trinity and Old Palace Schools. Frederick Percy is intending to relaunch his *Whitgift School: a history* published in 1991 in the year 2000, with a supplementary volume to cover the last decade of the century. An outline history leaflet of the Whitgift Foundation (John Whitgift, Archbishop of Canterbury (1583-1604) is issued.

Commercial publications:
There are two histories from Phillimore: *Addington: a history*, by Frank Warren, 1984; and *Croydon: a pictorial history*, by John Gent, 1991.
From Sutton: two collections *Croydon in old photographs* compiled by Stuart Bligh (now with Bexley Local Studies Library).

* SOME OTHER COUNCIL CONTACTS *

Agenda 21: Barbara Wilcox, Taberner House, Park Lane, Croydon, Tel: (020) 8760 5791.
Community arts development officer: Sally Aitken, *Tel*: (020) 8760 5400, ext. 1149.
Conservation: contact: Sharad Bawdekar, Urban Design Department, Taberner House, Park Lane, Croydon, *Tel*: (020) 8686 2051.
Nature conservation: contact: Jacki Lewis, Countryside and open spaces officer, *Tel*: (020) 8686 4433, ext. 2438.
South Norwood Country Park Visitors/Educational Centre: *Tel*: (020) 8646 5947. n 1988 the Parks Department published the profusely illustrated, and admirably researched book *Croydon parks: an illustrated history*, by Mrs M.A. Winterman. A more recent publication is a large fold-out sheet *Hidden history in Croydon's Parks*. There are also leaflets such as *South Norwood Country Park, Celebrating South Norwood*, and the *Waddon community trail* (green trail connecting the Waddon Estate with the Croydon Clocktower). A seasonal guide to free guided wildlife walks is also issued.

* SOME NON-COUNCIL CONTACTS *

Business information:
CROYDON CHAMBER OF COMMERCE. 1 Wandle Rd, Croydon CR9 1HY, *Tel*: (020) 8781 7770.

Voluntary organisations:
CROYDON VOLUNTARY ACTION. 97 High St, Thornton Heath, Surrey CR7 8RY, *Tel*: (020) 8684 3862.

* LOCAL PRESS *

Croydon Advertiser, Advertiser House, 19 Bartlett St, South Croydon CR2 6TB, *Tel*: (020) 8763 6666.
Croydon Guardian (free newspaper), Guardian House, Sandiford Rd, Sutton, Surrey SM3 9RN, *Tel*: (020) 8770 2215.
Croydon Post (free newspaper), published by the Croydon Advertiser (see above).
Croydon Reports, London Borough of Croydon quarterly magazine, edited by Richard Gibbs, Press and Public Relations Office, Taberner House, Park Lane, Croydon, CR9 3JS, *Tel*: (020) 8760 5644.

MERTON

* LONDON BOROUGH OF MERTON *

[467] **MERTON LOCAL STUDIES CENTRE**. Morden Library, Merton Civic Centre, London Rd, Morden SM4 5DX, *Tel*: (020) 8545 3239; *Fax*: (020) 8545 4037. *Contact*: Heather Constance. *Hours*: Mon, Tues, Wed, Fri 10-7; Thurs 10-1; Sat 10-5. There are special collections on: Lord Nelson, William Morris, and Tennis in Wimbledon. Guides to sources published on: parish registers, the census 1841-1891 (for family history), and materials for the study of local history of the London Borough of Merton.

[468] **MERTON HERITAGE CENTRE**. The Carons (in basement), Madeira Rd, Mitcham CR4 4HD, *Tel/Fax*: (020) 8640 9387. *Heritage officer*: Miss Sarah Gould. Opened in 1994, there are changing displays on panels and in glass cases.

Recent publications from London Borough of Merton, Education and Libraries:
1992: *A century of change*: Merton teacher resource pack.
1996: PAYNE, John. *William Morris and London*: a personal view.
1997: BRULEY, Sue, *and* EDWARDS, Nick. *Factory life in Merton and Beddington 1920-1960*. 25pp, illus.
1998: *St Helier Estate* (in Morden). 52pp, illus. (Merton in Pictures, Book 4).

The *Heritage pack of local history notes* consists of updated sheets with bibliographies on a range of places, people and topics:
On places: The Carons; Colliers Wood; The Liberty site; Merton; Merton Priory; Mitcham; Morden; Pollards Hill; St Helier Estate; The Snuff Mills; Wimbledon; Wimbledon Windmill.
On famous people: John Innes; William Morris at Merton; Nelson and Merton; William Wilberforce and Wimbledon; The women's suffrage movement in Wimbledon.
Subjects: Cinemas in Merton; Film studios in Merton; Inns and taverns in Merton; The London Borough of Merton; Public libraries in Merton since 1887.

Merton Heritage Trails: a pack of five walks (A5 laminated cards) published by 'Addax' in 1992 for London Borough of Merton. Covers: Wandle walk; Merton Park trail; Morden Park heritage trail; Mitcham village; Wimbledon village and Cannizaro Park.

Other publications from the library, still available:
Merton in pictures series: 1: *Wimbledon: an historical glimpse*, 1985; 2: *Mitcham: an historical glimpse*, 1988; 3: *Mitcham Fair*.
Mizens of Mitcham, by Gerald A. Morris, 1989; *Origin, growth and development of Nelson Hospital*, Merton by Frank & Di Deas, 1981.

A wide range of publications from societies, commercial publishers and individuals is also stocked, and a useful categorised title list (with publishers and dates) is issued.
From Historical Publications: *Wimbledon past*, by Richard Milward, 1998.
From Phillimore: *Merton and Morden*: a pictorial history, by Judith Goodman, 1995; *Mitcham*: a pictorial history, by Eric Montague, 1991; *Old Mitcham*, by Tom Francis, edited by Eric Montague, 1993.
From SB Publications: *Wimbledon then and now*, 1995, compiled by Richard Milward.
From Sutton: *Merton, Morden and Mitcham*, old photographs compiled by Patrick Loobey; and *Wimbledon*, also compiled by Patrick Loobey.
From Tempus: *Wimbledon, 1865-1965*, by Richard Milward, 1997; and *Mitcham*, by Nick Harris, 1996.
From Enigma Publishing (51 Cecil Rd, London SW19; 4 Charmwood Avenue, London SW19): *Mysterious Wimbledon*, by Ruth Murphy, 1994; *More mysterious Wimbledon*, by Ruth Murphy and Clive Whichelow, and *Pubs of Wimbledon village* (past and present), by Clive Whichelow, 1998.

* MUSEUMS AND HISTORIC PROPERTIES *

[469] **SOUTHSIDE HOUSE**. The Administrator, The Pennington - Meller - Munthe Charity Trust, Southside House, Wimbledon Common, London SW19 4RJ, *Tel*: (020) 8946 7643. *Hours*: open for guided tours (lasting about 1½ hours) on Tues, Thurs, Sat and Bank Holidays 2pm, 3pm, 4pm (between December 1st and Mid-summer's day). Old family villa, still lived in by the descendants of Robert Pennington who built the house in 1687. House is noteworthy for its many portraits and historic objects. A guide and postcards are available.

[470] **WANDLE INDUSTRIAL MUSEUM**. Vestry Hall Annexe, London Rd, Mitcham CR4 3UD, *Tel*: (020) 8648 0127. *Hours*: Every Wednesday 1-4, and the first Sunday of each month 2-5; other times by appointment. Tells the story of the Wandle valley and its industrial heritage (especially snuff and tobacco, and textiles). Publications: *Hour passed at Merton Abbey*, by Tony Deseife, 1987; *Hour passed at Mitcham Grove*, by John Viger, 1988; *Hour passed at Morden Hall Park*, by John Viner, 1988; *Hour passed at Ravensbury Park*, by Kevin Leyden, 1990.
A Wandle trail Watermeads-Ravensbury Park-Morden Hall Park was issued in 1992, with London Borough of Merton; and in 1996 a *Wandle trail map and illustrated guide* was published. There is a Friends support group contactable at the above address.

[471] **WIMBLEDON LAWN TENNIS MUSEUM**. The All England Club, Church Rd, London SW19 5AE, *Tel*: (020) 8946 6131. *Hours*: Tues-Sat 10.30-5; Sun 2-5. *Curator*: Miss Valerie Warren. Publications: *Changing face of Wimbledon*, by Alan Little, 1987; *Suzanne Lenglen: Tennis idol of the twenties*, also by Alan Little, 1988.

[472] **WIMBLEDON WINDMILL MUSEUM**. Windmill Rd, Wimbledon Common, London SW19 5NR, *Tel*: (020) 8947 2825. *Hon. curator*: Norman Plastow. *Hours*: Sat, Sun and public holidays 2-5, April to October; visits by groups at other times can be arranged. The museum is housed in a Grade II listed windmill built in 1817 and depicts the history of windmills and milling told in pictures, models and the machinery and tools of the trade. It came into being in 1976 and was set up on a budget of only £1,000. It is now run by a trust which has a lease of the building from the Commons Conservators for a nominal rent. Some £100,000 heritage lottery funding was obtained in 1998 for further improvements: the sails are due to turn again.

[473] **WIMBLEDON SOCIETY MUSEUM**. 22 Ridgeway, Wimbledon, London SW19 4QN, *Tel*: (020) 8296 9914. *Chairman of Museum Committee*: Cyril Maidment. *Hours*: May-August, 2.30-5 every Sat and Sun. School visits can be arranged at other times; there are teachers' packs and a 'handling' collection. The museum was founded in 1916; it was completely redesigned with new displays in 1994 and received a Civic Trust 'Pride of Place' award. Displays and exhibits range from pre-historic times to the present day: natural history, manor houses, churches, schools, transport, sports and leisure, politics and the two world wars. There are extensive records and archives, photographs, water-colours and prints.

* HISTORICAL/AMENITY SOCIETIES *

[474] **THE JOHN INNES SOCIETY** (for conservation in the John Innes Estate at Merton). *Chairman*: Bob Welchman, 21 Melrose Rd, London SW19 3HF, *Tel*: (020) 8540 3265 *Historical matters/publications*: David Roe, 105 Poplar Rd South, London SW19 3JZ. Covers the Merton Park Conservation Area and adjoining neighbourhoods: the estate of John Innes, the 'squire of Merton' in the 19th century. He gave his name to a local park and to the well-known horticultural institute, since moved from Merton. The society arranges a range of events and there is a bi-monthly newsletter. There is an active historical section which organises talks and exhibitions, and publishes booklets. A recent exhibition, in 1999, was of the fine drawings of Merton by the late John Wallace, architect, artist and local historian. The society has published two of his booklet histories: *Long Lodge at Merton Rush, buildings and people*: 267-269 Kingston Road; and *Spring House in Merton*: 205 Kingston Rd. There are also three booklets by Judy Goodman: *Dorset Hall, 1906-1935: a home, a family, a cause: votes for women* (on Rose Lamartine Yates and family); *John Innes and the birth of Merton Park (1865-1904)*; and *Merton Park: the quiet suburb (1904-14)*, 2nd edition, 1998. *Merton Park: the expanding suburb 1914-31* was published in 1986; and *Unfortunate infants*: an account of the Bermondsey Poor Law Institution for Children, Old Church House, Merton 1820-1845, in 1989.

[475] **MERTON HISTORICAL SOCIETY**. *Secretary*: Mrs Sheila Harris, 100 Cannon Hill Lane, London SW20 9ET. *Chairman*: Eric N. Montague, 9 Devonshire Rd, Sutton SM2 5HQ, *Tel*: (020) 8643 1608. *President*: J. Scott McCracken, archaeological consultant. The Society was est. in 1951 and aims 'to encourage a knowledge of local history and to foster an interest in history in general'. Lectures, meetings, conducted local walks and visits plus workshops. There is a quarterly bulletin and a wide range of publications. Publications currently available include: *The Amery Mills of Merton Priory, the Copper Mills and the Board Mills*, by Eric Montague; *The archaeology of Mitcham to AD700*, by Eric Montague, 1992; *Around Manor Road, Mitcham*, by Constance Pope; *Childhood memories of wartime Mitcham*, by Irene Baine, 1994; *The Elms*, by Eric Montague, 1969; *A history of Lord Nelson's Merton Place*, 1998; *The liberty print works: wartime remembrances*, by William J. Rudd, 1993; *Life at the Cranmers, Mitcham, before the 1914-18 war*, by Ethel Smith, 1998 (first edition: 1973); *The Long Thornton and District Improvement Society*, by Christine Munday, 1995 (first edition: 1990); *Last common lands - Merton Common*, by Evelyn Jowett, 1991; *Lost common lands - Morden Common*, by Evelyn Jowett, 1991; *Memories of Lower Morden*, by Lilian Grumbridge, 1990; *Memories of my side of the Common*, by Constance Curry, 1988; *Memories of service with Mitcham LDV/Home Guard 1940-42*, by J.B. Pritchard, 1995; *Morden Hall*, 1997; *Morden Park*, 1977; *More memories of Manor Road, 1920's*, by Constance Pope, 1991; *Patent steam washing factory at Phipps Bridge, Mitcham*, by Eric Montague; *The Railways of Merton*, 1998; *Ravensbury Manor House and Park*, by Eric Montague, 1981;

The Ravensbury Mills; Reminiscences of Park Place, Mitcham, by George O'Nash, 1969; *Some memories of Merton,* 1983; *Stane Street in Upper Morden,* by William J. Rudd, 1991; *Textile bleaching and printing in Mitcham and Merton, 1590-1870,* by Eric Montague.

NB: Some 12 of the above titles are in the 'Local History Notes' series.

There is also a series of three heritage trails to the River Wandle: 'Historic River Wandle': 1: *The mill in pictures;* 2: *Phipps Bridge to Morden Hall;* 3: *Ravensbury to Mill Green.*

A guide to the church of St Peter and St Paul, by Eric Montague, was published in 1992.

[476] **MERTON TOWN TRAILS ASSOCIATION,** *Secretary:* Alex Briggs, 6 Rutlish Rd, London SW19 3AL, *Tel:* (020) 8540 6541; *Chairman:* Tony Scott, 10 Edge Hill Rd, Mitcham, *Tel:* (020) 8640 0328. There have been nine trails published late 1970's, early 1980's, on Wimbledon, Merton Park, Morden, Mitcham and Wandle area. The association's main function nowadays is funding with small grants the publications of local societies.

[477] **WIMBLEDON SOCIETY.** *Secretary:* John Crossman, 38 Thornton Rd, Wimbledon SW19 4NQ, *Tel:* (020) 8947 4650. *Chairman:* Martyn Harman, 64 Marryat Rd, Wimbledon SW19 5BJ, *Tel:* (020) 8946 1238. *President:* Norman Plastow, Far House, Hillside, Wimbledon SW19 4NL, *Tel:* (020) 8947 2825. The Society evolved from the John Evelyn Club for Wimbledon founded in 1903. It was one of the first amenity societies and is still actively involved with local planning and conservation. It organises walks and lectures and monthly local history meetings.

Richard Milward (159 Coombe Lane, London SW20 0QX), is the leading Wimbledon historian. He was a history teacher until his retirement in 1985. He began writing on Wimbledon history in 1972, and has published some 23 titles. Some have appeared under the Wimbledon Society, others he has published himself. His major series of historical accounts is as follows:
I: *Early and medieval Wimbledon,* 1983; (there was a previous edition 'Early Wimbledon to c. 1540', published by the author in 1969); II: *Tudor Wimbledon,* 1972; III: *Wimbledon in the time of the Civil War,* 1976; IV: *A Georgian village: Wimbledon 1724-1765,* 1986; V: *Wimbledon 200 years ago,* 1996.
Volumes I and IV were published by the Society, the others by the author.
Outside the series, there is his *The Spencers in Wimbledon, 1744-1994,* published under his Milward Press in 1996.
The Society published his: *Cannizaro House and Park,* 1991 (situated in South-eastern corner of Wimbledon Park); *New short history of Wimbledon,* 1989; and *Wimbledon manor houses,* 1982.

He has also studied the Roman Catholic and Church of England parishes:
Portrait of a church: the Sacred Heart was published by himself in 1987; and *Triumph over tragedy: Edith Arendrup and the building of the Sacred Heart church* was published by Merton Priory Press in 1991; *Parish church since Domesday: St Mary's Wimbledon,* was published by the parish in 1993 to celebrate its 150th anniversary; *Rectory: Wimbledon's oldest house* was published by Artscan Ltd in 1992.

Other Wimbledon Society publications currently available are:
Bells of St Mary's, 1986, by A.P. Whitehead; *Memories of a Wimbledon childhood 1905-1918,* by Patrick Fawcett (John Evelyn Society, 1981, reprinted by the Wimbledon Society 1990); *Safe as houses: Wimbledon at war 1939-1945,* by Norman Plastow, 1990; *Wimbledon 1885-1965,* by Winifred Whitehead, 3rd edition, 1979, published by the John Evelyn society; *Wimbledon railways,* 1982, by Alan Elliot.

The Society (at its museum) also sells some specialist titles: *Crusader: the life and times of Sir Cyril Black* (a Wimbledon politician), published by his family in 1996, written by Hilary Kingsley.
Who was Atkinson Morley? by Kate Hayward was published by the Friends of the Atkinson Morley Hospital.
Sir Theodore Janssen, Huguenot (lord of the manor at Wimbledon, 1717-1721), by Elspeth Veale was issued as Vol 26, No 2, 1995 of the Proceedings of the Huguenot Society.
Wimbledon Park: from private park to residential suburb, written and published by Bernard Rondeau (now living in France) in 1995 is a major work of 111 pages, with illustrations and maps.
There is also a history of *Wimbledon Park Golf Club.*
Booklets written and mostly published by local historian Gillian Hawtin (now deceased) are sold:
Early radical Wimbledon (c. 1880-1931), 1993, was published by Sunray (16 Albert St, Belper, Derbyshire DE56 DA).
'A new view of old Wimbledon' is a series of three booklets: *Archaeology to Queen Anne,* 1994; *Wimbledon under the George's c. 1714-1830, retreat for the aristocracy,* 1993; and *Wimbledon during the twentieth century, c. 1905-1965,* 1993.

There is a booklet entitled simply *Wimbledon*, 1994; and *Wimbledon FC: an old central's man, Walter Ernest Hawtin, 1876-1916*, published in 1991.

There is also a range of historical maps.

* PARKS AND COMMONS *

[478] **FRIENDS OF CANNIZARO PARK** (south eastern corner of Wimbledon Common). Mail address: Robert Holmes & Co, estate agents, 35 High St, Wimbledon Village, London SW19, *Tel*: (020) 8947 9833.

[479a] **MITCHAM COMMON CONSERVATORS** (elected representatives from boroughs of Merton, Croydon, Sutton and the City of London). *Warden*: Martin Boyle, The Ecology Centre, Windmill Rd, Mitcham CR4 1HT, *Tel*: (020) 8288 0453. A series of five leaflets is in preparation.
Clerk: Mr G. Norris, 8 Langley Rd, Merton Park SW19 3NZ.
There is also a [479b] **MITCHAM COMMON PRESERVATION SOCIETY**. *Contact*: Janet Morris, 241 Commonside East, Mitcham, *Tel*: (020) 8648 0255. In 1970 the Society published Eric Montague's *A History of Mitcham Common*; a new edition will be published funds permitting. A history *Three hundred years of Mitcham Cricket 1685-1985*, by Tom Higgs was published by Mitcham Cricket Club in 1985.

[480] **WIMBLEDON AND PUTNEY COMMONS CONSERVATORS**. *Clerk and ranger*: Jim Reader; *Assistant ranger*: David Haldane. Manor Cottage, Wimbledon Common, London SW19 5NR, *Tel*: (020) 8788 7655. A *History of Wimbledon and Putney Commons*, edited by Normal Plastow was published in 1986. This is an updated edition of the centenary history by Myson, Parsloe and Williamson published in 1971. Other publications also appeared around this time: *Walks on Wimbledon Common*, by Professor Nicholson; a booklet: *Wimbledon & Putney Commons*, by Alan Phillips; and *A Field Guide to butterflies of Wimbledon Common and Putney Heath*, by Tony Drakeford. Tony Drakeford is also planning to publish his exhaustive study on the natural history of Wimbledon Common (Tel: contact: (020) 8947 3015). Lastly, in the 1980's Wandsworth Council published nature trail booklets on Putney Heath, Putney Lower Common, Mill Corner and Kingsmere.

[481] **WIMBLEDON PARK HERITAGE GROUP**. *Contact*: Timothy Ball (architect), *work tel*: (020) 8543 2196; *home*: (020) 8767 7636.

* SOME OTHER COUNCIL CONTACTS *

Arts: Mark Homer, Arts development officer, Civic Centre, *Tel*: (020) 8545 3571. Merton Arts Council: Wimbledon Library, *Chair*: Malcolm Parker, *Tel*: (0370) 307099.
There is an annual Merton Arts Festival May-August.
Business: A Merton business directory is produced by the Council's Business Partnerships Unit, contact: Rob Moran, Civic Centre, *Tel*: (020) 8545 3822.
Conservation areas/listed buildings: Lone Levay, Civic Centre, *Tel*: (020) 8545 3055. There are 29 conservation areas in Merton; booklets describing characteristics of about half have been issued.
Wimbledon Reference Library, Wimbledon Hill Rd, London SW19, *Tel*: (020) 8946 1136. A community information database MERLIN is maintained.
Parks/nature: Chris Mountford, Civic Centre, *Tel*: (020) 8545 3657.

* SOME NON-COUNCIL CONTACTS *

Voluntary organisations:
MERTON VOLUNTARY SERVICE COUNCIL. *Contact*: Chris Frost, Vestry Hall, London Rd, Mitcham CR4 3UD, *Tel*: (020) 8685 1771.

* LOCAL PRESS *

Merton Independent (free paper), 19 Bartlett St, South Croydon, *Tel*: (020) 8763 6666.
The New Merton Messenger, council paper, quarterly, edited by Paul Parry, Civic Centre, London Rd, Morden SM4 5DX.
Putney and Wimbledon Times, 144 Wandsworth High St, London SW18 4JJ, *Tel*: (020) 8874 4226.
Wimbledon Guardian (free paper), 34-44 London Rd, Morden SM4 5BR, *Tel*: (020) 8687 4385.
Wimbledon News, same address as above.

SUTTON

* LONDON BOROUGH OF SUTTON *

[482] **SUTTON HERITAGE SERVICE**. Central Library, St Nicholas Way, Sutton, Surrey SM1 1EA. *Heritage manager*: John Phillips; *Historic houses officer*: Valerie Murphy, *Tel*: (020) 8770 4781. *Archivist*: Kathleen Shawcross, *Tel*: (020) 8770 4745; *Email*: sutton.heritage@dial.pipex.com. There is a summer walks programme and exhibitions, and talks run at the historic properties. *Hours*: Tues, Fri 9.30-12; Wed, Thurs 2-7.30; 1st and 3rd Saturday of each month 9.30-1, 2-4.45; 1st and 3rd Sunday of each month 2-5.

The archive and the Local Studies Searchroom are situated on Level 5 West of the Central Library. There are guides to the archives and to the parish registers held. Original parish registers for the area have now been transferred to the department from Surrey County Record Office.

The Local Studies Centre sells only its own book publications. Postcards (and mail order requests) are sold at the Leisure Stop Shop, Central Library, *Tel*: (020) 8770 4444.

Recent publications:

1993: CUNNINGHAM, Margaret. *The story of the Oaks and Oaks Park*, 116pp. (A former country house occupied by the Earls of Derby and demolished in the late 1950's in South Carshalton). Author also wrote *The story of Little Woodcote and Woodcote Hall*, L.B.S. 1989.

1995: CLUETT, Douglas. *Discovering Sutton's heritage*: the story of five parishes, 68pp, illus. Author is a former Sutton Local Studies librarian and has written extensively on Croydon Airport.

1997: JACKSON, Patricia. *Whitehall and Cheam Village: a history and guide*. 32pp, illus. Author is curator at Whitehall.

Sutton Libraries publication programme has included general interest and specialist titles. It is well known for its series on Croydon Airport: (the original site was wholly in Sutton). *Croydon airport and the Battle for Britain, 1939-1940*, 1984; *Croydon Airport flypast: historic aircraft profiles in colours*, 1984; *Croydon airport: the great days 1928-1939*, published 1988; *Croydon Airport: the Australian connection*, 1988; *The first, the fastest and the famous: Croydon Airport in pictures*, 1985.

Also more personal accounts: *Croissants at Croydon: the memories of Jack Bamford* (former general manager of Air Union and subsequently Air France), 1986; and *Croydon Airport remembered: an aviation artist looks back*, by Charles C. Dickson, 1985.

Also still in print are photographic collections: *All our yesterdays*: a pictorial record of the London Borough of Sutton over the last century, compiled by Ian Bradley and others, 2nd edition, 1991; and *The past in pictures*: a further collection ..., 2nd edition, 1991, edited by June Broughton.

Frank Burgess compiled *Cheam village past and present*: comparative views from 1891-1991, published in 1991; he also compiled two earlier collections from Sutton Libraries: *No small change*, 1983; and *Now and then*, 1985. Frank Burgess is an elderly Sutton local historian, and Phillimore has published his *Sutton: a pictorial history*, 1993; and *Cheam, Belmont and Worcester Park: a pictorial history*, 1995.

John Phillips and Kathleen Shawcross (of the Heritage Service) are the compilers of a collection from Tempus: *Carshalton, Wallington and Beddington*; a collection on *Sutton* by Jane Jones is in preparation.

There are also two collections, *Cheam and Belmont*; and *Sutton*, compiled by Pamela Berry, from Sutton.

There have also been several more unusual items published by Sutton Libraries: *Five centuries of artists in Sutton*, compiled by former arts librarian Maureen Beasley, published in 1989, has over 200 entries on painters, sculptors and architects who lived or worked in the borough.

The story of lavender by Sally Festing was published as a second edition in 1989 and sells beyond the locality. Lavender and herb growing was an important Sutton industry. Alan Crowe's *Inns, taverns and pubs of the London Borough of Sutton*, now out of print, was published in 1980 and featured the author's line drawings of every pub in the borough. Sutton Libraries also published his historical/pictorial maps.

Margaret Thomas (Wigs Publishing, 47 Rookwood Avenue, Wallington, Surrey SM6 8HF, *Tel*: (020) 8669 5975, is adopting a more educational, national curriculum based approach. Her first publication *Victorian Sutton*, was published n 1998 and further books on Tudor Sutton and Sutton 1914-1945 are planned.

* HISTORIC PROPERTIES *

[483] **CARSHALTON HOUSE** stands at the west end of the old village and dates from the first decade of the 18th century. It has had a variety of owners. In 1893 it was acquired by the Daughters of The Cross and is today St Philomena's Convent School.

Sutton Libraries published a history *The story of Carshalton House*, by A.E. Jones in 1980. In the grounds there is a structure called the Water Tower - it contains the pump chamber, the orangery, the saloon and the unique bath room. The tower is open from 2.30-5 every Sunday in the summer, and from 10-5 when the house is open to the public. There is a [484] **FRIENDS OF CARSHALTON WATER TOWER** organisation, *Contact*: Mrs Julia Gertz, 136 West St, Carshalton, Surrey SM5 2NR, *Tel*: (020) 8642 2845. *Chair*: Jean Knight, 83 Grosvenor Avenue, Carshalton Beeches, Surrey SM5 3EN, *Tel/Fax*: (020) 8669 1546. Est. in 1991, members receive a newsletter and enjoy lectures, visits, social events, etc. There is a shop in the Orangery. In 1978 Sutton Libraries issued a facsimile reprint of the 2nd 1882 edition of *Some particulars relating to the history and antiquities of Carshalton*.

[485] **FRIENDS OF NONSUCH, NONSUCH MANSION AND PARK**. *Contact*: Mrs Joyce Shaw, 97 Grove Rd, Sutton SM1 2DB, *Tel*: (020) 8642 2845. *Chairman*: Gerald Smith, 57 St Margaret's Avenue, North Cheam SM3 9TV. Aims to assist the boroughs of Sutton, Epsom and Ewell to restore Nonsuch Mansion built in 1802-6 (in the locality of Nonsuch Palace, demolished in 1682) and prevent commercial development of the park. The service wing is to be restored to a working kitchen and the stables will become a visitors centre. The adult education branch of Sutton College of Liberal Arts occupy the upper rooms.

The borough's heritage centre is at [486] **HONEYWOOD**, Honeywood Walk, Carshalton SM5 3NX, *Tel*: (020) 8770 4297. *Hours*: Wed-Fri 10-5; Sat, Sun 10-5.30, also bank holidays. The centre opened in December 1990 and illustrates local history with photographs, maps and documents from the borough's collection. There are period rooms, a Tudor gallery, a River Wandle room and art gallery room showing changing exhibitions. Garden has an area planted with herbs associated with Sutton's past. There is a Friends organisation, *Secretary*: Mrs S. Horne, 7 Grosvenor Rd, Wallington SM6 0EG; *Membership secretary*: Mr Stan Coleman, 19 Meadow Walk, Wallington SM6 7EJ.

Another historic property in Carshalton is [487] **LITTLE HOLLAND HOUSE**, 40 Beeches Avenue, Carshalton SM1 3LW, *Tel*: (020) 8773 4555. *Hours*: 1.30-5.30 first Sunday of each month, and Sun and Mon of bank holiday weekends. This was the home from 1904-61 of artist, designer Frank Dickinson, built by himself, and filled with his own hand-made objects and paintings. In 1997 Valerie Murphy published a booklet on it and him: *A novice built his own ideal house*.

Also in Cheam is the [488] **LUMLEY CHAPEL**, St Dunstan's Churchyard, surviving part of the chancel of the old church, and important for its Tudor memorials (including the most impressive marble and alabaster monument to Jane, Lady Lumley, daughter of the 18th Earl of Arundel of Nonsuch Palace). For visits, contact the Custodian, John Davidson, *Tel*: (020) 8643 4404.

To the east of Nonsuch Park is Cheam Park, and overlooking it is [489] **WHITEHALL**, 1 Malden Rd, Cheam SM3 8QD, *Tel*: (020) 8643 1236, a timber-framed building of about 1500 run by the London Borough of Sutton. *Hours*: Summer: 2-5.30 Tues-Fri, Sun; 10-5.30, Sat; Winter: 2-5.30 Wed, Thurs, Sun; 10-5.30 Sat. There are permanent displays on Cheam, Nonsuch Palace, and changing exhibitions. Curator Patricia Jackson has written a history and guide. There is a Friends organisation which helps to run and support Whitehall. *Contact*: Mrs E. Thornton, 25 Lavender Rd, Carshalton SM5 3EF, *Tel*: (020) 8647 2574.

* HISTORICAL AND AMENITY SOCIETIES *

[490] **BEDDINGTON, CARSHALTON & WALLINGTON ARCHAEOLOGICAL SOCIETY**. *Secretary*: Miss Mary Pugh, 57 Brambledown Rd, Wallington SM6 0TF, *Tel*: (020) 8647 8540. *Publications officer*: Dr Beryl Palmier, 75 Beddington Gardens, Carshalton SM5 3HL, *Tel*: (020) 8395 8472. Aims 'to extend knowledge of local history, preserving objects of beauty in the district (natural and man-made), undertaking archaeological work and preserving the finds'. Also lectures and visits. A library is maintained. There have been 5 occasional papers. No 2 was Ron Michell's *The parish of Beddington in the year 1837*, issued in a revised edition in 1991. No 5 is *Celebrating our past*: studies in local history and archaeology on the occasion of the 75th anniversary of the society (8 papers). There is also a newsletter.

[491] **BEDDINGTON SOCIETY**. *Contact*: Dennis Philpott, 1 Church Lane, Wallington, *Tel*: (020) 8647 5165.

Beddington has long connections with the Carew family. The [492] manor house of the Carews in Beddington Park is now a school, noteworthy for its Great Hall, probably late 15th century, which can be visited together with the cellars on specific days in the summer.

The Carew Manor octagonal dovecote (over 250 years old) in the grounds can also be visited on a few days in the summer. *Contact*: Valerie Murphy, Historic houses officer, *Tel*: (020) 8770 4781. In 1989 Sutton Libraries published John Phillips' booklet *Carew Manor: a short guide*.

[493] **CARSHALTON SOCIETY**. *Secretary*: J.S. Thornton, 25 Lavender Rd, Carshalton SM5 3EF, *Tel*: (020) 8647 2574. *Chairman*: Adrian Mann, 43 Denmark Rd, Carshalton SM5 2JF. Est. in 1963 'for the conservation of the amenities of Carshalton'. There is a quarterly newsletter and a leaflet *Walk around Carshalton Village Conservation Area.*

[494] **CROYDON AIRPORT SOCIETY**. *Contact*: Tom Samson, 18 Great Woodcote Park, Purley, Surrey CR0 3QS, *Tel*: (020) 8660 8821. *Membership secretary*: Mrs Margaret White, 38 long Walk, Tattenham Corner, Epsom, Surrey KT18 5TW, *Tel*: (01737) 357887. Est. in 1978 with the object of perpetuating the history and the traditions of Croydon Airport and the men and women who worked and flew from there. The ultimate aim is the establishment of a civil aviation museum within the control tower and terminal building and to replace with replicas the original wireless aerials. The society has some 700 members, including many overseas, and meets monthly usually at Airport House (the old terminal building). Organises an annual 'aerodrome walkabout', and visits to aviation interest sites are arranged. There is a journal twice a year, editor: Peter Cooksley. A booklet on the aviation inspired street names of the Roundshaw estate was published recently.

[495] **NONSUCH ANTIQUARIAN SOCIETY**. *Contact*: Charles Abdy, 17 Seymour Avenue, Ewell, Surrey KT17 2RP, *Tel*: (020) 8393 0531. Concerned with archaeology, history and conservation in Epsom, Ewell, Cheam, Sutton.

Sutton Libraries have published two books on Nonsuch. In 1981 they reissued John Dent's *The quest for Nonsuch*, 320pp, first published by Hutchinson in 1970; and in 1992 published a work by his daughter Lalage Lister: *Nonsuch: pearl of the realm*, 112pp.

[496] **SUTTON AND CHEAM SOCIETY**. *Secretary*: Mrs E.M. Woodward, Little Orchard, Cuddington Way, Cheam SM2 7JA, *Tel*: (020) 8643 1964. *Chairman*: Mr A.J. Colledge, Torridon, Cuddington Way, Cheam SM2 7JA, *Tel*: (020) 8642 5996. *President*: Roger Lamplugh. Est. in 1959 'to protect and improve surroundings in the former borough of Sutton and Cheam' (Belmont, North Cheam and Worcester Park). There are meetings, lectures and visits; a Design award is made. Newsletter issued. Three guided *Walks around Sutton* have been issued, but are currently out of print.

[497] **THE WANDLE GROUP**. *Secretary*: Mrs N. Cunningham, 25 Pine Ridge, Carshalton SM5 4QQ, *Tel*: (020) 8647 7878. A committee of representatives from member organisations and individuals concerned with the whole of the River Wandle, its archaeology, ecology and nature conservation, history and planning matters, from the river's source in Carshalton and Waddon Ponds to its confluence with the Thames in Wandsworth.

* SOME OTHER COUNCIL CONTACTS *

Business: The Sutton Business Directory is published regularly; contact: Philip James, Environmental Services Department, 24 Denmark Rd, Carshalton SM5 2JG, *Tel*: (020) 8770 6255.

Conservation areas/listed buildings: Contact: Simon Grainger, Planning area manager, *Tel*: (020) 8770 6200. There are 14 conservation areas, A guide to buildings, the 'Sutton Local List' is to be published in 1999.

Nature conservation/ecology: Contact: Richard Barnes, Senior ecology officer, *Tel*: (020) 8770 6246.

Ecology Centre at: Old Rectory, Festival Walk, Carshalton SM5 3NY, *Tel*: (020) 8770 5820. A wide range of environmental leaflets is produced; there are nature trails on *Oaks Park, Sutton Countryside*, and *Wilderness Island* (Carshalton).

Parks: there are a number of Friends of parks organisations, including Beddington Park, Cheam Park, Roundshaw Park and Sutton Common; contact: John Palmer, parks department, *Tel*: (020) 8770 4627.

Reference Library: Central Library, St Nicholas Way, Sutton SM1 1EA, *Tel*: (020) 8770 4785. A database on community organisations, including residents associations is maintained.

* SOME NON-COUNCIL CONTACTS *

Arts:

SUTTON ARTS COUNCIL. *Secretary*: Mr Roy Brisley, 12 Devonshire Avenue, Sutton SM2 5JL, *Tel*: (020) 8642 3743. There is an open annual arts exhibition at the Europa Gallery at Central Library. Visual art contact is John Thornton, of the Carshalton Society.

Voluntary organisations:
SUTTON COUNCIL FOR VOLUNTARY SERVICE. Unilink House, Ground Floor, 21 Lewis Rd, Sutton SM1 4BR, *Tel*: (020) 8643 3277.

* LOCAL PRESS *

Sutton Advertiser; Sutton Independent (free papers). 19 Bartlett St, Croydon, *Tel*: (020) 8763 6666.
Sutton Borough Guardian (free paper); *Sutton Comet*. Guardian House, Sandyford Rd, Sutton SM3 9RN, *Tel*: (020) 8644 4300.
Sutton Council may launch its own newspaper/magazine in 1999.

WEST LONDON BOROUGHS
(north and south of Thames):

Ealing, Hammersmith, Harrow, Hounslow, Kingston, Richmond

EALING

* LONDON BOROUGH OF EALING *

[498] **EALING LOCAL HISTORY CENTRE**. *Archivist*: Jonathan Oates, Central Library, 103 Ealing Broadway Centre, London W5 5JY, *Tel*: (020) 8567 3656, ext. 37 (reference library at this number). *Hours*: Tues 9.30-7.45; Thurs 9.30-7.45; Wed, Fri, Sat 9.30-5.00. The collection is on closed access. There is no publishing programme at present, but currently on sale are: extensive range of postcards, greetings cards and coloured prints; four collections of photographs published jointly with Hendon Publishing: *Acton as it was*, 1980; *Ealing as it was*, 1981; *Environs of Ealing in old photographs*, 1984; and *Ealing in the 1930's, and 40's*, 1985.
Children's colour book of Ealing; and *Hanger Hill Garden Estate*, by M. Pointing, 1986; also publications of the Ealing M.A.H. Society and Southall Local History Society.

There are three collections of old photographs from Sutton publishing: *Acton*, by T. Harper-Smith; *Ealing and Northfield*, by R. Essen; *Ealing, Hanwell, Perivale and Greenford*, by R. Essen. From Historical Publications: *Ealing and Hanwell past*, 1991, by Peter Hounsell (he works at Ealing Libraries Library Support Centre).

Acton from A-Z: a compendium of street names together with the history of Old Acton, by R.N.G. Rowlands (1912-1994), third edition, 1977 was published by the borough in association with the Central Acton Partnership.

* MUSEUMS AND HISTORIC PROPERTIES *

[499] **GUNNERSBURY PARK MUSEUM**. *Curator*: Sean Sherman. *Education*: Sue McAlpine; Adam Senior. Gunnersbury Park, London W3 8LO, *Tel*: (020) 8992 1612; *Tel*: (education): (020) 8992 2247; *Fax*: (020) 8752 0686. *Hours*: 9-5, April-October (weekends and bank holidays 1-6); 9-4, November-March. The local history museum for the London Boroughs of Ealing and Hounslow, opened in 1929, housed in the decorative rooms of part of the Large Mansion, built 1800-01 and once home of the Rothschild family. Collections cover social history, local industries, fashion, childhood, etc. Vehicles include two Rothschild carriages and a hansom cab. The Victorian kitchens have been restored, and there is also a museum shop. Programme of temporary exhibitions. The Orangery and the Small Mansion terrace room in the beautiful park can be hired for functions: (020) 8862 5851.

The museum is supported by a Friends organisation which organises fund raising and social events and helps with museum projects. *Chairman*: James Wisdom, 25 Hartington Road, Chiswick, London W4, *Tel*: (020) 8994 4231. *Membership Secretary*: Joan Catterall, 39 Lionel Road, Brentford, *Tel*: (020) 8560 4262. *Newsletter (quarterly) editor*: Helen Poskitt, 14 Manor Gardens, London W3 8JU, *Tel*: (020) 8993 1773.

In 1993 Hounslow Leisure Service published *Gunnersbury Park and the Rothschilds*, by Anne and James Collett-White.

[500] **PITSHANGER MANOR**, Mattock Lane, Ealing, London W5 5EQ, *Tel*: (020) 8567 1227; *Fax*: (020) 8567 0595. *Hours*: Tues-Sat 10-5. Bought by John Soane, famous architect, in 1800 and rebuilt to create a Regency villa. Set in Walpole Park, rooms are being restored and refurbished to their early 19th century style. A Victorian wing houses a large collection of Martinware pottery and provides a large exhibition and workshop space.

[501] **ST BERNARDS (lunatic) HOSPITAL MUSEUM AND CHAPEL**. Uxbridge Road, Southall UB1, *Tel*: (switchboard): 020) 8574 2444.

* AMENITY AND HISTORICAL SOCIETIES *

[502] **ACTON HISTORY GROUP**. *Secretary*: David Knights, 30 Highlands Avenue, Acton, London W3 6EU, *Tel*: (020) 8992 8698; *Email*: dcknights@iee.org. *Editor*: Dr T Harper Smith, 48 Perryn Road, London W3 7NA. Resuscitated in 1986. There are lectures and visits. Recently raised £5000 for the recovery and restoration of the village pump and the Turnpike Road milepost. Indexing the Acton Gazette from 1890 until 1965.

T & A Harper Smith are the compilers of *Acton in old photographs*, from Sutton Publishing. The two are prolific authors on all aspects of Acton and their research is published in a wide ranging series: *Acton Past and Present* (commenced in 1984): 1: *Acton Parish 1484-1984*; 2: *The charities of St Mary's, Acton*; 3: *The stained glass in St Mary's, Acton*; 4: *A corner of Acton* (on High Street, Market Place, Churchfield Road, Grove Road); 5: *The Elms* (now Twyford High School); 6: *Guide to St Mary's Church*; 7: *The rectors of Acton*; 8: *The Atlees of Acton, Ealing, Hammersmith, Hillingdon and the USA*; 9: *Another corner of Acton* (King Street, High Street, Rectory Road, Horn Lane); 10: *Fifty years of West Acton School*; 11: *A brief history of electricity in Acton* (NB: this is by D Knights); 12: *Memorials in St Mary's, Acton*; 13: *Acton schools, 1817-1965*; 14: *Soapsud Island* (Acton laundries); 15: *Acton Hearth Tax assessments*; 16: *Gas in Acton* (NB: by D. Knights); 17: *Acton's Montessori schools*; 18: *Acton inns and pubs*; 19: *Acton people, 1200-1700*; 20-22: *Acton farms and farming* - the Tithes, 1842; The common fields; a new landscape; 23: *Dr Featley of Acton, Chelsea and Lambeth*; 24: *Acton people 1700-1900*; 25: *The building of Bedford Park*; 26: *The brickfields of Acton*; 27: *The story of Ealing Common*; 28: *Acton people III*; 29: *The Uxbridge Road*; 30: *Directory of Acton laundries 1843-1990*; 31: *Opening ceremony of the London United Electric tram to Ealing, 1901*; 32: *A brief history of Acton*; 33: *East Acton Village*; 34: *Thomas Boddington and the glass of St Mary's, Ealing*; 35: *St Mary's Church, Acton*; 36: *Andrew Hunter Dunn in South Acton*; 37: *Acton people IV*; 38: *The Gunnersbury Housing Estates*; 39: *Acton people V*; 40: *St Mary's, Ealing*; 41: *The drainage of Acton 1866-1965*; 42: *Berrymead, Acton 1660-1985*; 43: *Acton people VI*.

Also by T. Harper Smith (but not part of the numbered series):
Acton Hospital 1897 to 1997; *John Winter 1755-1843* (solicitor to the Bank of England, lived at Heathfield Lodge, Gunnersbury Lane; employed John Sloan).
Kensall New Town 1840-1990; *Poores of Acton: the story of a business* (hardware store); *St Thomas, Kensal Town 1889-1989*.
The Acton Pump Cookery Book, 1990 is a compilation of recipes to raise funds for restoration of the Acton Pump; edited by Sheila Ross.

The journal *The Acton Historian* is issued twice a year. Some recent issues:
No. 24, Nov. 1997: Golden Meadow; Adam Faith; G. Spencer & Sons; Acton's heritage.
No. 25, May 1998: Adam Faith; Cambrian buses in Acton; Acton Role of Honour; Acton industry; Baker's stores.
No. 26, Nov. 1998: The house I would like to live in; Allotments in Acton; Umbrellas; Acton surveyors books 1775-1811; Air raid shelters.
An index for numbers 1 -26 has been issued.

[503] **BRENTHAM SOCIETY**. *Secretary*: Rosana Henderson, 47 Meadvale Road, London W5 1NT, *Tel*: (020) 8998 6550. Britain's first co-operative garden suburb laid out by Parker and Unwin. The residents' society concerns itself with the estate. There is a local May festival and an annual garden party. Several booklets on the estate and its history have been issued and there is a quarterly newsletter. The Brentham Club is at 38 Meadvale Road, London W5, *Tel*: (020) 8997 2624.

[504] **BRENT RIVER AND CANAL SOCIETY**. *Membership Secretary*: Mary Hall, 72 Half Acre Road, Hanwell, London W7 3JJ, *Tel*: (020) 8579 7599. The society was est. in 1973 by Luke Fitzherbert to 'press for the creation of a continuous four and a half mile park along the River Brent from Hanger Lane to Brentford'; this now exists and in 1985 a park ranger was appointed - based at the Brent River Park Environmental Centre in Brent Lodge Park, *Tel*: (020) 8566 1929. The society has currently some 250 members, and has issued a booklet of five walks.

[505] **EALING CIVIC SOCIETY**. *Chairman*: Robert Gurd, 60 Beaufort Road, London W5 3EA, *Tel*: (020) 8998 4417. *Secretary*: Brian Harris, 72 The Knoll, London W13 8HY, *Tel*: (020) 8997 8824. *Membership secretary*: Mr K.W. Cordon, 5 Woodville Road, London W5 2SE. Aims to 'preserve, conserve and improve'. There is a publication *Housing in Ealing*.

[506] **EALING MUSEUM, ART AND HISTORY SOCIETY**. *Secretary*: Mrs M. Parrott, 52 Baronsmede, London W5 4LT, *Tel*: (020) 8567 9003. Aims 'to promote interest in the history of the London Borough of Ealing and region, and in museums and art galleries in general'. Its activities include lectures, excursions and publishing. Recent publications are: *The dangerous years: life in Ealing, Acton and Southall in the Second World War 1939-45*, by Dennis Upton; and *A farm in Perivale*, by Eva Farley. *The Grover family of Ealing* by Eric H. Whittleton, published in 1982, is still in print, as is *Scenes of 18th century life* by Peggy Ivie, 1983; a 57 page survey of Christian churches: *Art, architecture and history of Ealing churches* was published in 1978.

[507] **FRIENDS OF ST MARY'S PERIVALE**. *Secretary*: Robin MacGibbon, 34 Crossway, Ealing London W13 0AX, *Tel*: (020) 8997 1307. *Chairman*: Alan Gillett, 51 Park View Road, London W5 2JF, *Tel*: (020) 8997 2526. Robin MacGibbon is the author of a book on the church. The church is much used for a wide range of musical events highlighting young musicians.

[508] **OLD HANWELL RESIDENTS ASSOCIATION.** *Chairman*: Derek Smith, 70 St Dunstan's Road, London W7. *Tel*: (020) 8567 3708. The Hanwell Preservation Society is now defunct. (published *The street names of Hanwell* in 1977). Residents and council workers are represented on the **HANWELL STEERING GROUP**.

[509] **SOUTHALL LOCAL HISTORY SOCIETY.** *Chairman/Secretary*: George Twyman, 119 Dormers Wells Lane, Southall, Middx. UB1 3JA, *Tel*: (020) 8574 5047. Est. in 1958 aiming to research and record the history of the Southall area. Meetings are held in the archive room at Southall Library.
Contents of Transactions:
No 1: Manors of Norwood and Southall; The Elisha Biscoe School; Transport in Southall and district; History of the gas industry in Southall.
No 2: The Story of St Mary's Church, Norwood Green.
No 3: Historical maps of the Southall area. *No 4*: Maps in cardboard tube.
No 5: Street names of Southall; The charities of Southall.
No 6: The story of Holy Trinity Church, Southall. *No 7*: Ernest A.L. Ham, local artist.
No 8: The Martin brothers: the Southall potters. *No 9*: 'Northcott otherwise Southall', a b/w video giving a brief history of Southall up to 1958.

A self-published book is *The chronicles of a manor house*, by Miss E.M. Barnett (on Southall Manor House, the Green).

A brief history of Southall (62pp) by Paul Kirwan was published by Ealing Public libraries in 1980.

* SOME OTHER COUNCIL CONTACTS *

Agenda 21: Michael Calderbrook, Perceval House, 14-16 Uxbridge Road, London W5 2HL, *Tel*: (020) 8758 5269.
Arts: Principal arts and museums officer: Neena Sohal, Pitshanger Manor, *Tel*: (020) 8567 1227; Community arts development officer: Keith Waithe, Perceval House, *Tel*; (020) 8758 5906.
Countryside Service: (parks, open spaces): Keith Townsend, Perceval House, *Tel*: (020) 8758 5916. Events brochure *Enjoy the great outdoors* issued. The West London Waterways Walks leaflets (partnership between Brent, Ealing, Hillingdon, Houslow, Richmond, The National Rivers Authority and the Ramblers Association): pack includes *Brent River Park Walk*; *Dog Rose Ramble* (10 mile circular walk beside brooks and part of the canal); *River Crane Walk*; *Thames Path national trail in Hounslow*; *Willow tree wander* (5 mile walk along Yeading Brook from North Harrow Station to Ickenham Station).
Conservation officer: Ray Rogers, Perceval House, *Tel*: (020) 8758 5676.
Tourism: Yvonne Johnson, Perceval House, *Tel*; (020) 8758 5626.
There is a new series of attractive guided walks leaflets (part funded by the European community Regional development Fund, and produced in conjunction with local societies):
2: *A Brentham walk* (Brentham Garden Suburb), with the Brentham Society.
3: *Ealing Common walkabout*, with the Ealing Common Society.
4: *Ealing Green*, with the Walpole Residents Association.
5: *Hanger Hill Garden Estate*, with Hanger Hill Garden estate Residents Association and Ealing Civic Society
6: *Hanger Hill, Haymills Estate*, with Hanger Hill East Residents Association and Ealing Civic Society.
8: *Southall Town trail*, with the Southall Local History Society.
11: *Ealing Town Hall.*
Other walks are in preparation for; Acton, Hanwell, canals, transport heritage.
There are also two tourist brochures: *Enjoy yourself in Ealing*; and *Surprise yourself in Southall*.
There are many residents' associations in the borough, and Yvonne Johnson is a contact point for information on them.

* SOME NON-COUNCIL CONTACTS *

Business:
EALING CHAMBER OF COMMERCE. 42 The Grove, London W5, *Tel*: (020) 8840 6332. A business directory for Ealing was published by the council in 1997.

Voluntary organisations:
EALING VOLUNTARY SERVICE/EALING VOLUNTEER BUREAU: 24 Uxbridge Road, London W5, *Tel*: (020) 8579 6273.

* LOCAL PRESS *

Around Ealing, edited by Rachel Blake, council magazine, from Perceval House, 14-16 Uxbridge Road, London W5 2HL, *Tel*: (02058 5704.

The Middlesex County Press publishes three Ealing newspapers: *Ealing Gazette, Southall Gazette, Northolt and Greenford Gazette*; and two free papers *The Leader, The Informer* from 134 Broadway, London WL3, *Tel*: (020) 8579 33131.

HAMMERSMITH

* LONDON BOROUGH OF HAMMERSMITH *

[510] **HAMMERSMITH ARCHIVES AND LOCAL HISTORY CENTRE**, The Lilla Huset (close to 'The Ark'), 191 Talgarth Road, London W6 8BJ, *Tel*: (020) 8741 5159. *Fax*: (020) 8741 4882. *Hours*: Mon 9.30-8; Tues 9.30-1; Wed closed; Thurs 9.30-4.30; Fri closed; Sat 9-1.00 (first Saturday in month only).
Librarian: Christine Bayliss. Compiler with Jerome Farrell of *Hammersmith and Shepherds Bush in old photographs*, from Sutton. *Archivist*: Jane Kimber. Compiler of *Fulham in old photographs* from Sutton.
Two earlier collections of photographs *The instant past: old Hammersmith in pictures*, 1984; and *Life in Fulham: old Fulham in pictures*, 1985, were published by the library.

The centre sells a range of publications from commercial sources and societies as listed below. Also some specialist items: two church histories: *Hammersmith parish church: history and guide*, by Jean Grinstead; *St Matthew's, Fulham 1895-1995*, by S. Pierson; *The exhibitions: Great White City, Shepherds Bush, London: 70th anniversary 1908-1978* was written and published by Donald R. Knight in 1978.
A walk around Fulham Palace and its garden, was published by Sibylla Flower and Friends of Fulham Palace; this organisation was est. in 1970 and currently has some 20 members; *Contact*: Ms S. Flower, 16 Cloncurry Street, London SW6.

The centre has special collections on: William Morris, A.P. Herbert, and the White City exhibitions.

Postcards:
Black and white sets are on: 'A summer's day'; 'Shopping with a shilling'; 'At work'; Fulham Palace.
Coloured postcard sets on: Paintings from the Cecil French bequest; Fulham Palace, Hammersmith; Exhibitions. Also greetings cards showing paintings from the Cecil French bequest, and Fulham Palace.
Prints of four works by Evacustees Phipson (1854-1931)
Information packs:
Hammersmith Bridge: centenary of present bridge, 1987.
Ravenscourt Park: centenary of park, 1988.

[511] The **HAMMERSMITH AND FULHAM URBAN STUDIES CENTRE** in also based at the above address, *Tel*: (020) 8741 7138. It aims 'to assist people of all ages to understand and become involved in the process of environmental change'; An attractive, unusual publication is their *Places to visit along the Thames path in Hammersmith and Fulham: a guide by local children.*

* MUSEUMS *

[512] **THE MUSEUM OF FULHAM PALACE.** *Curator*: Miranda Poliakoff. Bishop's Avenue, London SW6 6EA, *Tel*: (020) 7736 3233. (close to Putney Bridge underground). *Hours*: March-Oct Wed-Sun 2-5; Nov-Feb Thurs-Sun 1-4, and Bank Holiday Mondays. The museum is a new project run by the Fulham Palace Trust, and collects artefacts and information relating to all aspects of the palace's architecture, archaeology, garden history and all who have lived and worked there. Based currently in two major historic rooms: Bishop Howley's dining room and the Porteus Library.
Site was first acquired by Bishop Waldhere in 704 and continued as a residence of the Bishops of London until 1973. Part of the long moat remains. The historic gardens include botanic beds, herb garden and wisteria pergola within the old walled kitchen garden. There is a friends organisation: Museum of Fulham Palace associates. A newsletter is issued.

* AMENITY AND HISTORICAL ASSOCIATIONS *

[513] **BROOK GREEN ASSOCIATION**. *Contact*: Mrs D.P. Johnston, 22 Phoenix Lodge Mansions, London W6 7BG, *Tel*: (020) 7603 6096. (area lies to the north of Hammersmith Road).

[514] **ETHNIC COMMUNITIES ORAL HISTORY PROJECT (ECOHP)**. *Co-ordinator*: Sav Kyriacou, The Lilla Huset (above local studies library), 191 Talgarth Road, London W6 8BJ, *Tel*: (020) 8741 4076; *Fax*: (020) 8741 8435. The project is an educational, registered charity which provides a voice to ethnic community groups throughout London by publishing their life-stories and experiences. It also gives people the opportunity to express themselves through innovative arts activities. It is committed to recording and publishing in the mother tongue.
The following books have been published since 1988:
No 1: *The Irish in exile: stories of emigration*, 1988. 24pp, illus.
No 2: *Passport to exile: the Polish way to London*, 1988. 40pp, illus. (in English/Polish).
No 3: *In exile: Iranian recollections*, 1989. 40pp, illus. (in English/Farsi).
No 4: *The motherland calls: African-Caribbean experiences*, 1992. 2nd ed. 24pp, illus.
No 5: *The forgotten lives: travellers on the Westway site*, 1989. 24pp, illus.
No 6: *Xeni-Greek-Cypriots in London*, 1990. 64pp, illus. (in English/Greek).
No 7: *Ship of hope: the Basque children*, 1991. 24pp, illus. (in English/Spanish).
No 8: *Aunt Esther's story* African-Caribbean), 1996. 2nd ed. 20pp, illus.
No 9: *Sorry, no vacancies: lifestories from the Caribbean*. 32pp, illus. (out of print).
No 10: *Asian voices: life stories from the Indian sub-continent*, 96pp, illus. (in English, Urdu and Bengali).
No 11: *Sailing on two boats: second generation perspectives*. 72pp.
No 12: *Such a long story: Chinese voices in Britain*. 88pp, illus. (in English/Chinese)

[515] **FULHAM AND HAMMERSMITH HISTORICAL SOCIETY**. *Secretary*: Rosamund Vercoe, 37 Paddenswick Road, London W6 0UA, *Tel*: (020) 8748 9493. *Publications*: Sonia Crutchlow, 29 Ellerby Street, London SW6 6EX. *Chairman*: Keith Whitehouse, 85 Rannoch Road, London W6 9SX, *Tel*: (020) 7385 3723. Est. in 1971, by the amalgamation of the Fulham History Society (est. in 1934) with the Hammersmith Local History group (est. in 1954). A newsletter is issued three times a year. There are lectures and visits.

Publications issued in the 1990's (including reprints):
1990: WHITTING, Phillip David, *editor. A history of Hammersmith*, based upon that of Thomas Faulkner published in 1839. First published by the Hammersmith Local History Group in 1965.
1991: VERCOE, Rosamund. *Ravenscourt*. 50pp, illus.
1992: HASKER, Leslie. *Hammersmith and Fulham through 1500 years*. 84pp, illus.
1993: DENNY, Barbara. *Ladybirds on the wall: growing up in West Kensington 1920-1940.*
Barbara Denny (now deceased) is also the author of *Fulham past*, 1997; and *Hammersmith and Shepherds Bush past*, 1995 both from Historical Publications.
1995: *Fulham as it was*; (a reissue of a collection of old photographs first published with Hendon in 1983).

Other society publications currently in print, and available at the local history centre:
Fulham Bridge, 1729-1886: the predecessor of Putney Bridge, 1986, by George Dewe and Michael Dewe; *Fulham in the second world war*, 1984, by Leslie Hasker; *Hammersmith Bridge*, 1987, by Charles Hailstone; *Medicine in the parish of Fulham from the 14th century: Fulham Hospital, 1884-1959*, published 1988, by A. Wyman; *Pope's corner: Roman Catholic institutions in Hammersmith and Fulham*, 1980, by D. Evinson; *West London nursery gardens*, by Eleanor Joan Willson, 1982.

[516] **FULHAM ARCHAEOLOGICAL RESCUE GROUP**. *Contact*: Keith Whitehouse, 85 Rannoch Road, London W6 9SX. *Tel*: (020) 7385 3723.

[517] **FULHAM SOCIETY**. *Secretary*: Michael Plumbe, 104 Drive Mansions, Fulham Road, London SW6 5JH, *Tel*: (020) 7371 7530. *Chairman*: John Putnam, 44 Ranelagh Gardens Mansions, Ranelagh Gardens, London SW6 3UQ, *Tel*: (020) 7736 0924. Est. in 1971. Sub-committees deal with the environment, traffic and noise, conservation and listed buildings.

[518] **HAMMERSMITH AND FULHAM COMMUNITY TRUST**. The Emerald Centre, Hammersmith Road, London W6 *Tel* (020) 8748 5863. Also runs an information/visitor centre at 20 Broadway Shopping Centre, W6.

[519] **HAMMERSMITH AND FULHAM HISTORIC BUILDINGS GROUP.** *Chair*: Mrs Angela Dixon, 31 St Peter's Square, London W6 9NW, *Tel*: (020) 8748 7416. Another contact: Michael Burrell, *Tel*: (020) 8746 3994. Publications include: *Bradmore House, Hammersmith*, by Keith Whitehouse, Roger White and Ian McInnes, edited by Michael Burrell. A new guide to buildings of historic interest is in preparation.

[520] **HAMMERSMITH SOCIETY.** *Chair*: Jane Mercer, 27 Westcroft Square, London W6 0TD, *Tel*: (020) 8741 1665.

[521] **RAVENSCOURT SOCIETY.** *Contact*: John Jones, 221 Goldhawk Road, London W12 8ER. Est. in 1971, currently with some 100 members; concerned with preserving and enhancing the environment of Ravenscourt Park, London W6, both for the residents of Ravenscourt and Starch Green Conservation Area and park users. Newsletter issued.

[522] **SHEPHERDS BUSH LOCAL HISTORY SOCIETY.** *Secretary*: Mrs J. Blake, 22a Collingbourne Road, Shepherds Bush, London W12 0JQ, *Tel*: (020) 8743 4865. Est. in 1982, currently with some 60 members. Monthly meetings; quarterly newsletter. Maintains a collection of local photographs and slides and is willing to give illustrated lectures on request. 1990's publications: *Shepherds Bush - the Dickens connection*, 1992; 48pp, illus. (the story of Urania Cottage in Lime grove, a 'home for fallen women' founded by Charles Dickens and Angela Burdett-Coutts). *The Scrubs*, 1998; 32pp, illus. (on Wormwood Scrubs: the prison, Hammersmith Hospital, military uses, airships and air flights, Linford Christie Stadium and the history of the area). *Markets and traders* was reissued in 1999, 23pp, illus. and covers Shepherds Bush Market and the Norland Market. Still available are: *Around the bush: a history of Shepherds Bush*, 1984; and *Around the bush*: the war years, 1914-18, published in 1986.

Also available through the society: *The Fantasy Factory: the story of Lime Grove Studios, 1915-1991*, compiled and published by Jocelyn Lukins (a specialist on Doulton ceramics) (14 Keith Grove, London W12 9EZ).

West Kensington and Shepherds Bush in old picture postcards was complied by Pamela D. Edwards and published in 1995 by the European Library Publishers (Zaltbommel/Netherlands) in their "Back in Time Series".

Other organisations for small localities:
In addition to the above, there are many residents associations, some covering public open spaces: Bishops Park (Fulham Palace) Residents Association; St Peters Square R.A.; Westcroft Square R.A. (north and south of King Street).
A council contact for all amenity groups in the borough is Nada Yocic, planning information office, ext. 3330.

* SOME OTHER COUNCIL CONTACTS *

Business information*:* A Hammersmith Business directory is published; *contact*: Nigel Gee, Regeneration Unit, Town Hall. There is also a 'Media West' directory for media companies in West London.
Conservation: Head of Design and Conservation: Barbara Woda, Town Hall, King Street, London W6, *Tel*: (020) 8748 3020, ext. 2315. There are 43 conservation areas, and 'character profiles' are currently being published.
Fulham Regeneration: Central Fulham Steering Group. *Contact*: John Whitwell, Town Hall, King Street, London W6, *Tel*: (020) 8748 3020, ext. 3393.
Fulham Centre Regeneration Project. Fulham Broadway, London SW6. *Tel*: (020) 7381 5085.
Nature conservation: contact: Richard Adam, policy and projects officer, ext. 3332.
Reference libraries: Hammersmith Reference Library, Shepherds Bush Road, London W6 7AT, *Tel*: (020) 8576 5053; Fulham Reference Library, 598 Fulham Road, London SW6 5NX, *Tel*: (020) 8576 5254.

* SOME NON-COUNCIL CONTACTS *

Residents Associations*:*
HAMMERSMITH & FULHAM FEDERATION OF TENANTS AND RESIDENTS ASSOCIATIONS. Ashcroft Square, Leamore Street, London W6, *Tel*: (020) 8748 4114/9313.

Voluntary organisations:
VOLUNTARY SECTOR RESOURCE AGENCY. Palingswick House, King Street, London W6, *Tel*: (020) 8748 6449.

* LOCAL PRESS *

Hammersmith & Fulham Gazette, (and free paper *Hammersmith & Fulham Leader*), 134-136 Broadway, London W13 0LT, *Tel*: (020) 8579 3131.

Hammersmith & Fulham Guardian (free paper). North West London Newspaper Group, Scrubs Lane, London NW10, *Tel*: (020) 8962 6868.

Hammersmith Chronicle/Fulham Chronicle. Newspaper House, Winslow Road, London W6, *Tel*: (020) 8741 1622.

Hammersmith, Fulham and Chiswick Times. 134 Broadway, London W13, *Tel*: (020) 7381 6262.

Street Life, Hammersmith council newspaper, issued ten times a year, edited by Louise Raisey, *Tel*: (020) 8576 5562.

HARROW

* LONDON BOROUGH OF HARROW *

[523] **HARROW LOCAL HISTORY COLLECTION** at: Civic Centre Library, PO Box 4, Civic Centre, Harrow, Middx. HA1 2UU, *Tel*: (020) 8424 1056. *Local History Librarian*: Robert W. Thomson. *Assistant Librarian*: Miss Amanda Wood. The collection is on the same floor as the lending and reference libraries. *Hours*: Mon, Tues, Thurs 9.30-8; Fri 9.30-1; Sat. 9-5. The library has published a number of general and specialist books over the years, on localities and specific institutions. In 1978 chief librarian Alan W. Ball's book *Paintings, prints and drawings of Harrow on the Hill 1562-1899* (159pp) was published. A companion volume by him *The countryside lies sleeping, 1685-1950*; paintings, prints and drawings of Pinner, Stanmore and other former villages now in the London Borough of Harrow was published by the London and Home Counties Branch of the Library Association in 1981 (352 pp). Recent publications:

1993: THOMSON, R.W. *Place names of Stanmore and district*, 35pp.

1994: THOMSON, R.W. *Hatch End: an alphabetical history.* revised edition. 14pp.

1997: HAMLIN, John F. *History of the Royal Air Force, Bentley Priory and Stanmore Park.* 142pp. illus. maps.

The library also sells some publications of local history societies, and some commercially published books.

Postcards: 16 are currently sold individually; also commercial postcards.

In preparation (to be published probably by the library) is a millennium history of Harrow, by Don Walter, Tithegate, London Road, Harrow on the Hill, HA1 3JJ, *Tel*: (020) 8422 9892.

* MUSEUMS *

[524] **HARROW MUSEUM AND HERITAGE CENTRE**. Headstone Manor, Pinner View, Harrow, Middx HA2 6PX, *Tel*: (020) 8861 2626; *Fax*: (020) 8863 6407. *Curator*: David Whorlow. *Hours*: Wed-Fri: 12.30-5; Sat, Sun: 10.30-5. Headstone Manor was a working farm until the 1920's. It was sold to Hendon Rural District Council in 1925 and in 1928 became Headstone Park. It was designated the home of Harrow Museum and Heritage Centre in 1968, owned by the London Borough of Harrow and managed by Harrow Arts Council. The complex consists of manor house with moat, tithe barn, small barn and granary. Restoration work is now proceeding following £1 million lottery funding.

A Friends organisation assists with its promotion, support and development. *Hon. Secretary*: Mrs Lona Price, 52 Embry Way, Stanmore HA7 3AZ, *Tel*: (020) 8954 3443. *Membership Secretary*: Mrs June Noah, 50 Montrose Road, Wealdstone, Harrow HA3 7DU. There is a quarterly newsletter, and a 'Friendly Guide' was published in May 1996.

* HISTORICAL, AMENITY AND ENVIRONMENTAL SOCIETIES *

[525] **FRIENDS OF BENTLEY PRIORY NATURE RESERVE.** *Hon. Secretary*: Margaret Wood, 26 Bentley Way, Stanmore HA7 3RD, *Tel*: (020) 8954 3060.

[526] **FRIENDS OF ST LAWRENCE, LITTLE STANMORE.** *Hon. Secretary*: Miss S.H. Woodward, 8 Hereford House, Stratton Close, Edgware, Middx HA8 6PP, *Tel*: (020) 8952 3897. Formed in 1971 to raise funds for the restoration of the church and its paintings and to encourage interest in this unique 18th century Continental baroque church, with paintings by Bellucci, Brunetti, Laguerre, Sleter and wood carving by Grinling Gibbons. The church is situated in Whitchurch Lane, Edgware, next to Canons Park, and is open for viewing on Sundays 2-5 (2-4 in winter). A booklet guide was published in 1985.

[527] **HARROW COMMUNITY TRUST.** Central Depot (Unit 4), Forward Drive, Wealdstone HA3 8NT, *Tel*: (020) 8424 1167.

[528a] **HARROW HERITAGE TRUST**. *Chairman*: Martin Verden, The Fives Court, Moss Lane, Pinner, Middx HA5 3AG. Est. in 1985 by the late Councillor Peter Pitt during his year as Mayor of Harrow; it aims to provide a focus for activity and funds which can be directed towards enhancing the environment of Harrow: environmental improvement, preservation of buildings, development of walks, trails and sites, promotion of high quality design in new buildings and landscaping projects. Leaflets have been published on: walks, nature reserves, tree planting and graffiti removal.

[528b] **HARROW HILL TRUST**. *Hon. Secretary*: Mrs Margaret Robathan, Merrick, Mount Park Road, Harrow on the Hill HA1 4JY, *Tel*: (020) 8864 9992. Founded in 1959 as the amenity society for Harrow on the Hill and surrounding area.

[529] **HARROW NATURAL HISTORY SOCIETY**. *Hon. Secretary*: Miss E. Stainthorpe, 6 Bellamy Court, Stanmore HA7 2DF, *Tel*: (020) 8907 1348.

[530] **HARROW WEALD COMMON CONSERVATORS**. Founded in 1899 to manage Harrow Weald Common. *Hon. Secretary*: Mr. G. Mount, 33 Lappetts Lane, South Heath, Great Missenden, Bucks HP16 0RA, *Tel*: (01494) 863035.

[531] **HATCH END ASSOCIATION**. *Hon. Secretary*: Mrs Anne Swinson, 6 Thorndyke Court, Westfield Park, Hatch End, Pinner, Middx HA5 4JG, *Tel*: (020) 8428 1415. *Membership Secretary*: Peggy Anderson, 21 Lonsdale Close, (town?) HA5 4RY, *Tel*: (020) 8421 2996. *Bulletin editor*: Paul Samet, 3 Tooke Close HA5 4TJ, *Tel*: (020) 8428 0344. Founded in 1929 as an amenity organisation for the Hatch End environment and surrounding Green Belt. The membership consists of residents, currently 1,800 households and local business people. The Hatch End Bulletin is issued three times a year. In 1995 it published *The natural history of Hatch End*, by Ernest Venis (with maps by Tony Venis and illus. by David Muriss).

[532] **HEADSTONE RESIDENTS ASSOCIATION**. *Hon. Secretary*: Mrs Brenda Cunnamer, 172 Headstone Lane, Harrow HA2 6LY, *Tel*: (020) 8428 1840. Publishes a quarterly bulletin.

[533] **PINNER ASSOCIATION**. *Hon. Secretary*: Mrs Cynthia Wells, 97 West End Lane, Pinner, Middx HA5 3NU, *Tel*: (020) 8866 8699. One of the largest amenity societies in the country, est. in 1932. It aims to stimulate public interest in the area of Pinner, to promote development and improvement of all things of historic or public interest in Pinner. A magazine *The Villager* is published three times a year. *Ten walks around Pinner*, first published in 1992 is to be reprinted in 1999. In 1995 the association published *The villager at war: a diary of home front Pinner, 1939-1945*, 120pp, illus., maps.

[534] **PINNER LOCAL HISTORY SOCIETY**. *Hon. Secretary*: Beryl Newton, 2a Willows Close, Pinner HA5 3SY, *Tel*: (020) 8866 3372. *Membership Secretary*: Joan Duckett, 26 Hazeldene Drive, Pinner HA5 3NJ, *Tel*: (020) 8868 1499. *Chairman*: Bernard Harrison, 2 Ashridge Gardens, Pinner HA5 1DU, *Tel*: (020) 8886 7719. *Publications sales*: Harold Harley, 30 St Michael's Crescent, Pinner HA5 5LG, *Tel*: (020) 8866 5827. *Newsletter editor*: Henry Rockwell, 5 Eastglade, Pinner HA5 3AN, *Tel*: (020) 8866 1561. *Research*: Jim Golland, 49 Azalea Walk, Pinner HA5 2EH, *Tel*: (020) 8866 6722.
The society was est. in 1972 and currently has over 200 members. There are meetings and outings, and a newsletter is issued three times a year. There is an occasional journal *The Pinn*. Pinn Four, edited by Patricia Clarke has articles on the local gas works, the horse bus, suffragettes, and an epidemic in 1741. Recent publications:
1992: KIRKMAN, Ken, *Pinner chalk mines*. 80pp, illus., maps. The story of a site containing some of the deepest chalk mines in the country.
1994: CLARKE, Patricia A., and the Pinner Local History Society. *Pinner, Hatch End, North Harrow and Rayners Lane: a pictorial history*. Published by Phillimore, not the society. 128pp, illus.
1994: LONG, Iris, *editor. Pinner old cemetery, Paines Lane*. 38pp, illus. An index to the names on the inscriptions on the graves.
1995: CLARKE, Patricia, *editor. Our houses: an account of five houses in Pinner and district*. 24pp, illus., maps.
1995: GOLLAND, Jim, *editor. Pinner to paradise* (The Langthorn letters), written 1883-1927 to an emigrant from Pinner, Middlesex to Australia. 124pp, illus. Letters from family and friends to a young man who emigrated to Australia in 1883; they tell of a family struggling against illness, unemployment and poverty in an age when the Metropolitan Railway came to Pinner.

[535] **STANMORE AND HARROW HISTORICAL SOCIETY**. *Hon. Secretary*: Mrs S. Baker, 39 Tenby Avenue, Harrow HA3 8RU, *Tel*: (020) 8907 5727. Est. in 1932, the society has active sub-sections concerned with archaeology, buildings and research. There are monthly meetings, and weekly members' evenings; local visits and further afield during summer months. A newsletter is issued. In 1992 the society published *Salubrious air: people and places of Stanmore and Harrow*. 43pp, illus. Two booklets, by R.D. Abbott on the buildings of Great Stanmore, and of Little Stanmore where published by the society in 1977 and 1978.

[536] **STANMORE SOCIETY**. *Chairman*: Mr A.J. Raymond, 8 Old Forge Close, Stanmore HA7 3EB, *Tel*: (020) 8954 2257.

* SOME OTHER COUNCIL CONTACTS *

Conservation officers: Roger Mascall, Carole Davies at the Civic Centre's Planning Department, *Tel*: (020) 8424 1467. There are conservation and historic building publications on: Mount Park Estate; Pinnerwood Park Estate; Canons Park Estate; Pinner Hill Estate; West Towers; Harrow Park; South Hill Avenue; Harrow on the Hill Village; Roxborough Park and the Grove; Sudbury Hill; directory of statutory and locally listed buildings; Headstone Manor development plan.
Parks: Peter Brown; Steve Wood, at the Civic Centre. *Tel*: (020) 8424 1753. Guided walks leaflets are available: Bentley Priory circular walk; Pinner Grimsdyke circular walk; Roxbourne Rough local nature reserve; Stanmore Common local nature reserve.

HARROW AGENDA 21 ENVIRONMENTAL FORUM. *Contact*: Julie Tallentire, PO Box 38, Civic Centre, Harrow HA1 2UZ, *Tel*: (020) 8424 1913. Set up in November 1996 as a partnership between the Council, community groups, businesses and individuals. Two 'Green Guides' have been produced, and there is also an 'Environment Challenge for Schools' teachers' pack.
The Environmental Information Centre, is at the Civic Centre, third floor, and is managed by Julie Tallentire, *Tel*: (020) 8424 1993.

* SOME NON-COUNCIL CONTACTS *

Arts:
HARROW ARTS COUNCIL, Harrow Arts Centre, Uxbridge Road, Hatch End, Pinner HA5 4EA, *Tel*: (020) 8428 0123.
In 1995 Harrow Arts Council published:
EDWARDS, Ron. *Commercial Travellers' schools*. 16pp. illus. bibliog.

Business information:
The Harrow Business Guide (a directory) is published by Harrow in Business (local enterprise agency), Enterprise House, 297 Pinner Road, Harrow HA1 4HS, *Tel*: (020) 8427 6188.

Voluntary organisations:
HARROW ASSOCIATION FOR VOLUNTARY SERVICE, The Lodge, 64 Pinner Road, Harrow HA1 4HZ, *Tel*: (020) 8863 6707.

* LOCAL PRESS *

Harrow Observer, 326 Station Road, Harrow HA1 2DR, *Tel*: (020) 8427 4404. (part of the South News Group). Also here, free newspapers *Harrow Informer, Harrow Independent, Harrow Leader*.
Harrow People, magazine published by the council, PO Box 57, Civic Centre, Harrow HA1 2XF, *Tel*: (020) 8442 1739; Editor: Jo Lloyd.
Harrow Times. 71 Church Road, Hendon NW4 4DN, *Tel*: (020) 8203 0926. (part of Newsquest Group).

HILLINGDON

* LONDON BOROUGH OF HILLINGDON *

[537] **HILLINGDON HERITAGE SERVICE/LOCAL STUDIES COLLECTION**: at Central Library, High Street, Uxbridge, Middx UB8 1HD, *Tel*: (01895) 250702. Senior staff: Carolynne Cotton, Maria Newbery. *Hours*: Mon 9.30-8; Tues-Thurs 1-5.30; Fri 10-5.30.
The museum collection is currently in store.
Hillingdon libraries have not issued any new local history publications in recent years, but the following titles are currently available:
Archaeology of West Middlesex, by Cotton, Clegg and Mills, 1984.
A concise history of Hayes, 1989, by Catherine Kelter (a community librarian with London Borough of Hillingdon); *Eastcote: from village to suburb*, 1987, by Ron Edwards; *The goodliest place in Middlesex: a history of the ancient parish of Ruislip from the Domesday Book to modern times*, 1989, by Eileen Bowlt (winner of the Alan Ball award for local history research in

1990); *Gregory King's Harefield: an English village in the 1690's*, 1992, by Fiona Cuthbertson; *Harefield's old buildings*, 1982, by Margaret Evans; *The history of Heathrow*, 2nd edition, 1993 by P. Sherwood; *A history of the bells of St Martins's, Ruislip, 1992*, by Dr R.D. Andrews; *Life and work in a Middlesex village: oral history of Harefield*, 1984, by Geoffrey Tyack; *The story of Ickenham*, 1983, by Morris W. Hughes; *Stand and deliver: highwaymen in East Middlesex*, 1986, by Brian Williams (a community librarian with London Borough of Hillingdon); *Uxbridge: a concise history*, 2nd edition, 1984, by Carolynne Hearmon (i.e. Cotton); *West Drayton and Yiewsley through the centuries*, 1983 (reprinted 1995), by A.H. Cox.

History trails cover: Hayes, Hillingdon, and Ruislip, manor farm and village.
Nature trails cover: Bayhurst Wood Country Park; Yeading Valley circular; Yeading Woods.
Gardens of excellence, 1996 is a booklet on Hillingdon's public gardens, prepared by the Parks Department.

In addition to its own publications, the library also sells publications from commercial publishers, societies and individuals:
The London Borough of Hillingdon is well covered by Phillimore and Historical Publications: *Bygone Ruislip and Uxbridge*, by Dennis E. Edwards, 1985; from Phillimore.
Hayes past, by Catherine Kelter, 1996; *Ickenham and Harfield past*, by Eileen M. Bowlt, 1996; *Ruislip past*, also by Eileen M. Bowlt, 1994; and *Uxbridge past*, by Carolynne Cotton, 1994, all these four from Historical Publications.
From Tempus, there is a collection of old photographs: *Around Ruislip*, compiled by local history library staff Maria Newbery, Carolynne Cotton, Julie Ann Packham and Gwyn Jones.
From Sutton there are two collections on *Hayes and West Drayton*, compiled by Philip Sherwood; and two collections on *Uxbridge*, compiled by K.R. Pearce.
James Skinner (43 Fairway Avenue, West Drayton UB7 7AP is the author and publisher of *St Mary's story* (a Roman Catholic school in Uxbridge), and (with J. Nelson) of *St Catherine's 125 years on* (a Roman Catholic church in West Drayton).
A brief guide to Ickenham is written and published by Sheena Rosser (1 Whitney Close, Ickenham UB10 8EL).

* HISTORICAL/AMENITY SOCIETIES *

[538] **FRIENDS OF RUISLIP NATURE RESERVE**. *Contact*: Mr M.E. Morgan, 40 Keswick Gardens, Ruislip Gardens, Ruislip, Middx HA4 7XN, *Tel*: (01895) 635565.

[539] **HAREFIELD HISTORY SOCIETY**. *Secretary*: Mrs K.M. Davey, 20 Hinkley Close, Harefield, Middx UB9 6AA. Est. in 1980 by a group of residents of the village who had just completed a three year study of its history organised by the W.E.A. (publication: *Harefield at that time of day*); meetings, visits. A newsletter is issued twice a year.

[540] **HAYES AND HARLINGTON LOCAL HISTORY SOCIETY**. *Secretary*: John Walters, 7 St Jerome's Grove, Hayes, Middx. *Membership secretary*: Mr. C. Berridge, 202 Balmoral Drive, Hayes, Middx *Tel*: (020) 8561 5651. *Publications editor*: Mr P.T. Sherwood, 5 Victoria Lane, Harlington, Middx, *Tel*: (020) 8564 9098. Est. in 1952. Monthly meetings; visits; the society maintains a museum collection and has a large photographic local buildings archive.
P.T. Sherwood is the author of two collections on *Hayes and West Drayton* from Sutton; *Heathrow past and present* from Hendon; *Villages of Harmondworth* from the West Middx. F.H.S. and the *History of Heathrow* from Hillingdon Libraries.
Contents of recent issues of the society's journal:
Spring 1993: Harlington recalled; The Hayes National Schools 1836-1861; Harvesting at Harlington. *Autumn 1993*: William Byrd 1543-1993; Harvesting and threshing at Dawley Manor Farm; A poem on Heathrow. *Spring 1994*: Discovering the people of Hillingdon; Requiem for Harlington Village; Duplication in the census returns. *Autumn 1994*: 'The Regent' at Hayes; 'The Lilacs' (Overburg House), Harlington; The Harlington Sparrow, Starling and Rat Club; History of the Perry Oaks Sludge Works; *Spring 1995*: Obituaries as a source of local history; Grandfather George; *Autumn 1995*: What's in a name; Charles Dickens and his local connections; The Shropshire strawberry pickers in Harlington. *Spring 1996*: The Fairey Aerodrome at Heathrow; Recollections of Harlington; The Minet Family. *Autumn 1996*: Beside the main line and a little further; Violence in Hayes Parish Church; Paul Pry and Bo-Peep in Hayes c 1840. *Spring 1997*: Chapel House, Hayes; Hatton Gore, Harlington. *Autumn 1997*: More violence at Hayes Church; Diary of an air-raid warden; Sale details of the 'Coach and Horses'. *Spring 1998*: The Rawlinson manuscripts; Archives of the Minet Estate; A survey of the Parish of Harlington 1692. *Autumn 1998*: Harlington Baptist Church 1798-1998; The 1793 perambulation of the boundary of Hayes Manor; John Syme - a Harlington policemen. *Spring 1999*: The Car Caravan Cruiser Company; Caesar's Camp at Heathrow; Auctioneer's notices as a source of information.

[541] **RUISLIP, NORTHWOOD AND EASTCOTE LOCAL HISTORY SOCIETY**. *Secretary*: Mrs Eileen Watling, 7 The Greenway, Ickenham, Middx UB10 8LS, *Tel*: (01895) 673534. Monthly meetings, visits and walks.
Recent publications: 1992: *The three 'R's in Ruislip*; (on the history of the schools in the old parish of Ruislip); 1996: *Highways and byways* (10 walks round historic Ruislip, Northwood and Eastcote).

Articles in the Society's journal, 1993-8:

1993: The Rickmansworth-Pinner turnpike; Graffiti in St Martin's Church; Struck by lightning; Powick Bridge; Harry Edgell and his commemorative window; The Roumieu's; Methodism; Childhood memories; Northwood Hills 1930's and 40's; A rediscovered sand mine in Northwood.

1994: Eastcote Grange: report on the fabric; St Martin's church: the reredos and chancel East window; The head and the quadruped (wall paintings); Some Ruislip cases in the Court of Requests; Home Farm, Ickenham; Ruislip war memorial; Ruislip cottagers' Allotments Charity.

1995: The Ship public house, Ickenham; John Kirton, 17th century tilemaker; The end of hostilities in Eastcote; Field End Farm, Eastcote; The distressed areas; Remembering a raid some 50 years ago; The war comes to St Martin's Approach, Ruislip; From blacksmith's cottage to village tea rooms; A windmill on Haste Hill; The donkey tale; Highgrove and Hume-Campbell's: the east window in St Martin's Church.

1996: Ickenham Manor moat; The Gawdy papers; Mad Bess and a local wood; The nave west window in St Martin's Church; Scout camp in Ruislip in 1915; Many-quartered coats of arms; Scout chapel in Mad Bess Wood; The American base, South Ruislip 1949-72; The Oerlikon Gun Factory, Ruislip Gardens; Four Maintenance Unit and RAF records; Griffinhurst.

1997: W.A. Telling and the development of the Grange Estate, Northwood; The changing face of The Fells; Hilliard Road, Northwood: the early years; Charms Hall and the Decharms family in Ruislip; A cottage at Eastcote 1835; Memories of a Hole by the Lido; Ian Tait 1909-97; Reminiscences of Coteford; The soldier-saints and two wheat sheaves: more St Martin's stained glass; Update on St Martin's 19th century stained glass.

1998: Archaeological discoveries at Manor Farm; An archaeological survey in Bury Street: April 1998; Ruislip in 1841; The story of Ruislip Common water pumping station and its curious aftermath; St Martin's chancel south window; Memories of Acre Way; Kenneth James McBean 1912-98; Munitions in Ruislip during the First World War; The stone cross at the Grange, Northwood; The Horn End fete; Ruislip Bowls club: the early years 1911-1924; John and Paul Rowe of Northwood.

[542] **UXBRIDGE LOCAL HISTORY AND ARCHIVES SOCIETY**. *Membership secretary*: P. Dengel, 8 High Beeches, Gerrards Cross, Bucks SL9 7HU, *Tel*: (01753) 880000. *Chairman*: K.R. Pearce, 29 Norton Road, Uxbridge UB8 2PT. Est. in 1949. The society meets monthly from September to May and arranges outings to places of historic interest in the summer.

A recent publication is *Moviemania: memories of an Uxbridge cinemagoer*, by James Skinner, 36pp, illus.

K.R. Pearce, is the author of *Uxbridge at war 1939-1945*, published by the society; and of *Uxbridge, Hillingdon and Cowley in old photographs*, from Sutton; a second collection of photographs from Sutton *Uxbridge people* is forthcoming.

Recent issues of the journal the *Uxbridge Record* have contained the following articles:

No 62, Spring 1994: Kirby Bros. Ltd. 1939-1971.

No 63, Autumn 1994: The Place, Uxbridge and its owners up to the Civil War.

No 64, Spring 1995: Trams, trolleybuses and buses in the area (part 1); The Uxbridge spitfire. *No 65, Autumn 1995*: Trams, trolleybuses and buses (2); Centenary of cinematography. *No 66, Spring 1996*: Trams, trolleybuses and buses (3). *No 67, Autumn 1996*: Autobiography of Cyril Pheby. *No 68, Spring 1997*: Trouble in Uxbridge in 1633. *No. 69, Autumn 1997*: The Beach family. *No 70, Spring 2998*: Memories of the '20's; Cowley Mill Road. *No 71, Autumn 1998*: Frays River and Cowley Hall Mill; The Tomlinson family.

[543] **WEST DRAYTON & DISTRICT LOCAL HISTORY SOCIETY**. *Secretary*: Peter Furness, 86 Castle Avenue, Yiewsley, West Drayton, Middx UB7 8LQ, *Tel*: (01895) 444246. Another contact (Treasurer and curator): Dr R.T. Smith, 36 Church Road, West Drayton, Middx UB7 7PX, *Tel*: (01895) 442610. Est. in 1949, currently with some 100 members. A journal is issued twice a year. There have been no new publications in the 1990's, but the following are still available:

Before and after Domesday, 1986, (a chronology of Harmondsworth, West Drayton and Yiewsley), by Miss M.M. Swatton; *Post H remembered*, 1989 (a tribute to the air raid wardens of World War II), also by Miss M.M. Swatton (now deceased); *A Yiewsley benefactor*: the story of B.S. Liddall, 1833-1894. by A.H. Cox (now deceased), 1974.

M.M. Swatton also edited a book on *Victorian Cookery*, published in 1987.

* SOME OTHER COUNCIL CONTACTS *

Agenda 21: Dennis Judge, Civic Centre, High Street, Uxbridge UB8 1UW, *Tel*: (01895) 250111, ext. 7521.

Arts: Contact: Joan Gallacher, at Central Library, Uxbridge, ext. 3711.

A business directory for Hillingdon is produced regularly by the Economic Development Unit; contact: Ron Dane, Civic Centre, ext. 7513.

Conservation areas/listed buildings: Jon Finney, principal architect/planner, Civic Centre, High Street, Uxbridge UB8 1UW, *Tel*: (01895) 250111, ext. 3536. There are 25 conservation areas. Publications on the areas and on listed buildings are in preparation.

Nature conservation/ecology: Colin Eastman, ext. 3620. A leaflet on nature reserves in the borough is issued; another contact: Colin Roome, recreation/education department, ext. 3456. A new River Pinn walk (from Pinner Station to Cowley) is in preparation.

Reference Library: Central Library, 14-15 High Street, Uxbridge UB8 1HD, *Tel*: (01895) 250600. Lists of historical societies; and of environmental societies (includes nature reserves, and members of the Hillingdon Conservation Council, chairmen of the 10 conservation area advisory panels) are issued.

* SOME NON-COUNCIL CONTACTS *

Voluntary organisations:

HILLINGDON ASSOCIATION OF VOLUNTARY ORGANISATIONS. 1st Floor, Kirk House, 97-109 High Street, Yiewsley UB7 7HJ, *Tel*: (01895) 442722.

* LOCAL PRESS *

Uxbridge Gazette (four editions), Gazette House, 2nd Floor, 28 Bakers Road, Uxbridge UB8 1RG, *Tel*: (01895) 451000. Also two free papers *The Informer* and *The Leader*.

Hillingdon People, published bi-monthly by Hillingdon Council, editor: Toni McConville, Civic Centre, ext. 3530.

HOUNSLOW

* LONDON BOROUGH OF HOUNSLOW *

[544] Two local studies collections are maintained, at Hounslow and Chiswick:

Hounslow Library, 24 Treaty Centre, High Street, Hounslow TW3 1ES, *Tel*: (020) 8570 0622, ext. 7879; *Fax*: (020) 8569 4330. *Hours*: Mon, Wed, Fri, Sat 9-5.30; Tues, Thurs 9.30-8. *Assistant Librarian*: James Marshall (author of *History of the Great West Road*, 1995). Andrea Cameron is now retiring after many years service. In 1995 Phillimore published her *Hounslow, Isleworth, Heston and Cranford: a pictorial history*. She has been especially active in the Hounslow and District History Society.

Chiswick Area Library, Duke's Avenue, London W4 2AB, *Tel*: (020) 8994 1008. *Local studies Librarian*: Carolyn Hammond. *Hours*: Mon, Thurs 9.30-8; Tues, Fri, Sat 9.30-5.30; Wed closed.

Carolyn Hammond is the author of *Chiswick library: 100 years service to the community*, published in 1991 by Hounslow Council; and with her husband Peter Hammond she compiled two collections of old photographs for Tempus: *Chiswick* and *Brentford*.

Chiswick and Brentford, compiled by Patrick Loobey is from Sutton Publishing.

Recent publications from Heritage Publications (Hounslow Leisure Services):

1994: MAXWELL, Gordon S. *Highwayman's Heath*. 413pp. illus. Reissue of book first published in 1935 by Thomason Ltd (Hounslow Chronicle).

1995: MARSHALL, James. *History of the Great West Road*. 112pp. illus.

1995: *Reminiscences of the Afro-Caribbean community in Hounslow*. 30pp.

1996: *Reminiscences of the Asian community in Hounslow*. 40pp. Both edited by Neil Chippendale.

1997: Portfolio of Hogarth prints illustrating 'Hudibras'. (The library owns the plates).

Non-book material:

Maps: Moser Glover, Map of the manor of Isleworth-Syon 1635; Growth of Feltham 1827-1934; Norden/Speed map of Middlesex 1610.

Videos: Hounslow in World Ward II; coronation of HM Queen Elizabeth (programme of events in the Borough of Heston & Isleworth); Bygone West Middlesex.

There is a range of postcards featuring historic properties, including Chiswick House, The Chiswick Empire, Boston Manor and Hogarth's House.

The local studies libraries sell a range of publications from societies, commercial publishers and authors.

Publications from Hounslow Council, still available, include:

And so a city make here, by G.E. Bate, 1990 (reprint of book published n 1948 on the history of most of Hounslow); *Chiswick*, by Warwick Draper (1973 edition, reissued, 1990); *On Q: Jack and Beatie de Leon and the Q Theatre*, by Kenneth Barrow, 1992.

Collections of old photographs published in the 1970's and 1980's in collaboration with Hendon Publishing Co. are still available: *Brentford and Chiswick as it was*, 1978; *Brentford as it was*, 1983; *Chiswick as it was*, 1986; *Hounslow as it was*, 1977; *Isleworth as it was*, 1982; *Looking back at Hounslow High Street*, 1984; *Old photographs of Bedfont, Feltham and Hanworth*, 1980.

Looking back: a personal look at S.W. Middlesex is a collection of articles by Eddie Menday first published in the Middlesex Chronicle, published in 1995 by Ad Pontes Books, 59 Woolseley Road, Ashford.

Publications published by their authors include:
3 volumes of autobiography by Sybil Pearce (died 1998, aged 98): *An Edwardian childhood*, 3rd. edn. 1992; *A post Edwardian girlhood*, 1991; *The years between 1919-1939 in Bedford Park*.
The Battle of Turnham Green is a children's colouring booklet published in 1992 by Ian Caddy, (32 Esmond Road, London W4); and *Stamford Brook: an affectionate portrait* is by Shirley Seaton (7 South Side, London W6 0XY - see advert).
Specialist publications include: *Exploring the Thames foreshore in Hounslow*, from the Thames Explorer Trust; *Hanworth Air park 1916-1949*, from Feltham Arts Association and a booklet on *Heston aerodrome*, (Airfield Focus Series No 24), from GMS Enterprises (67 Pyhill, Bretton, Peterborough PE3 8QQ, *Tel*: (01733) 265123.

* TOURISM *

[545a] **HOUNSLOW HERITAGE GUIDES ASSOCIATION.** *Contacts*: Janet McNamara, 31b Brook Road South, Brentford TW8 0NN, *Tel*: (020) 8560 3718; Brian Pett, 12 Farnell Road, Isleworth TW7 6EX, *Tel*: (020) 8230 8583. Est. in 1994 some 30 guides offer 3 walks: in Brentford, Chiswick and Isleworth.

[545b] **HOUNSLOW TOURIST INFORMATION CENTRE**, *Contact*: Helen Evans, The Treaty Centre, High Street, Hounslow TW3 1ES, *Tel*: (020) 8572 8279; *Fax*: (020) 8569 4330. A visitor and accommodation guide is issued.

* HISTORIC PROPERTIES AND VISITOR ATTRACTIONS *

[546] **BOSTON MANOR HOUSE.** Boston Manor Road, Brentford, Middx TW8 9JX, *Tel*: (020) 8560 5441. Jacobean manor hose, built in 1623, run by the London Borough of Hounslow. *Hours*: April-October, Sat, Sun, bank holidays only 2.30-5. Short guide issued (written by Janet McNamara). Famous for its plaster ceilings in the state room on the first floor. The ground floor rooms date from the early 19th century and house part of the local collection of paintings.

[547] **CHISWICK HOUSE.** Burlington Lane, Chiswick, London W4 2RP, *Tel*: (020) 8995 0508. An English Heritage property, (grounds owned by London Borough of Hounslow). *Hours*: winter 10-4, Wed-Sun; summer 10-1; 2-6. daily. Important 18th century Palladian villa; ground floor exhibition on the evolution of house and gardens. Guide book published. There is a Friends organisation CHISWICK HOUSE FRIENDS, *Secretary*: John Armstrong, 76 Duke's Avenue, London W4 2AS, *Tel*: (020) 8994 0685. Est. in 1984 it assists and supports the bodies responsible for the restoration, conservation, preservation, enhancement and protection of the building, statues and grounds for the benefit of the public.

[548] **FULLER, SMITH AND TURNER PLC - GRIFFIN BREWERY.** Chiswick, London W4 2QB, *Tel*: (020) 8996 2063. Tours are held on Mon, Wed, Thurs, Fri, and start promptly at 11, 12, 1 and 2.

[549] **HEATHROW AIRPORT VISITOR CENTRE.** Newall Road, off Bath Road, *Tel*: (020) 8745 6655. *Hours*: Mon-Fri. 10-7; Sat-Sun. 10-5.

[550] **HOGARTH'S HOUSE.** Hogarth Lane, Great West Road, London W4 2QN, *Tel*: (020) 8994 6757. *Hours*: Winter: Tues-Fri. 1-4.30. Sat-Sun. 1-5. Summer: Tues-Fri. 1-5; Sat-Sun. 1-6. Managed by the London Borough of Hounslow. The home of William Hogarth from 1749 to 1764. Permanent exhibition of some of his most famous engravings; also reproductions of paintings and interpretation panels. Guide book issued.

[551] **HOUNSLOW URBAN FARM.** Faggs Road, Feltham, Middx, *Tel*: (020) 8751 0950. *Hours*: Feb-Oct. 10-4. Opened in 1990. In 1995 the farm became an approved Rare Breeds Centre (the only one of its kind in Greater London).

[552] **OSTERLEY PARK HOUSE**. Osterley, Middx TW7 4RB, *Tel*: (020) 8560 3918. *Hours*: 1-5, Wed-Sat, 11-5; Sun and bank holidays 11-5; April-October.
National Trust, 18th century property set in 140 acres park.
There is a Friends organisation, *Membership secretary*: Mrs Audrey Ebison, 341 Jersey Road, Osterley, Middx TW7 5PJ, *Tel*: (020) 8560 6313; *Chairman*: Ian Conacher *Tel*: (020) 8560 8523. Est. in 1991, and since then the Friends have raised over £10,000 for projects in the house and grounds. There are special events and winter lectures at the house.

[553] **SYON HOUSE**, Syon Park, Brentford, Middx TW8 8JP, *Tel*: (020) 8560 0881. *Hours*: weekends and bank holidays, April-Sept. 11-5. Owned by the Duke of Norhumberland. Tudor house, with important collection of 17th and 18th century paintings.

* HISTORICAL AND AMENITY SOCIETIES *

[554] **BEDFORD PARK SOCIETY** (for the protection of the amenities of the earliest Garden Suburb). *Secretary*: Ruth Levy, Kara Lodge Studio, 14 Newton Grove, London W4 1LB, *Chairman*: Peter Eversden, 40 Abinger Road, London W4 1EX, *Tel/Fax*: (020) 8747 3281.
The Society has published: *Bedford Park houses: the care and protection of our architectural heritage*, 1987, by Ailwyn Best; *Gardening in Bedford Park*, 1988, by Fenja Anderson; and *Guide to Bedford park in the form of two walks*, 3rd edition, 1990, by Tom Greeves.
Tom Greeves was an architect/draughtsman; he died in 1997. Ann Bingley published his book *Bedford Park: the first garden suburb, a pictorial survey* in 1975. His book of drawings *Ruined cities of the imagination* was published by Images Publishing (Malvern) in 1994.

Lawrence Duttson (80 Esmond Road, London W4 1JF, *Tel*: (020) 8994 0409) researches and publishes on Bedford Park. His *Mainly about Bedford Park* is concerned with local residents. He is currently working on a history of Bedford House, and of the Bedford family

[555] **BRENTFORD & CHISWICK LOCAL HISTORY SOCIETY**. *Secretary*: Miss Mary E. King, 21 Homecross House, Fisher's Lane, Chiswick, London W4 1YA, *Tel*: (020) 8994 8257. *Membership secretary*: Miss Catharine Owst, 44 Oliver Close, Chiswick, London W4 3RL, *Tel*: (020) 8994 6814. *Journal editor*: Gillian Clegg, 4 Quick Road, London W4 2BU, *Tel*: (020) 8995 5333. *Chairman*: James Wisdom, 22 Hartington Road, London W4 3TL, *Tel*: (020) 8994 4231.
Nos 1-4 of the journal were produced 1980-1985; Nos 5-8 dates from the 1990's;
No 5, 1996: The Battle of Brentford, 1642; Linoleum: a Chiswick invention; Did Jack the Ripper die in Chiswick? The Thames Soapworks of Brentford; Patsy Hendren, Chiswick's famous cricketer; Lieut.Col. Shipway's pedigree; The Church of England Records Centre.
No 6, 1997: Camille Pissarro: paintings of Stamford Brook; A history of Brentford Bridge; Postboxes in W4; How Chiswick celebrated the 1897 Jubilee; The Great West Road then and now; Brentford's jewel: Boston Manor House; The estates around Chiswick House; Homes for the workers: Chiswick New Town; The first Chiswick golf club.
No 7, 1998: The Morice letters; Thomas Griffiths Wainewright; Mr Young of Young's Corner; An American President in Brentford; William Sargeant, Chiswick boatbuilder, electrical engineer and architect; The Royal Victoria Asylum in Chiswick; The Corona Stage Academy; Tracing Colonel Shipway's pedigree.
No 8, 1999: John Ranby and his house; Chiswick Library: the move to Duke's Avenue; A royal wedding day in Brentford; Chiswick's cinemas; Law and order in New Brentford; The Chiswick workhouse; Zoffany in Chiswick and Brentford.

Gillian Clegg is editor of LAMAS Transactions; and author of *Chiswick Past*, 1995; and *Clapham past*, 1998, both from Historical Publications.

Two Brentford walks have been compiled and published by Greater London Industrial Archaeology Society: *New Brentford & Grand Union Canal Walks*: and *Old Brentford and the River Thames walk*.

[556] **BUTTS SOCIETY**. *Secretary*: Michele Tinker, The Gables, 1 Brent Road, The Butts Estate, Brentford, Middx TW8 8BP, *Tel*: (020) 8560 2286; *Fax*: (020) 8568 8233. *Chairman*: Christopher Richardson, 16 The Butts, Brentford, *Tel*: (020) 8560 5764. Est. in 1960 to involve local residents with the preservation and protection of the conservation area located to the north of Brentford High Street, east of the River Brent. The houses represent some of the oldest in the borough of Hounslow dating back to the early 18th century. Current membership about 100. Newsletter issued.

Chiswick :

[557] **BURLINGTON LANE RESIDENTS ASSOCIATION**. *Secretary*: Hans Danziger, 44 Burlington Lane, London W4.

[558] **CHISWICK PROTECTION GROUP**, *Secretary*: Peter Eversden, 40 Abinger Road, London W4 1EX, *Tel*: (020) 8747 3281. A forum for some 14 Chiswick amenity and residents' associations.

[559] **EAST CHISWICK RESIDENTS ASSOCIATION**. *Secretary*: Lou Brown, 8 Netheravon Road, London W4.

[560] **OLD CHISWICK PROTECTION SOCIETY**. *Current secretary*: (changing 1999): Katherine Bull, Strawberry House, Chiswick Mall, London W4. Est. in 1957, the society's interests include the amenities of the River Thames and Chiswick Eyot preservation and planning, conservation of trees, road and traffic problems and flood defences. Conservation work in the churchyard of St Nicholas Parish Church (guide book published in 1998) has concentrated on restoration of some of the listed tombs: of P.J. de Loutherbourg, designed by Sir John Soane for his artist friend, of James McNeill Whistler, and the Earl of Burlington's bricklayer.
In 1991 Hounslow Council published a history trail *Worlds apart*, (with contributions from the OCPS) linking Hogarth's House and Chiswick House via old Chiswick; and in 1998 the society published a new edition of *Life and work in old Chiswick* by Humphrey Arthure (a perambulation of the riverside area - Church Street and Chiswick Mall.

Another Chiswick author is William Roe (14 Alwyn Avenue, Chiswick, W4 4PB). He has published himself two books: *Glimpses of Chiswick's place in history*; and *Glimpses of Chiswick's development* (reveiwed in the Times, February 5, 1999). The latter includes some local scenes painted by the author. (He worked for a surveying firm for 50 years).

[561] **GROVE PARK GROUP**. *Secretary*: Mr D.J. Webber, 26 Kinnaird Avenue, London W4 3SH, *Tel*: (020) 8994 2913. Est. in 1972, currently with some 600 members, it covers the area in South Chiswick bounded by the A4, A316, River Thames and Kew Bridge. There is an annual local history lecture.

[562] **HOUNSLOW AND DISTRICT HISTORY SOCIETY**. *Secretary*: Mrs M. Lodge, Albertine, Manor House Court, Shepperton, Middx TW17 9JS, *Tel*: (01932) 245688. *Membership secretary*: Mrs P. Cox, 142 Guildford Avenue, Feltham, Middx TW13 4EL, *Tel*: (020) 8890 4739. Est. in 1960 to promote the study of, and stimulate interest in, the history of Hounslow and the surrounding areas, formerly covered by Hounslow Heath; also to preserve old buildings, graveyards and open spaces. Specialist publications have been issued since 1964, and include: *Business and trade in High Street, Hounslow 1803-1982*, by Susan Higlett; *The history of Hounslow Manor and the Bulstrode family,* 1980, by Gillian Morris; *The history of the Royal Manor of Hanworth*, 1979, by Andrea Cameron; *History of the Spring Grove*, 1983, by Gillian Morris; and *One hundred years of art and further education in Bedford Park, Chiswick 1881-1981*, published in 1982.
In 1987 the Bedfont Research Group published *Bedfont: an outline history of the parish of East Bedfont with Hatton.* In 1988 *Bygone Feltham*, by Kenneth Baldwin was published.
In 1990 *Sarah Trimmer of Brentford and her children with some of her early writings, 1780-1786* by Dorris M. Yarde was published (she was responsible for setting up the first industrial training school); and in 1996 *A family business*, 56pp, illus. by Geoff Thomason, on his family's newspaper enterprise (The Hounslow Chronicle).

[563] **ISLEWORTH SOCIETY**. (previously Isleworth Civic Trust). *Secretary*: John Daniels, 48 Algar Road, Isleworth, Middx, *Tel*: (020) 8568 3378. Preservation, protection and enhancement of the Isleworth Riverside Conservation Area and environs.

Mary and Kevin Brown are the compilers of two collections of old photographs *Isleworth,* 1995 and 1998 from Tempus.

Other booklets on Isleworth include: two school histories: *The first 200 years of the Green School*, Isleworth (Busch Close), by Wendy Mott, 1996; and *Isleworth Blue School* by Gillian Morris, 1986/7.
Isleworth: a guide and some of its history edited by Martin Jenkins was published by the Isleworth Community Council in 1991; and *Isleworth thro' 4000 years*, by Andrea Cameron was published by All Saint's Church, Isleworth in 1983.

[564] **STRAND-ON-THE-GREEN ASSOCIATION**. *Secretary*: John Ormsby, 70 Strand-on-the-Green, London W4, *Tel*: (020) 8995 0890. *Email* ormsby@cwcom.net. Has some 140 members. Two newsletters issued annually.

* SOME OTHER COUNCIL CONTACTS *

Businesses in Hounslow are listed in an on-line/database directory, contact: Chris Rowlinson, Economic Development Department, *Tel*: (020) 8862 5976.

Conservation areas/listed buildings: Andrew Dick, Principal conservation area officer, Civic Centre, Lampton Road, Hounslow TW3 3DW, *Tel*: (020) 8862 5234. Publications include: ring binder on conservation areas; *Statutory list of buildings of special architectural or historic interest.*

Nature conservation: Stephen McAndrew. Ecologist, environmental co-ordinator, (ecology of private land), *Tel*: (020) 8862 5973.

Tom Keatley, *Tel*: (020) 8862 5859, for public parks and open spaces.

Hounslow Heath nature reserve: *Tel*: (020) 8577 3664; Bedfont Lakes Country Park, *Tel*: (01784) 423556.

Wide range of leaflets issued.

Reference libraries: reference and lending stock are 'integrated' at Hounslow Library; there is a separate reference department at Chiswick Library, *Tel*: (020) 8994 5295. The 'Viewdata' computerised information system covers community organisations of all kinds.

* SOME NON-COUNCIL CONTACTS *

Arts:

Arts and Events (part of independent Community Initiatives Partnerships Ltd), Contact: Philip Butterworth, Chiswick Town Hall, *Tel*: (020) 8862 6567.

Festivals include the May Isleworth Festival, (classical music, jazz), and the summer time Chiswick Festival, music, film, using the amphitheatre in Chiswick House grounds.

Voluntary organisations.
HOUNSLOW VOLUNTEERS BUREAU, Civic Centre, Hounslow, *Tel*: (020) 8570 8630.

* LOCAL PRESS *

Brentford, Chiswick and Isleworth Times, 13-14 King Street, Richmond TW9 1LF, *Tel*: (020) 8940 6030.
The Chronicle; The Informer; The Leader (last two are free). 93 Staines Road, Hounslow TW3 3JB, *Tel*: (020) 8572 1816.
Feltham Leader, free paper. 11 The High Street, Egham TW20 9HP.
Heathrow Villager, free paper, 260 Kingston Road, Staines TW18 5PG, *Tel*: (01784) 453196.
Your Hounslow, quarterly Council magazine, edited by Simon Caplan, Civic Centre, Lampton Road, Hounslow, *Tel*: (020) 8862 5021.

KINGSTON UPON THAMES

* ROYAL BOROUGH OF KINGSTON UPON THAMES *

[565] **KINGSTON LOCAL HISTORY ROOM.** *Local history officer*: Tim Everson. *Archivist*: Jill Lamb. North Kingston Centre, Richmond Road, Kingston upon Thames, Surrey KT2 5PE, *Tel*: (020) 8547 6738; *Fax*: (020) 8547 6747. *Hours*: Mon-Fri 10-5; Tues 10-7.

Tim Everson, with wife Shaan Butters (a counsellor) is currently working on a history of faith in Kingston (emphasis on Christianity). Shaan Butters is the author of *The Book of Kingston*, 1994, 192pp, published by Baron-Birch. Kingston University has created a database on 19th century Kingston (based on the holdings of the local history collection, where it can be accessed).

The Brill Collection is a small collection of some 70-80 water-colours of Kingston, post 1955 mainly by students from the college.

A Borough Archives Guide is available.

No recent publications, but a number from the museum and heritage service are still in print, see below.

[566] **KINGSTON MUSEUM AND HERITAGE SERVICE.** *Heritage officer*: Anne McCormack. *Collections manager*: Paul Hill. Wheatfield Way, Kingston upon Thames, Surrey KT1 2PS, *Tel*: (020) 8546 5386. *Email*: king.mus@rbk.kingston.gov.uk. *Hours*: Mon-Sat 10-5; closed Wed. The museum reopened fully in 1996 after refurbishment. It has a new Town of Kings gallery (from the Anglo Saxon period to the 20th century), and a new Eadweard Muybridge gallery (a pioneer of early motion photography, he was born and died in Kingston). The exhibition catalogue is available, and there is also a Museum of the Moving Image publication *Muybridge and the chronophotographers*. There is a museum shop. A quarterly newsletter is issued.

There is a Friends organisation, est. in 1992 contactable at the above address, concerned with fund raising and providing volunteer help. There is also a lecture programme. For membership, *Tel*: (020) 8399 3009.

[567] **KINGSTON UPON THAMES TOURIST INFORMATION CENTRE**. Market House, Kingston upon Thames, *Tel*: 9020) 8547 5592. *Hours*: Mon-Fri 10-5; Sat 9-4.

Publications from a wide range of sources, publishers and individuals are sold both at the library and the museum.
Publications from the museum and heritage service, still in print, include *Royal Kingston*, 1988, by Anne McCormack and Marion Shipley; *Kingston upon Thames, a pictorial history*, 1989, Phillimore, also by Anne McCormack; *Kingston's kings 900-1016* a colouring book, and a teachers' handbook, both by Paul Hill published in 1991. *The Queen in Kingston*, 1992, by Anne McCormack is on Queen Elizabeth II's visits to Kingston.
Scandal on the corporation: royalists and puritans in mid 17th century Kingston, from the Kingston Borough Archives, was published in 1982.
How we worked is a collection of oral history transcripts, published in 1989 by the Royal Borough of Kingston with the Manpower Services Commission.

Commercial publishers:
Histories from Historical Publications: *Kingston past*, 1997, by June Sampson; and *Surbiton past*, 1996, by Richard Statham, (former education officer with Kingston M. & H. Service).
From Sutton Publishing: *Kingston, Surbiton and Malden in old photographs*, compiled by Tim Everson.
Marine Day publisher is the imprint of Mr A.G. Durrant (64 Cotterill Road, Surbiton, Surrey, KT6 7UN, *Tel*: (020) 8399 7625. His Marine Press is a book design and print consultancy. Titles currently available are: *All change*, by June Sampson; *Kingston and Surbiton; old and new*, by June Sampson; *Malden, old and new: a pictorial history* and *Malden old and new revisited*, a second pictorial history, both by Stephen H. Day.
Mysterious Kingston, and *Strange Kingston*, both by B. & T. Russell are published by Twilight Books (11 Mina Road, Wimbledon, London, SW19).
Two publications from the Kingston Numismatic Society available are: *A notable emission for Kingston* (on a bank note), 1994, and *A numismatic history of Kingston*, 1997, both by Norman Clarkson.

Author/Publishers:
From Mark Davison (77 Rickman Hill, Coulsdon, Surrey CR5 3DT, *Tel*: (01737) 221215): *Hook remembered*; *Long Ditton remembered*; *Surrey in the Seventies*.
From John Pink (St Ann's Court, Grove Road, Surbiton KT6 4BE): *Britons never will be slaves*: grievances aired by domestic servants in Kingston and Surbiton in 1872, 1997; *The excise officers and their duties in an English market town: Kingston upon Thames 1643-1973*, 1996 and *On strike: an account of Kingston, Surbiton and Norbiton washerwomen's strike of 1872*, 1996.
Spring Grove: birth of a community by Isobel Robinson (wife of David Robinson, Surrey Archivist), 1997. (Spring Grove is a Victorian estate area in South Kingston).

Church and School histories:
Church histories include: *History of Kingston parish Church* (all Saints), by Leonard W. Cowie; and *St Peter's, Norbiton*, by Shaan Butters (wife of Tim Everson).
St Paul's Church, Hook is the publisher of *Hook in Kingston* by Marion Bone.
Kingston Quakers, by John Fulford was published by the author in 1973.
Two school histories are currently in preparation: for Kingston Grammar School (by Rev. David Ward), and for Tiffin Girls' School.

* AMENITY AND HISTORICAL SOCIETIES *

[568] **KINGSTON UPON THAMES ARCHAEOLOGICAL SOCIETY**. *Contact*: Richard Watson, 14 Willow Way, Ewell, Surrey KT19 0EH. Meetings and talks; weekend surveying and field walking; some local excavations, processing of finds; visits; quarterly newsletter.

[569] **KINGSTON UPON THAMES SOCIETY**. *Programme secretary*: Philippa Hussey, Vane House, Warren Rise, New Malden KT3 4SJ, *Tel*: (020) 8942 7930. *Treasurer/Membership*: Douglas Ambrose, 9 The Crest, Surbiton KT5 8JZ, *Tel*: (020) 8399 2803. *Chair*: Sylvia Blanc, 19 Henley Drive, Coombe Hill, Kingston KT2 7ED, *Tel*: (020) 8942 1296. *Vice-chairman/editor*: Tony Leitch, 66 St Albans Road, Kingston KT2 5HH, *Tel*: (020) 8546 9216.
Deals with 'matters of planning, preservation, conservation and design'. Meetings, visits.

A newsletter *Kingston news* is issued three times a year. There are three attractive guided walks: *Kingston upon Thames: a walker's guide to the history and architecture of the Royal Borough's town centre*; *The Hogsmill: the nature and history of a Surrey stream*; and *Richmond Park: an illustrated pocket guide to the history, architecture and wildlife of the Royal Park at Richmond.*
A *Hogsmill Safari* leaflet is also published by the Surrey Wildlife Trust.

[570] **MALDEN AND COOMBE CIVIC SOCIETY.** *Secretary*: Mrs M.J. Soole, 19 Woodside Road, New Malden, Surrey, *Tel*: (020) 8942 5148. *Membership secretary*: Mr W.G.I. Warner, 93 Bodley Road, New Malden, Surrey FT3 5QJ, *Tel*: (020) 8949 0402. Est. in 1944, currently some 600 members. It aims 'to encourage all citizens of Malden and Coombe to take an active interest in local affairs, and aims to preserve and enhance the amenities of our locality'. There are exhibitions and lectures, visits and a very active social programme is organised. A newsletter is issued and in 1994 a booklet *Fifty years in Malden: civic society and town 1944-1994* was published, 88pp with a bibliography and index.

[571] **SURBITON AND DISTRICT HISTORICAL SOCIETY.** *Secretary*: Mrs Ann Glover, 3 Northcliffe Close, Worcester Park, Surrey KT4 7DS, *Tel*: (020) 8330 0339. Est. in 1955. Monthly meetings, lectures on varied topics, weekend outings. Monthly newsletter. Own local history library.

* SOME OTHER COUNCIL CONTACTS *

Arts development officer: Colin Bloxham, *Tel*: (020) 8547 6416.
A business directory is produced regularly by the Council in collaboration with the local chamber of commerce; Contact: John Mumford, Environmental Services, *Tel*: (020) 8547 4695.
Conservation/listed buildings: Martin Higgins, Guildhall, Kingston upon Thames KT1 1EU, *Tel*: (020) 8547 4706.
Nature Conservation: Andy Watson, Senior tree and landscape officer, *Tel*: (020) 8547 5569.
Reference Library: a reference collection is held at Kingston Library, Fairfield Road, *Tel*: (020) 8547 6402.

* SOME NON-COUNCIL CONTACTS *

Voluntary organisations:
KINGSTON UPON THAMES VOLUNTARY ACTION. Siddeley House, 50 Canbury Park Road, Kingston KT2 6TX, *Tel*: (020) 8255 3335.

* LOCAL PRESS *

Kingston Guardian, (free newspaper); and *Surrey Commet* from: 26 York Road, Twickenham TW1 3LT, *Tel*: (020) 8744 9977.
Kingston Informer, (free newspaper). Informer House, 2 High Street, Teddington TW11 8EW, *Tel*: (020) 8943 5171.
Kingston, Surbiton and New Malden Times, Kimberley Group, 144 High Street, Wandsworth SW18 4TT, *Tel*: (020) 9874 4226.

RICHMOND

* LONDON BOROUGH OF RICHMOND UPON THAMES *

[572] There are two local history collections:
The Albert Barkas Room for local Studies, Central Reference Library, Old Town Hall, Whittaker Avenue, Richmond TW9 1TP, *Tel*: (020) 8332 6820, covers: Barnes, East Sheen, Ham, Kew, Mortlake, Petersham, Richmond (former boroughs of Barnes and Richmond). *Librarian*: Jane Baxter, *Assistant*: Chris Turfitt. *Hours*: Mon closed; Tues 1-5; Wed 1-8; Thurs, Fri 1-6; Sats. 2nd, 4th (5th) Saturday in the month 10-12.30, 1.30-5.
The Twickenham Local Collections is at: District Library, Garfield Road, Twickenham TW9 3JS, *Tel*: (020) 8891 7271, and covers the Hamptons, Teddington, Twickenham and Whitton (former borough of Twickenham). *Hours*: Mon 1-6; Tues 1-8; Wed 1-5; Thurs closed; Fri 1-6; Sats: 1st and 3rd Saturdays in each month 10-12, 1-5.

[573] **TOURIST INFORMATION/BOROUGH INFORMATION CENTRE.** *Contact*; Flavia Gapper, Old Town Hall, Whittaker Avenue, Richmond, *Tel*: (020) 8940 9125. *Hours*: 10-6 Mon-Sat; Sun. (summer months) 10.15-4.15.

The council's Tourism Development Office is at: Langholm Lodge, Petersham Road, Richmond, *Tel*: (020) 8332 2191. *Contact*: Jacki Ellis. A new leaflet guide to attractions (with L.B. of Hounslow) is in preparation.

* MUSEUMS *

KEW BRIDGE STEAM MUSEUM: see entry 597.

[574] **MUSEUM OF RICHMOND**. Old Town Hall, Whittaker Avenue, Richmond TW9 1TP, *Tel*: (020) 8332 1141. *Fax*: (020) 8332 1141. *Curator*: Simon Lace. *Assistant*: Caroline Fallis. *Hours*: Tues-Sat 11-5. Sun 1-4 during summer. The museum was set up in 1988 and tells the story of Richmond, Ham, Petersham and Kew from pre-historic times to the present day. Special features include detailed models of Richmond Palace and Shere Charterhouse, two significant buildings in Richmond's medieval history. There are displays on the river, the parks, theatres and Richmond's many famous residents. There is a programme of temporary exhibitions and local artists of the past are often featured. A newspaper the *Museum Herald* is issued. The newsletter of the Richmond Society, No 176, Winter 1998 has an article on the museum. It needs new premises, and may move into the disused United Reformed Church building on the Green.
There is a Friends organisation, which helps with fund raising and provides volunteers. *Secretary*: Jean McKinnon, 229 Hospital Bridge Road, Whitton TW2 7AA, *Tel*: (020) 8755 0259.

[575] **MUSEUM OF RUGBY/RUGBY FOOTBALL UNION**, Twickenham. Rugby Road, Twickenham, *Tel*: (020) 8892 2000. There are guided tours/behind the scenes visits Tues-Sat 10.30-5, and Sun 2-5.

[576] **ORLEANS HOUSE GALLERY**. *Curator*: Jane Dalton, Assistant: Rachel Tranter. Riverside, Middx TW1 3DJ, *Tel*: (020) 8892 0221. Houses the permanent topographical collection (some 2,000 items) of Richmond views. A catalogue is planned. There are also temporary exhibitions.

* ARCHAEOLOGY *

[577] **RICHMOND ARCHAEOLOGICAL SOCIETY**. *Membership Secretary*: Joan Samuel, 5 Grove Terrace, Teddington TW11 8AU, *Tel*: (020) 8977 3075. Monthly meetings with lectures by archaeologists.

* ENVIRONMENT *

[578a] **ENVIRONMENT TRUST FOR RICHMOND UPON THAMES**. *Administrator*: Greta Attley, 55 Heath Road, Twickenham, *Tel*: (020) 8891 5455. *Hours*: weekdays, about 10-2.

Also at the above address: [578b] **RICHMOND ENVIRONMENTAL INFORMATION CENTRE**, *Administrator*: Sarah Bailey, *Tel*: (020) 8891 2930. Part-time, mornings only.
The Richmond Environmental Forum (contact: Terry Mills, 26 Chelsea Close, Hampton Hill, *Tel*: (020) 8783 1264) and the Riverside Forum meet here.

* HISTORICAL AND AMENITY SOCIETIES * (arranged by locality)

Barnes and Mortlake :
[579] **BARNES AND MORTLAKE HISTORY SOCIETY**. *Secretary*: Sara Bromfield, 43 Hertford Avenue, East Sheen, London SW14 8EH, *Tel*: (020) 8878 0983. *Membership secretary*: James Smith, 11 Beverley Close, Barnes, London SW13 10EH, *Tel*: (020) 8876 3651. *Chair* Mrs Maisie Brown, 1 Mill Hill Road, Barnes, London SW13 0HR, *Tel*: (020) 8878 1417. Est. in 1955 to promote interest in the local history of Barnes, Mortlake and East Sheen. There are monthly lecture meetings and visits. There is a quarterly newsletter and issues from 1955 to 1990 have been indexed. There are two series of publications: general interest books, and occasional papers, emanating often from lectures.
Books 1993-1996:
1993: FREEMAN, Leslie. *Going to the parish:Mortlake and the parish church of St Mary the Virgin,* 54pp. illus.
1994: *Halfpenny green* (i.e. the Victorian stamp); postcards from Barnes and Mortlake. 96pp.
1996: *Childhood memories of Barnes villages*, by Mary Atwell, edited by Nicholas Dakin.
Other books still available are: *Alleyways of Mortlake and East Sheen*, 1983 by Charles Hailstone (now deceased); *Hammersmith Bridge*, 1987, also by Charles Hailstone; and *Highways and byways of Barnes*, 1992, by Mary Grimwade and Charles Hailstone.
There have been nine occasional papers: 1: *Shopping in Barnes between the two world wars*, 1989 by Mary Grimwade; 2: *Murder and mystery in Barnes and Mortlake*, 1989, by Mary Grimwade and Charles Hailstone; 3: *Barnes and Mortlake people*

in the reign of Charles II, 1989 by Margaret Butler (out of print); 4: *Richmond Park in the seventeenth century*, 1990, by Raymond Gill; 5: *A scientific triad* (on Sir Edwin Chadwick, Sir Richard Owen and Sir Benjamin Ward Richardson) 1990, by Maisie Brown, Henry Shearman and Raymond Gill; 6: *Early working class education in Barnes*, 1992, by Maisie Brown; 7: *The growth of East Sheen in the Victorian era*, 1992, by Raymond Gill; 8: *John Dee: Magus of Mortlake*, 1995, by Dilys Henrik Jones: 9: *Lost properties in Barnes*, 1996, by Mary Grimwade.

Barnes, Mortlake and East Sheen Past, written by members of the society, and edited by Maisie Brown was published by Historical Publications in 1997.

Projects in progress (for publications); Mortlake tapestries (Maisie Brown); Richmond Park during World War II (David Catford); Local pubs (Richard Bushell).

Also available: paintings and prints of local views reproduced as coloured cards.

[580] **BARNES COMMUNITY ASSOCIATION.** *Secretary*: Jenny Martin; *Chair*: Eric Holmberg, Rose House, 70 Barnes High Street, London SW13, *Tel*: (020) 8878 2359.

[581] **FRIENDS OF BARNES COMMON.** *Contact*: Mr J.N. Baker, 1 Cardigan Road, Barnes, London SW13 0BH, *Tel*: (020) 8876 6377.

[582] **FRIENDS OF SHEEN COMMON.** *Secretary*: Judith Harry, 12 Warren Avenue, Richmond TW10 5DZ, *Tel*: (020) 8876 6478. *Chairman*: Ken Baker, 5 Martindale, London SW14 7AL, *Tel*: (020) 8876 2514. Est. in 1932 to work for better management of the Common, owned by the National Trust. A newsletter is issued and November 1998 has an account of the organisation since its revival in July 1988.

[583] **MORTLAKE WITH EAST SHEEN SOCIETY.** *Secretary*: Anne Groom, 15 Park Drive, East Sheen, London SW14 8RB, *Tel*: (020) 8876 4772; *Fax*: (020) 8286 4637. *Chair*: Michael Pearce, 6 Christchurch Road, East Sheen, London SW14 7AN, *Tel*: (020) 8876 2189. Est. in 1996, the society is concerned with preservation and improvement of features of historic interest, new buildings, planning, the natural environment, traffic and road, aircrafts noise and local amenities.

Hampton and Teddington :

[584] **FRIENDS OF BUSHY AND HOME PARKS.** *Membership secretary*: Julie Cohen, 31 Sutherland Grove, Teddington, Middx TW11 8RP. Est. in 1990 in response to the growing need to support conservation in both parks. Each year the Friends undertake a special project such as planting an endangered species in a natural habitat. There are walks and talks. A quarterly newsletter is issued.

A history of the park *Bushy Park: royals, rangers and rogues*, by Kathy White and Peter Foster, was published in 1997 by The Foundry Press (Clarence Cottage, Hampton Court Road, KT8 9BY).

[585] **FRIENDS OF THE WILDERNESS.** *Contact*: Mrs I. King, 106 Broom Park, Teddington, Middx TW11 9RR, *Tel*: (020) 8977 9378.

[586] **HAMPTON COURT ASSOCIATION.** *Chairman*: Dr Louis Marks, Paddock Lodge, The Green, Hampton Court KT8 9PW, *Tel*: (020) 8979 5254.

[587] **HAMPTON HILL ASSOCIATION.** *Secretary*: Mrs Anne Wood, 136 Uxbridge Road, Hampton Hill, Middx TW12 1BG, *Tel*: (020) 8979 1431. *Membership Secretary*: Mrs J. Jennings, 12 Cranmer Road; *Archivist*: Mrs E. McLean, 28 St James's Road, *Tel*: (020) 8287 3407. Est. in 1964 to preserve the amenities of Hampton Hill and to foster a community spirit. Social activities include visits and every other year there is an exhibition of local arts, crafts and hobbies. A music circle meets once a month. A new history of Hampton Hill is in progress, contact: Ron Salmons, *Tel*: (020) 8979 6580. The internet will be utilised and the first item to be included will be *The birth and growth of Hampton Hill*, edited by Margery Orton, out of print for many years.

The Hampton Hill Gallery, 205 High Street, Middx TW12 1NP, *Tel*: (020) 8977 1379 are specialists in watercolours, etchings, and antique engravings, many of local scenes.

[588] **HAMPTON SOCIETY** (formerly Hampton Residents' Association). *Secretary*: John Farndon, *Tel*: (020) 8979 3973. *Chairman*: Bill Weisblatt, *Tel*: (020) 8979 3089.

[589] **HAMPTON WICK ASSOCIATION.** *Chairman*: Colin Pain, 41 Lower Teddington Road, Hampton Wick KT1 4HQ, *Tel*: (020) 8977 4074.

[590] **TEDDINGTON SOCIETY**. *Chair*: Ms Daphne Windel, 115 Munster Road, Teddington TW11, *Tel*: (020) 8977 0817.

Richmond, Kew, Ham, Petersham :

[591] **CAMPAIGN AGAINST TRAFFIC IN RICHMOND PARK**. *Contact*: Mary Thorpe, 226 Sheen Lane, East Sheen, London SW14 8LB. Est. in 1994 by Mary Thorpe and John Waller. The immediate purpose of the campaign was to provide information to the Dame Jennifer Jenkins Royal Parks Review Group concerning the damage being done to Richmond Park by the ever-increasing flow of traffic.

[591] **FRIENDS OF OLD DEER PARK**. *Contact*: John Treasurer, 20 Queensbury House, Friars Lane, Richmond, *Tel*: (020) 8940 3435. Set up to oppose redevelopment schemes.

[593] **FRIENDS OF RICHMOND PARK**. *Secretary*: Mr H. Stafford, 75 March Court, Warwick Drive, London SW15 6LD, *Tel*: (020) 8789 4601. Est. in 1961 'to protect Richmond Park as a place of natural beauty and public pleasure'. Meetings, guided walks; quarterly newsletter. A large colour slide library of park scenes is maintained.

[594] **FRIENDS OF THE ROYAL BOTANIC GARDENS KEW**. *Contact*: Michael Godfrey, 37 Kew Green, Royal Botanic Gardens, Kew, Richmond TW9 3AB, *Tel*: (020) 8332 5000; 8940 1171; *events tel*: (020) 9332 5655.
Kew Gardens Gallery: *Tel*: (020) 8332 5618. Changing exhibitions of contemporary and historical flower and botanical paintings/illustrations.
Kew Palace and Queen Charlotte's Cottage, *Tel*: (020) 8940 1171. *Hours*: 11-5.30, April-September. Owned by the Historic Royal Palaces Agency; built in 1631. Bought by the Crown in 1781 and used as a Royal palace until 1899, when it was opened to the public by Queen Victoria. Has recently undergone external restoration (awarded a Richmond Society award in 1998).
Marianne North Gallery, *Tel*: (020) 9332 5621. The natural history paintings of Marianne North, Victorian explorer in the 1870's and 1880's.

[595] **HAM AMENITIES GROUP**. *Secretary*: Ron Chave, 24 Cowper Road, Kingston-upon-Thames KT2 5PQ, Tel: (020) 8549 6363. *Chair*: Gwen Dornan, 3 Ham Ridings, Richmond, Surrey TW10 5HJ, *Tel*: (020) 8940 9489. Est. some 20 years ago to improve the local environment and to provide the opportunity for local contact in Ham, which lies half way between the two centres of Richmond and Kingston. There are visits, lectures, social events. An art group and a theatre group are attached. There is an annual fair on Ham Common. A regular newsletter is issued.

[596] **HAM AND PETERSHAM SOCIETY**. *Chair*: Mrs Sylvia Pele, 147 Petersham Road, Richmond,TW10 7AH, *Tel*: (020) 8940 3424.

[597] **KEW BRIDGE STEAM MUSEUM**. Green Dragon Lane, Brentford, Middx TW8 0EN, *Tel*: (020) 8568 4757. *Hours*: Daily, 11-5. Museum is housed in a magnificent 19th century pumping station and houses an important collection of water pumping machinery. A new gallery tells the history of water supply and usage in London. There is also a waterworks railway line.

[598] **THE KEW SOCIETY**. *Secretary*: John Deane, 2 Hatherley Road, Kew TW9 3LN. *Membership secretary*: Karen Baker, 38 Pensford Avenue, Kew TW9 4HP. Currently has some 700 members; it aims 'to protect the architectural and natural environment of Kew and to improve Kew's public amenities'. The riverside between the railway bridge and Chiswick Bridge will be developed and the society will continue to campaign for sympathetic development for all the different sites. There is a programme of social events, lectures and visits. A regular newsletter is issued.

[599] **RICHMOND HISTORY SOCIETY**. *Secretary*: Elizabeth Velluet, 9 Bridge Road, St Margaret's, Twickenham TW1 1RE, *Tel*: (020) 8891 3825. *Membership Secretary*: Jane Lewis, 1 Cole Park View, St Margaret's, Twickenham TW1 1W, *Tel*: (020) 8892 7381. *Journal editor*: David Blomfield, 7 Leyborne Park, Kew, Richmond TW9 3HB, *Tel*: (020) 8940 8749, *President*: John Cloake, 4 The Terrace, 140 Richmond Hill TW10 6RN.
The society was est. in 1985 'to promote and foster interest in the local history of Richmond, Kew, Petersham and Ham'. The society replaces the history section of the Richmond Society formed ten years earlier. Three newsletters a year are issued.

Publications 1992-5:
1992: PASMORE, Stephen. *The life and times of Queen Elizabeth I at Richmond Palace*. 72pp. illus.
1993: CLOAKE, John. *The growth of Richmond* (revised and enlarged editions). 48pp. illus.
1995: WINDSOR, Fred. *Richmond boy: memories of Richmond 1914-1933*. 41pp. illus.
1995: PRITCHARD, Evelyn. *Ham House and its owners through four centuries*. 73pp.

John Cloake is an eminent Richmond local historian. Historical Publications have published his *Richmond past*, 1991, reprint 1998, and the two volume work on Richmond palaces: *Palaces of Shene and Richmond*, 1995, and *Richmond Lodge and Kew Palaces*, 1996.

David Blomfield has written on Kew: his *Kew past* was published by Phillimore in 1994; in 1996 he published himself the second edition of his *The Story of Kew*.

Contents listing for Richmond History Journal:
No 14, 1993: Curates and ministers of Richmond Parish Church before 1660; Queen Elizabeth I at Richmond, a footnote; Richmond miscellania; Sudbrook Lodge, Petersham Road; The mystery of the Tower in Friars Lane; A brief history of Gordon, Forbes and Langham Houses on Ham Common; The Richmond conveyance company; Late Victorian politics in Richmond: the 1895 Parliamentary election; Topiary Square, Richmond.
No 15, 1994: Richmond lock and weir, 1894-1994; Cardigan House and its architects; Queen Charlotte visits Ham; The Coade stone River God of Richmond; The site of the Cassel Hospital; A white doe in Richmond Park; A German Richmond, Schloss Richmond in Brunswick: The Lady Bountiful of Kew; Richmond's Maids of Honour; Charles Dickens at Petersham; The first Royal loo.
No 16, 1995: The Queensberry folly; The first monarchs of the Richmond roads; Cardinal Newman and his boyhood in Ham; Shene in 1314; The fraudulent tax collectors of Kew; The May Family of Richmond and the Lisbon Factory; The history of St Michael's Convent, Ham Common; Sir William Herrick, jeweller to the King; The war of the terrace hedge; Anglo-Spanish relations-1555.

The Richmond Local History Society was responsible for the collection of old photographs *Richmond* from Sutton.
Richard Essen is the compiler of a collection *Richmond and Kew* from Tempus.

[600] **RICHMOND RESIDENTS ACTION GROUP.** *Secretary*: Martin Anderson, 3 Maids of Honour Row, The Green, Richmond TW9 1NY, *Tel*: (020) 8948 8800. Aims to act on behalf of local residents in civic matters.

[601] **THE RICHMOND SOCIETY.** *Secretary*: Mrs Pat Spaight, 5 Kelvin Court, Marlborough Road, Richmond TW10 6JS, *Tel*: (020) 8948 0643. *Membership secretary*: Mrs Sylvia Ruggier, 5 Northumberland Place, Richmond TW10 6TS. *Chairman*: David Church, 38 Sheen Road, Richmond TW9 1AW, *Tel*: (020) 8940 3484. Est. in 1995 to provide 'a focus for the conservation and development of the town, its amenities and unique character'. The society is also concerned with traffic and public transport, with tree planting and landscaping and environmental improvements. There is a full programme of events including the summer season of heritage walks. Since 1977 it has been making annual awards for good projects. Four folding leaflet heritage walks have been issued: *Richmond Town*; *Richmond Green*; *Richmond Palace*; *Richmond Hill*. There is also a quarterly newsletter.

Twickenham :
[602] **BOROUGH OF TWICKENHAM LOCAL HISTORY SOCIETY.** *Secretary*: Mr R.S. Knight, 14a Enmore Gardens, London SW14 8FR, *Tel*: (020) 8878 7041. *Membership secretary*: Miss S. Brooke, 86 Cole Park Road, Twickenham TW1 1JA, *Tel*: (020) 8892 4395. *Publications*: Mike Cherry, 75 Radnor Road, Twickenham TW1 4NB, *Tel*: (020) 8892 0950. *Newsletter editor*: Mr. I. Franklin, 52 Briar Close, Hampton TW12 3YX, *Tel*: (020) 8941 5632. Est. in 1965 to 'generally awaken and foster an informed interest in the history of various parts of the former borough of Twickenham (Twickenham, Whitton, Teddington, Hampton, Hampton Wick, Hampton Hill)'. There are meetings and visits.
Its series of papers began in 1965 and a wide range of specialist topics have been covered: specific individuals, specific buildings and sites, localities, trades, etc. Although the society has a small membership of some 180, many of its publications have a print run of up to 1,000 copies. Prolific authors in the past have included: T.R.Cashmore, Alan Charles Bell Urwin, and Donald Herbert Simpson.

Numbered papers since 1990:
No 64: URWIN, A.C.B. *St Margaret's: a banker's house and its contents in 1817*. 1990. 45pp. illus., plan.
No 65: FRANCIS, J.M. *and* URWIN, A.C.B. *Francis Francis 1822-1866: angling and fish culture in Twickenham, Teddington and Hampton*. 1991. 29pp. illus., map.
No 66: HITCHINSON, Frank W. *A Twickenham fireman remembers, 1929-1933*. 1991. 38pp.
No 67: PEARCE, Brian L. *The fashioned reed: the poets of Twickenham from St Margaret's to Hampton Court from 1500*. 1992. 49pp. illus.
No 68: BUNCH, Maureen. *Cambridge Park, East Twickenham: the building of a suburb*. 1992. 31pp.
No 69: ALLAN, D.G.C. Some noble and patriotic men and women: RSA members and prize-winners of the Twickenham area. 1994. 37pp.

No 70: NELSON, Helen McCutcheon, *and* PEARCE, Brian C. *The happiest days...a history of education in Twickenham, Part I, 1645-1918.* 1994. 32pp.

No 71: SHEAF, John. *Hampton in the 1890's through the eyes of Captain Christie of Beveree.* 1995. 26pp.

No 72: URWIN, A.C.B. *Richard Earl of Cornwall and King of Almayne, 1209-1272.* 1995. 54pp.

No 73: NELSON, Helen McCutheon. *The happiest days: a history of education in Twickenham Part II:* twentieth century schools. 1996. 44pp.

No 74: *A tribute to Horace Walpole and Strawberry Hill House on the occasion of the bicentenary of his death on 2 March 1797.* 1997. 29pp. Four essays by Brian Pearce, Michael Srodin, Clive Wainright and Stephen Calloway.

No 75: URWIN, Alan. *The second Earl of Kilmorey and his mausoleum in St Margarets.* 1997. 15pp.

No 76: SHEAF, John. *Edwardian Hampton: the story of Hampton and Hampton Hill from 1900-1914.* 1997. 44pp

No 77: CARROLL, Kathleen. *Lady Frances Waldegrave: political hostess at Strawberry Hill 1856-1879.* 1998. 36pp.

There is also a small series of 'Occasional papers'. No 6 on *Dr Langdon Down and the Normansfield Theatre*, by John Earl, 40pp, was published in 1997. No 5 was *2000 years of history*, a paper to accompany the 1995 exhibition (on Twickenham), by D. Simpson. Also still in print is No 4, on York House, Twickenham.

A member of the society Anthony Beckles Willson (44 Popes Avenue, Twickenham TW2 5TL) has written two important research books on Alexander Pope and Twickenham: In 1996 he published himself his *Mr Pope and others at Cross Deep Twickenham*; and in 1998 The Twickenham Museum (of which his is a trustee) and the Garden History Society published his *Alexander Pope's grotto in Twickenham*.

Other members' work published recently: John Sheaf (4 Thames Street, Hampton TW12 2FH and Ken Howe (1 Cedar Road, Teddington TW11 9AN) are the authors of *Hampton and Teddington past* from Historical Publications, 1995; together with Mike Cherry they also compiled the two collections of old photographs *Twickenham, Teddington and Hampton* from Sutton. Donald Simpson's *Twickenham Past* was published by Historical Publications in 1993, reprinted 1998.

[603] **EEL PIE ISLAND ASSOCIATION.** *Contact:* Dr Jack Betteridge, *Tel:* (020) 8891 4159.

[604] **FRIENDS OF TWICKENHAM GREEN.** *Secretary:* John Bell, 34 Albion Road, Twickenham TW2 6QJ, *Tel:* (020) 8898 9618. Aims 'to maintain and improve the environment of the Green and its associated conservation area'.

[605] **MARBLE HILL SOCIETY.** *Chair:* Janet Clarke, 25 Marble Hill Close, Twickenham TW1 3AY, *Tel:* (020) 8892 0588. *Membership secretary:* at: 9 Bridge Road, St Margaret's, Twickenham TW1 1RE. Est. in 1987 to 'bring together people with an interest in Marble Hill, to encourage wider interest in this historic museum and park and to help English Heritage to preserve and enhance its amenities'. The house is an outstanding example of Palladian architecture, designed by Colen Campbell. It contains an important collection of early Georgian paintings and furniture.

[606] **TWICKENHAM SOCIETY.** *Secretary:* Mrs Ann Sutton, 36 Gothic Road, Twickenham TW2 5FH, *Tel:* (020) 8241 9011. *Chairman:* Mr B. Parker, 17 The Green, Twickenham TW2 5TU, *Tel:* (020) 8894 1348. Est. in the 1960's, currently with some 130 members. There are monthly talks. A biannual newsletter *Eel Pie* is issued.

[607] **YORK HOUSE SOCIETY.** *Secretary:* Mrs Patricia Woram, 48 Lebanon Road, Twickenham TW1 3DG. The society dates back to 1922 and its name commemorates the founding members' success in persuading the council then to purchase York House, then under threat of demolition. It also played an important part in the acquisition of Orleans House, and in 1962 initiated and set up the Borough of Twickenham Local History Society. It continues to campaign for the preservation of the Twickenham riverside, and is also concerned with the central area of Twickenham. There are also social activities such as the Twelfth Night Ball.

* SOME OTHER COUNCIL CONTACTS *

Principal Arts Officer: Nigel Cutting, Longholm Lodge, 146 Petersham Road, Richmond TW10 6UX, *Tel:* (020) 8831 6137.

Business: A Richmond Business directory is issued, *Contact:* Kate Vogelsang, Publicity Officer, Old Town Hall, *Tel:* (020) 8940 6838.

Conservation/listed buildings: Russell Morris, Senior conservation officer, Civic Centre, 44 York Street, Twickenham TW1 3AA, *Tel:* (020) 8891 7335. A series of 'guidance notes' for the 63 conservation areas is in preparation.

Nature conservation: Emma Wilson, assistant ecology officer, *Tel:* (020) 8831 6135.

Reference Library: at Central Library, Old Town Hall, Whittaker Avenue, Richmond TW9 1TP, *Tel:* (020) 8940 5529.

* SOME NON-COUNCIL CONTACTS *

Arts:
RICHMOND UPON THAMES ARTS COUNCIL: *Contact*: Annie Stevens, 21 Paradise Road, Richmond TW9, *Tel*: (020) 8940 7217.

Business:
RICHMOND UPON THAMES CHAMBER OF COMMERCE. 3rd Floor, Regal House, 70 London Road, Twickenham TW1 3QS, *Tel*: (020) 8891 2535.

Voluntary organisations:
COUNCIL FOR VOLUNTARY SERVICE. 1 Princes Street, Richmond TW9 1ED, *Tel*: (020) 8255 8500.

* LOCAL PRESS *

Richmond and Twickenham Times. Dimbleby Newspapers Group, 14 King Street, Richmond TW9 1NF, *Tel*: (020) 8940 6030.
Richmond Comet. Newsquest Media Group, Guardian House, Sandyford Road, Sutton SM3 9RN, *Tel*: (020) 8644 4300.
Richmond Guardian, free newspaper from same group.
Richmond Informer. (free newspaper). Southnews PLC, 21 High Street, Teddington TW11 8EW, *Tel*: (020) 8943 5157.

LONDON WIDE AND NATIONAL ORGANISATIONS:

Subjects arranged alphabetically:

for headings see Contents page

vision *for* **London**

* ACADEMIC RESEARCH ORGANISATIONS (London wide) *

[608] **CENTRE FOR METROPOLITAN HISTORY**. Institute of Historical Research, Senate House, Malet Street, London WC1E 7HU, *Tel*: (020) 7862 8790. *Contact*: Miss Olwen Myhill (Administration assistant). *Director*: Derek Keene. *Deputy director*: Helen Creaton. Aims 'to provide a forum for the interchange of ideas on metropolitan history through seminars, conferences and other meetings; to undertake original research into the society, economy, culture and fabric of London with regard to its role both within the British Isles and in the world at large; to undertake bibliographical work and publish news of research in progress; to promote research into the history of other metropolitan centres by inviting scholars from other parts of the world to take part in its activities'. Conferences, study days and seminars are organised. An annual newsletter and an annual report are issued. *A bibliography of printed sources for the history of London to 1939* was published in 1994 by the Library Association; a ten-year supplement is in preparation. *Sources for the history of London 1936-45* was published by the British Records Association in 1998, and a checklist of unpublished London diaries of all periods is being compiled. Current research projects examine: Metropolitan market networks, 1300-1600; Markets and fairs to 1540; Mortality in the metropolis, 1860-1920. Completed projects include: Feeding the city, 1250-1400; Growth of the skilled workforce, 1500-1750; Metropolitan London in the 1690's; English merchant culture, 1660-1720; Oral history of the stock jobbers.

[609] **CENTRE FOR THE STUDY OF MIGRATION**. *Contact*: Dr Ann Kershen, Queen Mary and Westfield College, Mile End Rd, London E1 4NS, *Tel*: (020) 7975 5555, ext. 5009. Her publications include: *Trade unionism among the tailors of London and Leeds, 1870-1939*, published by Frank Cass.

[610] **GREATER LONDON INDUSTRIAL ARCHAEOLOGY SOCIETY**. *Secretary*: Bill Firth, 49 Woodstock Avenue, London NW11 9RG, *Tel*: (020) 8455 7164. *Membership secretary*: Sue Hayton, 31 The High St, Farnborough Village, Orpington, Kent BR6 7BQ, *Tel*: (01689) 852186. There is a winter series of lectures, summer walks and site recording with training. Also visits to industrial sites both in the capital and outside. There is a bi-monthly newsletter which includes short research reports, and an occasional journal. Recent publications:
1994: *London's Industrial Archaeology No 5*. Contents: Coachbuilding in London; Two East London breweries; Haringey Greyhound Stadium, totalisator and George Alfred Julius; Three bridges, Hanwell.
1995: *25 years of GLIAS*: a miscellany to commemorate the society's silver jubilee. Contents: The early years of GLIAS; 25 years of GLIAS accounts; Industrial archaeology successes; 25 years of GLIAS events; GLIAS publications; The changing face of London, the losses, the new, the converted, the refurbished and the threatened; The steam engine in London; London's IA in print; Do you remember?
1997: *London's Industrial Archaeology No 6*. Contents: Industrial archaeology and the historical imagination; Railway coke ovens; The forgotten workforce; Women gasworkers of the First World War; Silvertown Way and Silvertown By-pass.
1998: *Lewisham Silk Mills and the history of an Ancient Site*. The story of armour, small arms, silk, and gold & silver wire drawing. Second (corrected and enlarged) edition published in 1998 by the Lewisham Local History Society in association with GLIAS.

The national organisation to which most IA societies are affiliated is the **ASSOCIATION FOR INDUSTRIAL ARCHAEOLOGY**, *Contact*: Isabel Wilson, School of Archaeology Studies, University of Leicester, Leicester LE1 7RH.

[611] **THE HISTORY OF PARLIAMENT TRUST**. Wedgwood House, 15 Woburn Square, London WC1H 0NS, *Tel*: (020) 7636 0272; *Fax*: (020) 7255 1442. Est. in 1929 under the editorship of Colonel J.C. Wedgewood MP, who published 1439-1509 in two volumes in 1936 and 1938. The history was re-launched in 1951. Twenty-three volumes have been published between 1965 and 1992 (by HMSO, Secker and Warburg, and Alan Sutton); they are available on a CD-ROM published by Cambridge University Press. The series collates exhaustive biographical information, and includes constituency and introductory surveys. Five further sections are in preparation and research for a section of the House of Lords begins in April 1999.

[612] **THE LONDON AT WAR STUDY GROUP**. *Secretary*: Sid Holyland, 81 Harrowdene Gardens, Teddington, Middx TW11 0DL, *Tel*: (020) 8977 6559. Est. in 1995 and open to all interested in any aspect of the social/military history of the Greater London region during the two World Wars. It supports the Defence of Britain Project, and other interests include: ARP, Home Guard, fire/police/ambulance, cinema and theatre, evacuation and wartime schools, BBC, sport, big bands, transport, Allied HQ in London, London Docks. There are meetings and visits. There is a monthly newsletter/journal (*editor*: F.R. Goodey, 40 Causeyware Rd, Edmonton, London N9 8BS), and an Annual Review.
1997 Annual Review: Recruiting in London in 1902; The tubes as shelters in WW1; Naval memories of London at war 1943-44; Nork Park: a cadet remembers; Railways, rum and radar; Memorial to the London Blitz; Behind the lines in Jugoslavia.

1998 Annual Review: At Chelsea Hospital 1902; Railway air raid shelters in WW1; Life on a barrage balloon site; An ARP messenger in Leyton; For Kingston and country; At school in Peckham 1943-44.

[613] **LONDON RECORD SOCIETY**. *Secretary*: Miss H.J. Creaton, c/o Institute of Historical Research, Senate House, Malet Street, London WC1E 7HU, *Tel*: (020) 7862 8798. *General editors*: Vanessa Harding, S.J. O'Connor. *Chairman*: H.S. Cobb. Est. in 1964 'to publish transcripts, abstracts and lists of primary sources for the history of London, and generally to stimulate interest in archives relating to London'. Some 34 volumes have been published since 1965. Recent publications, of the 1990's are:

No 27: *The overseas trade of London: exchequer customs accounts, 1480-1*, edited by H.S. Cobb, 1990.

No 28: *Justice in 18th century Hackney*: the Justicing notebook of Henry Norris and the Hackney Petty Sessions Books, edited by R. Paley, 1991.

No 29: *Two Tudor subsidy assessment rolls for the city of London, 1541 and 1582*, edited by R.G. Lang, 1993.

No 30: *London debating societies, 1776-99*, edited by D. Andrew, 1994.

No 31: *London Bridge: selected accounts and rentals, 1381-1538*, edited by V.A. Harding and L. Wright, 1995.

No 32: *London Consistory Court depositions, 1596-1611*: lists and indices, edited by L. Giese, 1997.

No 33: *The settlement and bastardy examinations of St Luke, Chelsea, 1730-66*, edited by T.V. Hitchcock and J. Black, 1998.

No 34: *Records of St Andrew Hubbard, 1454-1560*, edited by C. Burgess, 1999.

[614] **LONDON TOPOGRAPHICAL SOCIETY**. *Secretary*: Patrick Frazer, 36 Old Deer Park Gardens, Richmond, Surrey TW9 2TL, *Tel*: (020) 8940 5419. *Membership secretary*: Trevor Ford, 151 Mount View Rd, London N4 4JT, *Tel*: (020) 8341 6408. *Publications secretary*: Simon Morris, 22 Brooksby St, London N1 1HA, *Tel*: (020) 7609 0890. *Newsletter editor*: Penelope Hunting, 40 Smith St, London SW3 4EP, *Tel*: (020) 7352 8057. *Chairman*: Peter Jackson, The Vane, The Avenue, Northwood, Middx HA6 2NQ, *Tel*: (01923) 829079. The society, founded in 1880, is a publishing society: maps, plans, views, illustrating the history, growth and topography of London, as well as scholarly books and atlases. Publications can be seen and bought at the London Metropolitan Archives. The society prospectus and catalogue contains information on the publishing output in print from the 1960's to the present day, with listings of contents of the journal the *London Topographical Record*. The society issues a newsletter twice a year, and is a good source for reviews and notices of new books.

Books in print include: *Berkeley Square to Bond St: the early history of the neighbourhood* by B.H. Johnson, 1952; *The survey of the building sites in the City of London after the Great Fire of 1666*, by Mills and Oliver (reduced facsimile of manuscript, five volumes), 1962-67; *The London panoramas of Robert Barker and Thomas Girtin*, c. 1800, by H.J. Pragnell, 1968; *The public markets of the City of London, surveyed by William Leybourn, in 1677*, by Betty R. Masters, 1974; *The Park Town Estate and the Battersea Triangle*, by Priscilla Metcalf, 1968; *Robert Baker of Piccadilly Hall and his heirs*, by Frances Sheppard, 1982; *The London surveys of Ralph Treswell*, edited by John Schofield, 1987; *Hugh Alley's Caveat: the markets of London in 1598*, 1988; *good and proper materials: the fabric of London since the Great Fire*, edited by Hermione Hobhouse and Ann Saunders, 1989; *The Mercer's Hall*, by Jean Imray, 1991 (509pp, tracing history of site from Great Fire to present day); *Drawings of Westminster, by Sir George Scharf*, with text by Peter Jackson (drawings made between 1859 and 1874), 1994; *Topography of London*, facsimile of John Lockie's gazetteer, 2nd edition, 1813, introduction by David Webb, 1994; *The Royal Exchange* (a collection of 30 essays on the three Royal Exchange buildings, of 1566, 1669 and 1841), published in 1997.

Some of the hon. officials of the society are important London scholars: Penelope Hunting has written a number of histories: *Royal Westminster*, 1981; *Broadgate and Liverpool Street Station; History of the Drapers Company*, 1989, of the *Leathersellers Company*, 1994; and of the *Society of Apothecaries*, 1998.

Peter Jackson is a trained graphic artist, and his output of books includes: *London is stranger than fiction*, 1951; *London Explorer*, 1953; *Tallis's London street views*, 1969; *London Bridge*, 1971; and with Felix Barker: *London - 2000 years of a city and its people*, 1974.

Ann Saunders was archivist for the Borough of St Marylebone 1956-63. Her publications include *John Bacon*, 1960; *Regent's Park*, 1969, 1981; two re-written volumes on London for the Arthur Mee Counties of England series, and *The art and architecture of London*.

[615] **RAPHAEL SAMUEL CENTRE FOR METROPOLITAN CULTURAL HISTORY**. *Secretary*: Yvette Fitzgerald, Department of Cultural Studies, University of East London, Longbridge Rd, Dagenham, Essex RM8 2AS, *Tel*: (020) 8590 7000, ext. 2743; *Fax*: (020) 8849 3598; *Email*: y.fitzgerald@uel.ac.uk. Centre's office at: Brushfield Annex, Bishopsgate Institute, 230 Bishopsgate, London EC2M 4QH, *Tel*: (020) 7375 0176. The membership of the centre currently comprises: *Frank Mort* (working on a study of sexual London in the 1950's and 1960's and on consumption in post-war Britain); *Sophie Watson* (currently editing a companion to urban studies, and researching public space, feminist urban theory and globalisation); *Mica Nava* (working on cosmopolitanism, modernity and consumption in early 20th century London); *Phil Cohen* (working on radical constructions of the English working class in the 19th and 20th centuries, and on narratives of the nation); *John Marriott* (author of many articles on East London history; working on the relationship between metropolis and

empire, and on the political culture of the East End in the 19th and 20th centuries); *Linda Rozmovits* (working on 19th and 20th century Anglo-Jewish history, race and ethnicity in the 19th century).

The centre focuses on research and scholarship on the history of London since the 18th century: publications, conferences, seminars, etc., funded projects, cross-institutional research networks, working with community-based historians in East London.

[616] **VICTORIA HISTORY OF THE COUNTIES OF ENGLAND**. Institute of Historical Research, University of London, Senate House, Malet Street, London WC1E 7HU, *Tel*: (020) 7862 8770. *Internet*: http://www.ihrinfo.ac.uk/vch. The series began in 1899 and has been managed by the Institute since 1933; since 1947 it has been helped by local sponsorship. There is also a Victoria History Trust, c/o the above address. Ten volumes have been published between 1969 and 1995 in the Middlesex series. Volume IX is on Hampstead and Paddington, Volume X on Hackney Parish, 1995. Volumes XI and XII are in preparation.

There is one volume for London, covering religious houses, Roman London, Anglo-Saxon London and ecclesiastical history.

* AMENITY/CIVIC SOCIETIES *

[617] **THE LONDON FORUM OF AMENITY AND CIVIC SOCIETIES**. Office: 70 Cowcross St, London EC1M 6EJ, *Tel*: (020) 7250 0606. *Chairman*: Marion Harvey. *Secretary*: Peter Eversden, 40 Abinger Rd, London W4 1EX, *Tel/Fax*: (020) 8747 3281. *Membership secretary*: Helen Marcus, 5 Greenaway Gardens, London NW3 7DJ, *Tel/Fax*: (020) 7794 4213. *News Forum editor*: Tony Aldous, 12 Eliot Hill, London SE13 7EB, *Tel*: (020) 8318 1745, *Fax*: (020) 8333 0977. *Events co-ordinator*: Fred Trollope, 9 Suncroft Place, London SE26 4RH, *Tel*: (020) 8699 8197. Est. in 1988 'to help amenity and civic societies to work together to protect and improve the quality of life in London'. The London Amenity and Transport Association was incorporated into the London Forum in 1994. Some 100 local societies are in the membership (with a combined membership of some 100,000 Londoners), plus some 40 associate groups. It has representatives on the Traffic Advisory Panel, and the development team for the new Civic Forum that will be a link for organisations in London with the Mayor and the GLA assembly. It responds to consultation papers, and policy documents and organises conferences, discussions and exhibitions. There is a regular newsletter *News Forum*.

[618] **THE LONDON SOCIETY**. 4th Floor, Senate House, Malet Street, London WC1E 7HU, *Tel*: (020) 7580 5537. *Secretary*: Mrs Benita Jones. Est. in 1912, one of the first environmental, amenity societies. In its 80 years of existence the society has become 'a respected voice in matters of renewal and renovation of the built environment'. It continues to work for the enhancement of the city and development proposals and planning applications are considered monthly by the Executive Committee. A library of some 3,000 volumes is run as a special collection within the London University Library. There are lectures and visits, and a journal is published twice a year with short articles, and book reviews. There is also a quarterly newsletter.

* ARCHAEOLOGY *

Some directory sources:
The *Directory of British Archaeology* (arranged in regions) is published annually by the periodical *Current Archaeology*, Andrew and Wendy Selkirk, 9 Nassington Rd, London SW3 2TX, *Tel*: (020) 7435 7517; *Email*: editor@archaeology.co.uk; *Internet*: www.archaeology.co.uk. CBA's *British Archaeological Yearbook* was first published in 1995 and a new edition is being prepared. The CBA (see below) maintains database listings nation-wide (contact: Don Henderson).

Some national organisations:
[619] **COUNCIL FOR BRITISH ARCHAEOLOGY**. Bowes Morrell House, 111 Walmgate, York YO1 2UA, *Tel*: (01904) 671417; *Fax*: (01904) 571384; *Email*: archaeology@compuserve.com. Members have automatic membership of a CBA region, bringing local news. There is an illustrated magazine *British Archaeology*, ten times a year; and an information bulletin, *CBA Briefing*. The *British and Irish Archaeological Bibliography* is published twice a year and covers a wide range of literature, articles, reports, theses, etc.

[620] **COUNCIL FOR INDEPENDENT ARCHAEOLOGY**. *Secretary*: Mike Rumbold, 3 West St, Weedon Bec, Northampton NN7 4QU, *Internet*: www.archaeology.co.uk/cia/.

[621] **INSTITUTE OF ARCHAEOLOGY**. University College London, 34 Gordon Square, London WC1H 0PY, *Tel*: (020) 7387 7050; *Fax*: (020) 7383 2527; *Email*: f.goddard@ucl.ac.uk; *Internet*: www.ucl.ac.uk/archaeology.

Greater London organisations:
[622] **GREATER LONDON ARCHAEOLOGY ADVISORY SERVICE**. At: English Heritage, 23 Savile Row, London W1X 1AB, *Tel*: (020) 7973 3735; *Fax*: (020) 7973 3249.

[623] **LONDON AND MIDDLESEX ARCHAEOLOGICAL SOCIETY**. c/o The Museum of London, London Wall, London EC2Y 5HN, *Tel*: (020) 7600 3699; *Fax*: (020) 7600 1058; *Internet*: http://www.london-arch-soc.demon.co.uk/. Est. in 1855 'to further the study of archaeology, local history and the historic buildings of the London area and to publish the results of such research'. There are lectures, and two full-day conferences annually, the autumn one is for local history, the spring one for archaeology. The newsletter contains listings of meetings held by affiliated local societies. Transactions are published annually with academic reports on excavations, archaeological and historical research and book reviews. Special papers and offprints of the Transactions are listed in the MoL publications catalogue.
Some LAMAs contacts include: Jon Cotton, MoL secretary of LAMAS research committee; Mark Hassel, president, at Institute of Archaeology, UCL.

[624] **MUSEUM OF LONDON ARCHAEOLOGICAL ARCHIVE**. 46 Eagle Wharf Rd, London N1 7EE, *Tel*: (020) 7490 8447; *Fax*: (020) 7490 3955.

[625] **MUSEUM OF LONDON ARCHAEOLOGICAL SERVICE**. Walker House, 87 Queen Victoria St, London EC4V 4AB, *Tel*: (020) 7410 2200; *Fax*: (020) 7410 2201; *Email*: molas@molas.demon.co.uk. *Internet*: www.demon.co.uk/molas/index.html. Recent publications include: *The development of North-west Roman Southwark: excavations at Courage's brewery 1974-90*, 1999; *The eastern cemetery of Roman London: excavations 1983-90*, 1999; *Excavations at the Nunnery of St Mary de Fonte, Clerkenwell*, 1998; *Excavations at the priory and hospital of St Mary Spital*, 1997; *Excavations at the priory of the Hospital of the Order of St John of Jerusalem, Clerkenwell*, 1998; *Industry in North-west Roman Southwark: excavations at Courage's brewery, 1974-90*, 1999; *The palace in Southwark of the medieval bishops of Winchester: excavations at Winchester Palace, London 1983-90, part 2*, 1999; *Queenhithe: excavations at Thames Court, City of London EC4, 1989-95*, 1999; *Roman buildings on the Southwark waterfront: excavations at Winchester Palace, London 1983-90, part 1*, 1999; *Saxon economy and environment in London*, 1998. For full information on the organisation see its *Yearbook*.

[626] **STANDING COMMITTEE ON LONDON'S ARCHAEOLOGY**. *Secretary*: Pat Wilkinson, 1b Forest Drive East, London E11 1JX. Issues a newsletter; has an annual conference. Brings together a wide range of individuals; sponsored by the CBS, Society of Antiquaries, LAMAS, and the Surrey Archaeological Society.

[627] **THAMES ARCHAEOLOGICAL SURVEY**. *Contact*: Mike Webber, Museum of London, 150 London Wall, London EC2Y 5HN, *Tel*: (020) 7814 5741.

Adjacent South East counties:
[628] **WEST ESSEX ARCHAEOLOGICAL GROUP**. *Secretary*: Mrs Jane Stirling, 9 Ashvale Gardens, Collier Row, Romford, Essex RM5 3QA, *Tel*: (01708) 780564. Est. in 1958 to 'promote the advancement of knowledge and education by a study of archaeology, history and kindred subjects particularly in West Essex'. Excavations, recording work, lectures. Reports of all excavations are published. Newsletter twice a year.

[629] **KENT ARCHAEOLOGICAL RESCUE UNIT**. Roman Painted House, New St, Dover, Kent CT17 9AJ, *Tel*: (01304) 203279; *Fax*: (020) 8462 4737. Est. in 1971, covering Kent and S.E. London: excavations, surveys, watching briefs, and publications. Manages the Roman House, Dover and the Crofton Roman Villa, Orpington.

[630] **KENT ARCHAEOLOGICAL SOCIETY**. *General secretary*: A.I. Moffatt, Three Elms, Woodlands Lane, Shorne, Gravesend DA21 3HH, *Tel*: (01474) 822280; *Fax*: (01634) 812159; *Internet*: 70374.1002@compuserve.com; *Membership secretary*: Mrs M. Lawrence, Barnfield, Church Lane, East Peckham, Tonbridge TN12 5JJ, *Tel*: (01622) 871945. The society was est. in 1857 'to promote the study and publication of archaeology and history in all their branches, especially within the ancient county of Kent'. It includes the London boroughs of Bexley, Bromley, Greenwich and Lewisham. It has a Kent Historic Buildings Index, and listings have been published for: Bexley, 1995; Greenwich, 1996; and Lewisham, 1996. There is an annual journal *Archaeologia Cantiana*. The society's library is at Maidstone Museum. It has an expanding large collection of visual records.

[631] **SURREY ARCHAEOLOGICAL SOCIETY**. Castle Arch, Guildford GU1 3SX, *Tel/Fax*: (01483) 532454; *Email*: surreyarch@compuserve.com. Est in 1854 to 'promote the study of archaeology and antiquities' within the county of Surrey. A large library and collection of visual and research material is maintained. There is a journal *Surrey Archaeological Collections* and a bulletin, issued nine times a year, with notices of local society meetings.

* ARCHITECTURE/HISTORIC BUILDINGS *

In addition to the many amenity societies in Greater London, there are organisations at national level of many kinds: professional bodies for architects, government agencies, the National Trust, societies concerned with preservation and conservation, societies for specific periods and for building types and a range of bodies for churches.
A useful source for this network is the compiler's *The Marcan Handbook of Arts Organisations*.
The following listing is selective and does not include the specialist organisations.

[632] **ARCHITECTURAL DIALOGUE**. West Hill House, 6 Swains Lane, London N6 6QU, *Tel*: (020) 8341 1371; *Fax*: (020) 8342 9108; *Email*: hc@archdialogue.demon.co.uk. *Internet*: http://www.archdialogue.demon. co.uk. The organisation has been organising architectural tours of London for ten years, led by specialists. Guides include: James Abatti, John Brushe, Mick Foster, Bruce Gorrick, David Laurence, John Stevenson, Ken Taylor, William Wymshurst, and David Yandell. Specialist programmes can also be provided for organisations. Contemporary architecture maps of London are available.

[633a] **ARCHITECTURAL HERITAGE FUND**. Clareville House, 26-27 Oxendon St, London SW1Y 4EL, *Tel*: (20) 7925 0199; *Fax*: (020) 7930 0295. Publications include: *Funds for historic buildings in England and Wales: a directory of sources*, 1998; and *How to rescue a ruin by setting up a local buildings preservation trust* (revised edition: 1997).

[633b] The **ASSOCIATION OF PRESERVATION TRUSTS** is also at the above address: *Tel*: (020) 7930 1629; *Fax*: (020) 7930 0295.

[634] **ENGLISH HERITAGE**, London Region. 23 Savile Row, London W1X 1AB, *Tel*: (020) 7973 3000; *Fax*: (020) 7973 3001.
The following contact names were accurate at March 1999.
Regional director for London: Philip Davies, ext. 3710; *Landscape architect for London and South East*: Andy Wimble, ext. 3726.
There are three teams for Greater London, with a head of team, casework staff, and historic buildings inspectors and architects:
North and East London: Barking, Barnet, Camden, Enfield, Hackney, Haringey, Havering, Islington, Newham, Redbridge, Tower Hamlets, Waltham Forest. *Head of team*: Patrick Pugh, ext. 3740.
Central and West London: Brent, Ealing, Hammersmith, Harrow, Hillingdon, Hounslow, City of London, Richmond, City of Westminster. *Head of team and regional architect*: Paul Velluet, ext. 3767.
Inspector of ancient monuments (for Greater London): Ellen Barnes, ext. 3738; *Historic parks and gardens advice* (for Greater London): Chris Sumner, ext. 3777.
Kensington and South London: Bexley, Bromley, Croydon, Greenwich, Kensington & Chelsea, Kingston-upon-Thames, Lambeth, Lewisham, Merton, Southwark, Sutton, Wandsworth. *Head of team and regional planner*: Geoffrey Noble, ext. 3712.
Greater London Archaeology Advisory Service: Head of service: Jez Reeve, ext. 3730.
Government Historic Buildings Advisory Unit: Head of unit: John Thorneycroft, ext. 3800.

English Heritage is a major publisher on the historic environment. Its 400 historic properties are described with up-to-date information in the *English Heritage Visitor's Handbook*, 1998/99. There are separate site guides, which may be in a variety of formats and include: Albert Memorial; Chiswick House; Down House, Kent (Charles Darwin home); Eltham Palace; Jewel Tower, Westminster; Kenwood; Marble Hill House; Ranger's House; Westminster Abbey Chapter House.
Conservation publications include: *Conservation in London: a study of strategic planning policy in London* (published jointly with the London Planning Advisory Committee, 1995); *In the public interest: London's civic heritage at risk*, 1995; and *The value of conservation*: a literature review of the economic and social value of the cultural built heritage, 1996. A guide *Conservation areas in London and the South East* was published in 1990. The archaeology series includes studies on *St Brides Church*, by Gustav Milne, 1997; *The Temple of Mithras*, by John Shepherd, 1998; and an important handbook: *Teaching archaeology: a United Kingdom directory of resources*, edited by Don Henson (organisations, people, museums, sites, books, videos, computer software, etc).
Address for publications is: PO Box 229, Northampton NN6 9RY, *Tel*: (01604) 781163; *Fax*: (01604) 781714.

[635] **HERITAGE OF LONDON TRUST**. *Contacts*: Julian Spicer, Diana Beattie, 23 Savile Row, London W1X 1AB, *Tel*: (020) 7973 3809; *Fax*: (020) 7973 3792. The only building preservation trust covering the whole of London. It seeks help from commercial and private sources to complement the efforts of the public sector. It has undertaken over 250 projects throughout London.

Conservation officers in Greater London councils are often members of the London Branch of the [636] **INSTITUTE OF HISTORIC BUILDING CONSERVATION**, *Secretary*: Rosemary McQueen, City of Westminster, *Tel*: (020) 7641 2455; *Email*: rmcQueen@westminster.gov.uk.

[637] **LONDON OPEN HOUSE**. PO Box 6984, London N6 6PY, *Tel*: (020) 7347 6007, is part of the Architectural Dialogue organisation and co-ordinates the 'Open House' weekend each year when many little known buildings throughout London are opened free to the public. The Open House booklet guide is especially informative. There is also a monthly Broadsheet giving details of many other architectural events in London.

[638] **NATIONAL ASSOCIATION OF DECORATIVE AND FINE ARTS SOCIETIES (NADFAS)**. NADFAS House, 8 Guildford St, London WC1N 1DT, *Tel*: (020) 7430 0730; *Fax*: (020) 7242 0686. There are London branches in Chelsea, Hampstead, Kew, North London, Regents Park and Westminster.

[639] **THE NATIONAL TRUST** for places of Historic Interest or Natural Beauty. Regional office: Hughenden Manor, High Wycombe, Bucks HP14 4LA, *Tel*: (01494) 528051; *Fax*: (01494) 463310. *London centres/ associations*: *Ealing Association*: K. Goff, 41 Gloucester Rd, Ealing, London W5 4JA, *Tel*: (020) 8567 1129. *Hamstead Centre*: Miss S.A. Wilson, Flat 25, 5 & 7 Belsize Grove, London NW3 4UT, *Tel*: (020) 7586 9821. *Kensington and Chelsea Association*: Membership secretary, at 12 Saltcoats Rd, London W4 1AR, *Tel*: (020) 7373 2536. *London Centre*: Miss S. Martin, 144 Clarence Gate Gardens, Glentworth St, London NW1 6AN, *Tel*: (020) 7402 6799. *Wimbledon Association*: Miss S. Morrell, 15 Cambridge Close, London SW20 0PT, *Tel*: (020) 8947 2639. *Woodford Green Centre*: D. Weekes, 28 Albion Park, Loughton, Essex IG10 4RB, *Tel*: (020) 8508 9541.

[640] **PUBLIC MONUMENTS AND SCULPTURE ASSOCIATION**. *Administrator/contact for the Central London Archive*: Jo Darke, 72 Lissenden Mansions, Lissenden Gardens, London NW5 1PR, *Tel*: (020) 7485 0566; *Fax*: (020) 7267 1742; work tel (Courtauld Institute: (020) 7873 2614). Concerned with a long term nation-wide recording survey leading to publications.
Contact for the East London regional archive: Jane Riches, Faculty of Design, Engineering and the Built Environment, University of East London, Holbrook Rd, London E15, *Tel*: (020) 8590 7000/7722, ext, 3250/3263; *Fax*: (020) 8849 3686; *Email*: j.riches@uel.ac.uk.
Contact for South West London regional archive: Fran Lloyd, Head of Art and Design History, Kingston University, Knights Park, Kingston, Surrey KT1 2QS, *Tel*: (020) 8547 7112; *Fax*: (020) 8547 7011.

[641] **ROYAL COMMISSION ON THE HISTORIC MONUMENTS OF ENGLAND (RCHME)**. Kemble Drive, Swindon, Wilts SN2 2GZ, *Tel*: (01793) 414 6000. Recording projects often cover building types. London publications/reports include: *The buildings of London Zoo*, 1993; *Deptford Houses*, 1999; *Islington chapels*, 1992; *The London Custom House*, 1993; *Thames Gateway*. A current project is looking at London's town halls, with an exhibition and publication planned for mid 1999.
NB: RCHME is now part of English Heritage (see above), but the National Monuments Record is still at Swindon, and older publications are available from there.

[642] **SAVE BRITAIN'S HERITAGE**. 77 Cowcross St, London EC1M 6BP, *Tel*: (020) 7253 3500; *Fax*: (020) 7253 3400; *Email*: save@btinternet.com. Est. in 1975 (European Architectural Heritage Year) to campaign publicly for endangered historic buildings. Its long lists of reports includes the following London titles currently in print:
Capital opportunities, 1991 (a catalogue of listed buildings at risk in Greater London which are in need of restoration); *From splendour to banality*: rebuilding the City of London 1945-1983, published 1983 (photographic survey of demolished buildings and of those that have replaced them); *Hoop and Grapes*, 1981 (the historical and architectural importance of the pub, and its neighbour, 46 Aldgate High Street); *Mansion House Square scheme: stop it*, 1982; *Mies is great: London is greater* (Terry Farrell's conservation scheme for the Mansion House Square site); *Stop the destruction of Bucklesbury* (on number 1 Poultry site, a review of its two thousand year history); *Vanishing London: a catalogue of decay*, 1979.
Out of print titles include:
Billinggate report, 1980; *The colossus of Battersea* (Battersea Power Station), 1981; *Last chance for Limehouse?* 1986; *Save Broad Street Station*, 1982; *Save Union Chapel* (in Islington), 1981.

[643] **SURVEY OF LONDON** (Royal Commission on the Historical Monuments of England). 55 Blandford St, London W1H 3AF, *Tel*: (020) 7208 8242; *Fax*: (020) 7208 8240. The survey was founded by the architect C.R. Ashbee and friends in 1894 as the 'committee for surveying the memorials of Greater London', with the support of the London County Council. The partnership between the 'amateur' committee and the LCC ended in the early 1950's and the LCC and later the GLC took over responsibility for the series of parish volumes surveying general topography and architectural history, and the monograph

volumes studying specific buildings usually under threat or undergoing change. Since 1986 the survey has been part of the ROHME. In 1994 there was a special celebratory volume written by the general editor Hermione Hobhouse: *London survey'd: the work of the survey of London 1894-1994*, 96pp with 66 illustrations.

The current staff and their direct lines are as follows:

Head of Survey (General editor): John Greenacombe, *Tel*: (020) 7208 8250.

Team members: Alan Cox (expert on bricks), *Tel*: (020) 7208 8249; Malcolm Dickson, ext. 8243; Stephen Porter (expert on 17th century), ext. 8247; Harriet Richardson (expert on hospitals), ext. 8253; Catherine Steeves, ext. 8252; Philip Temple, ext. 8245; Colin Thom, ext. 8248; Rosalind Woodhouse, ext. 8251.

Area by area index to the Survey of London main series numbered volumes, and numbered monographs:

ACTON: *East Acton Manor House* (Mon. 7, 1921).

BARKING: *Eastbury Manor House* (Mon 11, 1917).

BLACKHEATH: *Morden College* (Mon 10, 1916).

BROMLEY BY BOW: Vol 1, 1900; *Old Palace* (Mon 3, 1901).

CHELSEA: Vol 2, 1909; Vol 4, 1913; *Old Church* (Vol 7, 1921); *Royal Hospital* (Vol 11, 1927).

CITY OF LONDON: *Crosby Place* (Mon 9, 1908); *St Helen, Bishopsgate* (Vol 9, 1924); *Church of All Hallows, Barking-by-the-Tower* (Vol 12, 1929, and Vol 15, 1934); *St Bride's Church* (Mon 15, 1944); *College of Arms* (Mon 16, 1963).

CLERKENWELL: Vols 47 and 48 in progress.

COVENT GARDEN: *Theatre Royal, Drury Lane; and Royal Opera House* (Vol 35, 1970); *Parish of St Paul* (Vol 36, 1970).

FULHAM: *Sandford House* (Mon 8, 1907).

GREENWICH: *The Queen's House* (Mon 14, 1937).

HACKNEY: *Brooke House* (Mon 5, 1904); Vol 28, 1960.

HAMMERSMITH: Vol 6, 1915.

HYDE PARK: Vol 46 in preparation.

ICKENHAM (Hillingdon): *Swakeleys* (Mon 13, 1933).

KENSINGTON: *Northern Kensington* (Vol 37, 1973); *Museums area* (Vol 38, 1975); *Brompton* (Vol 41, 1983); *Kensington Square to Earl's Court* (Vol 42, 1986).

KNIGHTSBRIDGE: Vol 45 in preparation.

LAMBETH: *South Bank & Vauxhall* (Vol 23, 1951); *Southern Lambeth* (Vol 26, 1956); *County Hall* (Mon 17, 1991).

LEYTON: *The Great House* (Mon 4, 1903).

MAYFAIR: *Grosvenor Estate, general history* (Vol 39, 1977); *Grosvenor Estate, buildings* (Vol 40, 1980).

POPLAR: *Poplar, Blackwall, and the Isle of Dogs* (Vols 43-44, 1994).

ST GILES-IN-THE-FIELDS: *Lincoln's Inn Fields* (Vol 3, 1912; Vol 5, 1914).

ST JAMES', WESTMINSTER: *South of Piccadilly* (Vols 29-30, 1960); *North of Piccadilly* (Vols 31-32, 1963).

ST MARTIN-IN-THE-FIELDS: *Charing Cross* (Vol 16, 1935); *Strand* (Vol 18, 1937); *Trafalgar Square area* (Vol 20, 1940).

ST PANCRAS: *Cromwell House* (Mon 12, 1926); *Highgate Village* (Vol 17, 1936); *Old St Pancras and Kentish Town* (Vol 19, 1938); *Tottenham Court Road area* (Vol 21, 1949); *King's Cross* (Vol 24, 1952).

SHOREDITCH: Vol 8, 1922.

SOHO (PARISH OF ST ANNE): Vols 33-34, 1966.

SOUTHWARK: *Bankside* (Vol 22, 1950); *St George's Fields* (Vol 25, 1955).

SPITALFIELDS & MILE END: *Trinity Hospital* (Mon 1, 1896); *Spitalfield & Mile End New Town* (Vol 27, 1957).

STEPNEY: *St Dunstan's Church* (Mon 6, 1905).

STRATFORD BOW: *St Mary's Church* (Mon 2, 1900).

WESTMINSTER (PARISH OF ST MARGARET): Vol 19, 1926; *Whitehall* (Vol 13, 1930; Vol 14, 1931).

---

* ARCHIVES: ORGANISATIONS FOR USERS AND PROFESSIONALS *

[644] **BRITISH RECORDS ASSOCIATION** ('working for archives'). 40 Northampton Rd, London EC1B 0HB, *Tel*: (020) 7833 0428; *Fax*: (020) 7833 0416. Est. in 1932, a forum for all interested in archives. The association's Records Preservation Section acts as a clearing house and rescue body for historic documents. The archives and the user series includes: *Sources for the history of London, 1939-45*, a guide and bibliography by Heather Creaton. There are also guides to the records of the established church in England, Irish history, schools, English non-conformity, manors, and the police.

[645] **BUSINESS ARCHIVES COUNCIL**. 101 Whitechapel High St, London E1 7RE, *Tel*: (020) 7247 0024. Publishes a *Directory of corporate archives* (4th edition: 1998).

[646] **GREATER LONDON ARCHIVES NETWORK (GLAN)**. *Secretary*: Kath Shawcross, Archive and Local Studies Section, Central Library, St Nicholas Way, Sutton, Surrey SM1 1EA, *Tel*: (020) 8770 4745. Est. in 1982, the network is open

to all those engaged in the care of archives and local studies collections in the Greater London areas. There are meetings, visits and training sessions. There are two directories: *London local archives*: a directory of local authority record offices and libraries; and *Film archives in London* (range and dates of London local authority film collections and viewing facilities, with the proceedings of a one-day conference on film archive). *Greater London History Sources* will be based on the individual guides produced by archives and libraries; to be a multi-volume series, published by the Corporation of London. The first volume covering the city of London is in preparation. There is also a newsletter *Metropolitan Lines*.

Issue No 37, February 1995 of *Metropolitan Lines* has articles on the records of London Transport, the Post Office, the Metropolitan Police, and the London Fire and Civil Defence Authority.

[647] **LABOUR HERITAGE**. *Contact*: Irene Wagner, 19 Museum Chambers, Bury Place, London WC1A 2NH, *Tel*: (020) 7405 5272.

[648] **LONDON ARCHIVE USERS FORUM (LAUF)**. *Publicity officer*: Simon Fowler (archivist at S.O.G.), 13 Grovewood, Sandycombe Rd, Kew, Richmond, Surrey TW9 3NF, *Tel*: (020) 8296 8794. *Membership secretary*: Mrs D. Bradley, 6 Ariel Court, Ashchurch Park Villas, London W12 9SR. Est. in 1986 to 'represent the interests of users of record offices, public and private, in the London area'. There are regular visits and an annual conference. There is a regular newsletter.

[649] **SOCIETY OF ARCHIVISTS**. 40 Northampton Rd, London EC1R 0HB, *Tel*: (020) 7278 8630; *Fax*: (020) 7278 2107. Est. in 1954 as the professional society for archivists, archive conservators and record managers. Publications cover preservation and conservation, records management and training.

[650] **VOLUNTARY ACTION HISTORY SOCIETY**. *Secretary* at: The National Centre for Volunteering, Regent's Wharf, 8 All Saints St, London N1 9RL, *Tel*: (020) 8520 8902; *Fax*: (020) 7520 8910. Est. in 1991 'for the historical analysis of voluntary action and the history of charitable and voluntary organisations'. Seminars are organised and there are plans to set up a major archive resource for charity records, and to develop a computerised bibliographic database. There is a newsletter *Voluntary Tradition* and there are plans to develop a journal.

* THE ARTS IN GENERAL *

[651] **THE FESTIVAL OF BRITAIN SOCIETY**. *Contact*: George Simner, 23 Langton Avenue, East Ham, London E6 6AN. Formed in 1989 to bring together people interested in the events of 1951 and the Festival of Britain, organised by Sir Gerald Barry as 'a tonic to the nation'. In 1998 there were two exhibitions - at Portsmouth Museum: 'Spirit of 51', and at Plumstead Museum, London Borough of Greenwich ' Remember 51: the Festival of Britain'. A newsletter is issued.

[652] **LONDON ARTS BOARD**. Elme House, 133 Long Acre, London WC2E 9AF, *Tel*: (020) 7240 1313; *Fax*: (020) 7670 2400; *Website*: http.//www.arts.org.uk/lab.

[653] **LONDON ARTS CAFE**. *Administrator/contact*: Mireille Galinou, 108 Boundaries Rd, London SW12 8HQ, *Tel*: (020) 8767 7148 (evenings). This small membership organisation has been established by a curator (Paintings, Prints and Drawings) at the Museum of London as 'a forum for viewing, expressing and discovering all forms of contemporary urban art. Its aim is to highlight urban artistic developments in the capital, in the United Kingdom and all over the world. Its mission is to encourage a reflection on cities through urban art'. A newsletter is issued and there is an interesting, unusual programme of specially curated exhibitions, related events, and cultural visits and parties in off-beat venues.

* BUSINESS AND REGENERATION *

[654] **CENTRAL LONDON PARTNERSHIP**. 1 Hobhouse Court, Suffolk St, London SW1, *Tel*: (020) 7665 1550.

[655] **CITY FRINGE PARTNERSHIP**. c/o Economic Development Unit, PO Box 270, Guildhall, London EC2P 2EJ, *Tel*: (020) 7332 3603. Formed in November 1995 by the Corporation of London and the London Boroughs of Hackney, Islington and Tower Hamlets aiming 'to examine ways to alleviate the economic deprivation and physical dilapidation evident in the areas immediately surrounding the City'. Its membership includes a wide range of funding and development agencies and community trusts.

[656] **ENGLISH PARTNERSHIPS** - London office (excluding Greenwich Peninsula and Royal Docks). 58-60 St Katharine's Way, London E1 9LB, *Tel*: (020) 7680 2000; *Fax*: (020) 7680 2040.

[657] **GOVERNMENT OFFICE FOR LONDON**. Riverwalk House, 157/161 Millbank, London SW1, *Tel*: (020) 7217 3222.

[658] **GREATER LONDON ENTERPRISE**. 28 Park St, London SE1 9EQ, *Tel*: (020) 7403 0300; *Fax*: (020) 7403 1742; *Email*: gle@geo2.poptel.org.uk.

[659] **LONDON CHAMBER OF COMMERCE AND INDUSTRY**. 33 Queen St, London EC4R 1AP, *Tel*: (020) 7248 4444; *Fax*: (020) 7489 0391; *Email*: lcc@london.co.uk. *Website*: www.london.co.uk.

[660] **LONDON DEVELOPMENT PARTNERSHIP**. 301 Central Market, Smithfield, London EC1A 9LY, *Tel*: (020) 7248 5555; *Fax*: (020) 7248 8877.

[661] **LONDON ENTERPRISE AGENCY**. 4 Snow Hill, London EC1A 2BS, *Tel*: (020) 7238 3000; *Fax*: (020) 7329 0226; *Email*: sbds@lenta.demon.co.uk.

[662] **LONDON FIRST/LONDON FIRST CENTRE**. 1 Hobhouse Court, Suffolk St, London SW1Y 4HH, *Tel*: (020) 7665 1550; *Fax*: (020) 7665 1501; *Email*: staff@london-first.co.uk; *Website*: www.london-first.co.uk.
London First is a business campaign group concerned with increasing skills levels in London and improving the transport system. The London First Centre involves business leaders in promoting London overseas as the world's business capital. It is concerned too with building and co-ordinating a network of partnerships to improve and promote London's subregions, with East London as the major unexploited opportunity area, and to market London as the Millennium City, especially facilitating the development of new hotels. A booklet *100 facts on London* is published (5th edition: 1998).

[663] **LONDON MANUFACTURING GROUP (LMG)** and **MADE IN LONDON**. *Contact*: Alia Ilyas, c/o London Chamber of Commerce, 33 Queen St, London EC4R 1AP, *Tel*: (020) 7203 1829; *Fax*: (020) 7203 1883. Issues a newsletter *Capital Goods*.

[664] **SOUTH BANK EMPLOYERS GROUP**. 99 Upper Ground, London SE1 9PP, *Tel*: (020) 7928 6193; *Fax*: (020) 7620 1608. The group is an association of the major businesses and cultural organisations based in the area between Westminster and Blackfriars Bridges and works to transform the area for employees, residents and visitors. The group's public art programme seeks to involve artists and the local community in transforming the locality and some 33 banners have been installed. There is also a marketing group. SBEG works with other local people: with residents, traders, local councillors and MP's through the *South Bank Partnership* and the *South Bank Forum*. It works with councils on both sides of the Thames through the *Cross River Partnership*. A booklet *South Bank at the crossroads* surveys recent achievements and preoccupations. A directory *South Bank First*, of local businesses and services is issued, and there is a quarterly magazine/newsletter *South Bank News*.

* CEMETERIES *

There are cemetery friends organisations in a number of boroughs: Camden, Hackney, Haringey, Kensington, Lambeth, Tower Hamlets.
The national organisation is [665] **NATIONAL FEDERATION OF CEMETERY FRIENDS**. *Hon. secretary*: Gwyneth Stokes, 42 Chestnut Grove, South Croydon CB2 7LH, *Tel*: (020) 8651 5090. The newsletter contains much useful information.
An associate member is the [666] **LIVING CHURCHYARD AND CEMETERY PROJECT**. *Contact*: David Manning, The Arthur Rank Centre, National Agricultural Centre, Stoneleigh Park, Warwick CV8 2LZ, *Tel*: (01203) 696969. It has successfully encouraged conservation and sympathetic management in many churchyards throughout Britain and cemeteries are now included.
An important publication, with much information, outstanding photographs, extensive bibliography and biographical index is: *London cemeteries: an illustrated guide and gazetteer*, by Hugh Meller, 3rd edition, 1994, published by Scolar Press.
The Society of Genealogists publishers *Greater London cemeteries and crematoria*, by P.S. Wolfson, revised by C. Webb (3rd edition: 1994).

* CHURCH: denominational societies *

[667] **BAPTIST HISTORICAL SOCIETY**. *Secretary*: Stephen Copson, 60 Strathmore Avenue, Hitchin, Herts SG5 1ST, *Tel*: (01462) 431816; *Fax*: (01462) 442548; *Email*: slcopson@dial.pipex.com.

[668] **CHAPELS SOCIETY**. *Secretary*: Christina Van Melzen, Rookery Farmhouse, Laxfield, Woodbridge, Suffolk IP13 8JA, *Tel*: (01986) 798308.

[669] **CONGREGATIONAL HISTORY CIRCLE**. *Secretary*: Dr Alan Argent, The Flat, Trinity Congregational Church, St Matthew's Rd, London SW2 1NF.

[670] **FRIENDS HISTORICAL SOCIETY**. *Secretary*: Howard F. Gregg, 44 Seymour Rd, Wandsworth, London SW18 5JA, *Tel*: (020) 8874 7727.

[671] **HUGUENOT SOCIETY**. *Secretary*: Randolph Vigne, 53 Cornwall Gardens, London SW7 4BG.

[672] **STRICT BAPTIST HISTORICAL SOCIETY**. *Secretary*: Kenneth Dix, 38 French's Avenue, Dunstable, Beds LU6 1BH.

[673] **UNITED REFORMED CHURCH SOCIETY**. *Secretary*: Rev. Elizabeth J. Brown, 7 Castle Grove Avenue, Leeds LS6 4BS.

[674] **WESLEY HISTORICAL SOCIETY**. *Secretary*: Mrs E. Dorothy Graham, 34 Spiceland Rd, Birmingham B31 1NJ.

The umbrella organisation is the [675] **ASSOCIATION OF DENOMINATIONAL/HISTORICAL SOCIETIES AND COGNATE LIBRARIES**. *Contact*: Howard F. Gregg (Friends Historical Society, above).

---

* CINEMA AND FILM *

[676] **CINEMA THEATRE ASSOCIATION**. *Membership secretary*: Neville Taylor, Flat 1, 128 Gloucester Terrace, London W2 6HP. *Sales officer*: Jeremy Buck, 32 Pelham Rd, Wood Green, London N22 6LN. Est. in 1967 by journalist Eric George. There is an illustrated magazine *Picture House* and a bulletin. Books on London cinemas currently stocked include: *Cinemas of Camden; The big five: Lewisham's super cinemas; London's Astorias; Gazetteer of Greater London suburban cinemas; London's West End cinemas*.

[677] **THE LONDON FILM ARCHIVE**. 78 Mildmay Park, Newington Green, London N1 4PR, *Tel*: (020) 7923 4074; *Fax*: (020) 7241 7929. Can supply a vast array of London images from 1895 onwards in colour or black and white on high quality 16mm and 35mm film.

[678] **LONDON FILM COMMISSION**. 20 Euston Centre, Regents Place, London NW1 3JH, *Tel*: (020) 7387 8787; *Fax*: (020) 7387 8788; *Email*: ifc@lonfon-film.co.uk.

---

* COMMUNITY ORGANISATIONS *

[679] **COMMUNITY DEVELOPMENT FOUNDATION**. 60 Highbury Grove, London N5 2AG, *Tel*: (020) 7226 5375.

[680] **COMMUNITY MATTERS** (previously the National Federation of Community Organisations). 8/9 Upper St, Islington, London N1 0PQ.

Community Trusts:
Some 8 Greater London community trusts are members of the [681] **ASSOCIATION OF COMMUNITY TRUSTS AND FOUNDATIONS**. 4 Bloomsbury Square, London WC1, *Tel*: (020) 7831 0033. Current membership of some 50 organisations nationally. A small London Unit exists to encourage expansion in the Greater London area.

[682] **LONDON NORTH-EAST COMMUNITY FOUNDATION**. *Director*: Christopher Legge, PO Box 77, Ilford, Essex IG1 1EB, *Tel*: (020) 8553 9469. Currently covers Barking, Newham and Redbridge.

[683] **SOUTH EAST LONDON COMMUNITY FOUNDATION**. *Director*: Kevin Ireland, Room 6, Winchester House, 11 Cranmer Rd, London SW9 6EJ, *Tel*: (020) 7582 5117. Covers Greenwich, Lambeth, Lewisham and Southwark.

[684] **THAMES COMMUNITY FOUNDATION**. *Director*: Sandy Gilmour, Laboratory of the Government Chemist, Victoria House, Queen's Rd, Teddington, Middx TW11 0LY, *Tel*: (020) 8943 5525. Covers Richmond and Kingston.

Development trusts:
[685] **DEVELOPMENT TRUSTS ASSOCIATION**. 20 Conduit Place, London W2 1HZ, *Tel*: (020) 7706 4951; *Fax*: (020) 7706 8447; *Email*: info@dta.org.uk. Development trusts are 'Community based organisations working for the sustainable regeneration of their area through a mixture of economics, environmental, cultural and social initiatives'. Heritage and tourist projects are often involved.

Funding:
[686] **LONDON BOROUGHS GRANTS**. 5th Floor, Regal House, London Rd, Twickenham TW1 3QS, *Tel*: (020) 8891 5021; *Fax*: (020) 8891 5874; *Email*: info@lbgrants.uk; *Website*: www.lbgrants.uk. Funds some 650 organisations from an annual budget of currently £28.3 million. Press and public relations manager: Ian Brown, *Tel*: (020) 8831 6919.

[687] **THE TRUST FOR LONDON**. 6 Middle St, London EC1A 7PH, *Tel*: (020) 7606 6145; *Fax*: (020) 7600 1866. Est. in 1986 with an endowment resulting from sales of assets of the former GLC, the trust is managed by the City Parochial Foundation also at the above address, and funds small groups in any London borough concerned with helping disadvantaged and minority people. A historical account of the City Parochial Foundation 1891-1991, by Victor Belcher is available.

* 'UMBRELLA' ORGANISATIONS/COUNCILS FOR ADJACENT COUNTIES *

Essex:
[688] **ESSEX ARCHAEOLOGICAL AND HISTORICAL CONGRESS**. *Secretary*: Martin Stuchfield, Lowe Hill House, Stratford St Mary, Suffolk CO7 7JX, *Tel*: (01206) 37239. *Editor of Essex Journal*: Michael Beale, The Laurels, The Street, Great Waltham, Chelmsford, Essex CM3 1DE, *Tel*: (01245) 360344.

Hertfordshire:
[689] **HERTFORDSHIRE ARCHAEOLOGICAL COUNCIL**. *Secretary*: Mrs W. Parry, Mill Green Museum, Hatfield, Herts AL9 5PD, *Tel*: (017072) 271362.

[690] **HERTFORDSHIRE ASSOCIATION FOR LOCAL HISTORY**. *Chairman*: David Short. *Secretary*: Bridget Howlett, 15 Coleridge Close, Hitchin, Herts. Est. in 1949, and until 1991 known as the Hertfordshire Local History Council. Publishes a journal *Hertfordshire's Past* twice a year. Talks, and an annual symposium with exhibitions in November; and maintains a register of research and writing in local history. Network of people throughout county recording changes taking place in localities today.

Kent:
[691] **COUNCIL FOR KENTISH ARCHAEOLOGY**. *Contact*: Brian Philp, 5 Harvest Bank Rd, West Wickham, Kent BR4 9DL. Publishes the quarterly *Kent Archaeological Review*.

[692] **KENT HISTORY FEDERATION**. *Contact*: Miss E.I. Oxley, 48 Beverley Avenue, Sidcup DA15 8HE. Publishes *Journal of Kent History*.

Surrey:
[693] **SURREY LOCAL HISTORY COUNCIL**. *Secretary*: Mrs A.E. Mitton-Worsell, c/o Guildford Institute of University of Surrey, Ward St, Guildford, Surrey GU1 4LH, *Tel*: (01483) 65821.

* ESSEX ORGANISATIONS *

[694] **ESSEX ARCHITECTURAL RESEARCH SOCIETY**. *Contact*: Kathleen Pollard, 4 Nelmes Way, Hornchurch RM11 2QZ, *Tel*: (01708) 473646.

[695] **ESSEX HISTORICAL BUILDINGS GROUP**. *Contact*: Alan Bayford, 12 Westfield Avenue, Chelmsford CM1 1SF, *Tel*: (01245) 256102.

[696] **ESSEX SOCIETY FOR ARCHAEOLOGY AND HISTORY**. *Contact address*: 70 Duke St, Chelmsford CM1 1JP. Lectures, and excursions to historical sites. Annual newsletter *Essex Archaeology and History*.

[697] **FRIENDS OF ESSEX CHURCHES**. *Contact*: Mrs M. Blaxell, 5 Brookhurst Close, Springfield Rd, Chelmsford CM8 6DX.

[698] **FRIENDS OF HISTORIC ESSEX**. *Contact address*: 43 Bouverie Rd, Chelmsford CM2 0UF, *Tel*: (01245) 609543.

[699] **LOCAL HISTORY CENTRE**. University of Essex, Wivenhoe Park, Colchester CO4 3SQ.

[700] **COUNTY OF MIDDLESEX TRUST**. *Events director*: Clifford Batten, 23 Lowdell Close, Yiewsley, Middx, *Tel*: (01895) 420613.

[701] **FRIENDS OF THE COUNTY OF MIDDLESEX**. *Contact address*: PO Box 102, Feltham, Middx TW13 6SF. The organisation was est. in 1987 'to promote, protect and preserve the identity, heritage and history of the County of Middlesex ... to counteract the daily undermining of the County by the media, mapmakers and bureaucrats'. The Friends' local government sub-committee is in regular contact with government ministers and supports and works closely with the Association of British Counties and the Local Government Reform Group.

[702] **MIDDLESEX SOCIETY**. *Chairman*: Les Doble, 261 Greenford Avenue, Hanwell, London W7 1AD, *Tel*: (020) 8578 5182.

* FAMILY HISTORY AND GENEALOGY IN GENERAL *

[703] **ASSOCIATION OF GENEALOGISTS AND RECORD AGENTS (AGRA)**. *Secretariat at*: 29 Badgers Close, Horsham, W. Sussex RH12 5RH. Membership list available (£2.50).

[704] **FAMILY TREE MAGAZINE**. 61 Great Whyte, Ramsey, Huntingdon PE17 1HL, *Tel*: (01487) 814050; *Fax*: (01487) 711361. This highly popular, yet very specialist, commercially-run magazine is published by Armstrong, Boon & Marriott, and contains many adverts, book and appeal notices, and has many articles on the entire field of British family history and its diverse organisations. There is also a postal book service.

Family history societies are affiliated to the [705] **FEDERATION OF FAMILY HISTORY SOCIETIES**. Orders for FFHS publications to: 2-4 Killer St, Ramsbottom, Bury, Lancs BL0 9BZ. *Administrator*: Pauline Saul, 5 Morrington Close, Copthorne, Shrewsbury, Shropshire SY3 8XN, *Tel*: (01743) 65505 (author of FFHS *The Family Historian's Enquire Within*, 5th edition). Its newsletter *Family History News and Digest* is a useful source for new publications and there are also the catalogues *Current publications by member societies* (10th edition) and *Current publications by member societies on microfiche* (4th edition). There are practical guides such as *Dating old photographs,* by Robert Pols; *Forming a One-Name Group*, by Derek Palgrave, 4th edition; *Notes on recording monumental inscriptions*, 4th edition, by Penny Pattinson; as well as introductory guides to records.

The FFHS also sells the Genealogical Bibliography Series from S.A. and M.J. Raymond (PO Box 35, Exeter EX1 3YZ, *Tel*: (01392) 462158). This includes two volumes on London and Middlesex. *London occupations* is planned as a complementary volume to *Occupations: sources for genealogists*. The *Gibson Guides for Genealogists* cover a wide range of record sources and includes *Lists of Londoners*.

[706] **GUILD OF ONE NAME STUDIES**. 14 Charterhouse Buildings, Goswell Rd, London EC1M 7BA. *Internet*: www.one-name.org. Publishes a quarterly journal, and the *Register of One Name Studies* (14th edition).

[707] **INSTITUTE OF HERALDIC AND GENEALOGICAL STUDIES**. Northgate, Canterbury, Kent, *Tel*: (01227) 768664; *Fax*: (01227) 765617; *Email*: librarian@ihgs.ac.uk. Conducts academic research, runs courses, and has an extensive library.

[708] **SOCIETY OF GENEALOGISTS**. 14 Charterhouse Buildings, Goswell Rd, London EC1M 7BA, *Tel*: (020) 7251 8799. Est. in 1911 to promote and encourage the study of genealogy and heraldry. Runs lectures, courses and visits, and organises an annual Family History Fair at the Royal Horticultural Society Hall, Creycoat St, London SW1, and a comparable fair is planned for the National Exhibition Centre in Birmingham. There is a major library (Librarian: Sue Gibbons), and catalogues of holdings are published. There is also a bookshop which is now on-line at www.sog.org.uk. There is a series of guides *My ancestors were ...* (eg. Baptists, Jewish, Londoners). There are two quarterly journals *The Genealogists Magazine* and *Computers in Genealogy*.

* FAMILY HISTORY SOCIETIES *

The following societies were affiliated to the [709] **FEDERATION OF FAMILY HISTORY SOCIETIES**, The Benson Room, Birmingham and Midland Institute, Margaret St, Birmingham B3 3BS. The Federation's publications include: *Current* *publications by member societies* (9th edition: 1997), *Current publications on microfiche* (4th edition: 1997), and *Family History News and Digest*.

[710] **EAST OF LONDON FAMILY HISTORY SOCIETY**. *General secretary*: Mrs Vera Bangs, 23 Louvaine Avenue, Wickford, Essex SS12 0DP. *Membership secretary*: Mrs J. Crompton, 1 Pegelm Gardens, Hornchurch, Essex RM11 3NU. *Journal (Cockney Ancestor) editor*: Mrs J. Renton, 'Tawneys', 27 Lodge Lane, Locks Heath SO31 6QY. Est. in 1978, the society covers the London boroughs of Barking, Hackney, Havering, Newham, Redbridge and Tower Hamlets.

[711] **EAST SURREY FAMILY HISTORY SOCIETY**. *Secretary*: Rosemary Turner, 27 Burley Close, London SW16 4QQ. *Membership secretary*: Mrs Wyn Poate, 270 Tithe Pit Shaw Lane, Warlingham, Surrey CR6 9AQ. *Journal editor*: Peter Charlish, 9 Linden Close, Thames Ditton, Surrey KT7 0DE. Est. in 1977, the society includes the London boroughs south of the River Thames, formerly part of the ancient County of Surrey. Meetings are held in Sutton, Caterham, Croydon, Southwark and Richmond.

[712] **ESSEX SOCIETY FOR FAMILY HISTORY**. *Secretary*: Mrs Glynis Morris, 56 Armond Rd, Witham, Essex CM8 2HA, *Tel*: (01376) 516315. *Membership secretary*: Miss Ann Turner, 1 Robin Close, Great Bentley, Colchester CO7 8QH. *Journal editor*: (*Essex Family History* issued quarterly): Mrs G. Kelly, 66 Seymours, Harlow CM19 5NQ.

[713] **HERTFORDSHIRE FAMILY AND POPULATION HISTORY SOCIETY**. *Secretary*: Ken Garner, 2 Mayfair Close, St Albans, Herts AL4 9TN. *Email*: hfphs@binternet.com. *Editor of journal* (quarterly *Hertfordshire People*): Ian Waller, 16 Collingtree, Stopsley, Luton LU2 8HN. Publishes: directory of members interests; some 86 militia list (yearly records, prepared by the constable in each village of the able-bodied men fit for military service, from the mid 18th century to the Napoleonic wars); some 63 monumental inscriptions records.

[714] **HILLINGDON FAMILY HISTORY SOCIETY**. *Administrative secretary*: Mrs Gill May, 20 Moreland Drive, Gerrards Cross, Bucks SL9 8BB. *Email*: Gillmay@dial.pipex.com. The society covers the London Borough of Hillingdon, which embraces the nine ancient parishes once part of the county of Middlesex: Harefield, Ruislip, Ickenham, Hillingdon, Cowley, Hayes, West Drayton, Harlington and Harmondsworth. Publishes: Directory of members interests, 1977; a guide to sources *Family History in Hillingdon*; monumental inscriptions; *Church School, Ickenham, records of pupils and teachers 1873-1929*; and a series of 12 guides on Beginning Genealogy, by Arthur Dark.

[715] **LONDON AND NORTH MIDDLESEX FAMILY HISTORY SOCIETY**. *Secretary*: Mrs Susan Lumas, 7 Mount Pleasant Rd, New Malden, Surrey KT3 3JZ. *Membership secretary*: Mrs Julie Chapman, 76 Church Rd, Tottenham, London N17 8AJ. *Editor of journal* (quarterly *Metropolitan*): Harvey Haynes, 40 Cowper Rd, Harpenden, Herts AL5 5NG. Est. in 1978, the society covers the London boroughs of Brent, Camden, Enfield, Haringey, Islington, the City of London and Marylebone.

[716] **NORTH WEST KENT FAMILY HISTORY SOCIETY**. *Secretary*: Mrs S.M. Rhys, 6 Windermere Rd, Bexleyheath, Kent DA7 6PW. *Membership secretary*: Mr P. Gosney, 28 Ingram Rd, Dartford, Kent DA1 1JL. The society has a website at: http://users.ac.uk/~malcolm/NWKFHS. The society covers the London boroughs of Geenwich, Lewisham, Bromley and Bexley. Publishes: directory of members interests, 1994; a quarterly journal, 1851 census index series, monumental inscriptions, parish registers, indexes to the Bromley Journal and West Kent Herald, etc. Two recent publications are: *West Kent sources*: a genealogical guide to research in the Diocese of Rochester, 3rd edition; and *Memories of Lewisham in the late 19th century and early 20th century*. *Publications officer*: Mrs B. Attwaters, 141 Princes Rd, Dartford, Kent DA1 3HJ.

[717] **WALTHAM FOREST FAMILY HISTORY SOCIETY**. *Secretary*: J.F. Bowen, 1 Gelsthorpe Rd, Romford, Essex RM5 2NB.

[718] **WEST MIDDLESEX FAMILY HISTORY SOCIETY**. *Secretary*: Mrs Mavis Burton, 10 Westway, Heston, Middx TW5 0JE. *Membership secretary*: Peter Roe, 117 Fernside Avenue, Feltham TW13 7BQ. *Editor of quarterly journal*: Yvonne Mason, 65 St Margarets Grove, East Twickenham, Middx TW1 1JF. The society was est. in 1978 and covers the London boroughs of Ealing, Hammersmith, Harrow, Hounslow and Kensington.

[719] **WEST SURREY FAMILY HISTORY SOCIETY**. *Secretary*: Mrs S.E. McQuire, Deer Dell, Botany Hill, Sands, Farnham GU10 1LZ. *Membership secretary*: Miss Anne Ross, 5 Blaise Close, Farnborough GU14 7EW. *Publications officer*: Mrs Rosemary Cleaver, 17 Lane End Drive, Knaphill, Woking. Surrey GU21 2QQ. The society does not 'cover' any parts of Greater London, although many of its publications do so. The London and Middlesex publications are obtainable from Middx. societies: 41 research aids, many indexes, monumental inscriptions, and parish registers.

[720] **WESTMINSTER AND CENTRAL MIDDLESEX FAMILY HISTORY SOCIETY**. *Secretary*: Keith Rookledge, 2 West Avenue, Pinner, Middx HA5 5BY. *Email*: rookledge@compuserve.com. *Membership secretary*: Mrs June Brown, 901 Harrow Rd, Wembley, Middx HA0 2RH. *Journal editors*: Mr and Mrs Don Felgate, 80 Coaldale Drive, Stanmore, Middx HA8 2QF. Est. in 1978 the society covers Brent, City of Westminster, Ealing, Harrow and Hillingdon.

[721] **WOOLWICH AND DISTRICT FAMILY HISTORY SOCIETY**. *Secretary*: Mrs Pat Saunders, 132 Belvedere Rd, Bexleyheath, Kent DA7 4PF. *Membership secretary*: Peter Wood, 28 Marne Avenue, Welling, Kent DA16 2EY. *Journal editor*: Sue Holmes, 6 Barth Rd, Plumstead, London SE18 1SH.

* SPECIALIST FAMILY HISTORY SOCIETIES *

[722] **ANGLO-FRENCH FAMILY HISTORY SOCIETY**. *Secretary/Editor of 'French Ancestry' journal*: Patrick Pontet, 31 Collingwood Walk, Andover, Hants SP10 1PU.

[723] **ANGLO-GERMAN FAMILY HISTORY SOCIETY**. *Membership secretary*: Jenny Towey, 14 River Reach, Teddington, Middx TW11 9QL. Est. in 1987, the society has some 2,000 members. Publishes a quarterly journal *Mitteilungsblatt* and booklets on German institutions in England, occupations, civilian internment; and records on microfiche. Indexes of surnames are maintained; there is a postal bookshop service and an extensive library.

[724] **CATHOLIC FAMILY HISTORY SOCIETY**. *Secretary*: Mrs B. Murray, 2 Winscombe Crescent, Ealing, London W5 1AZ. *Editor of journal ' The Catholic Ancestor'*: Michael Gandy, 3 Church Crescent, Whetstone, London N20 0JR.

[725] **JEWISH GENEALOGICAL SOCIETY OF GREAT BRITAIN**. Address for all correspondence is: PO Box 13288, London N3 3WD. *Editor of quarterly journal 'Shemot'*: David Fielker, 66 Farquhar Rd, London SE19 1LT.

[726] **QUAKER FAMILY HISTORY SOCIETY**. *Secretary*: Barry Dackcombe, 32 Ashburnham Rd, Ampthill, Beds MK45 2RH. *Email*: qfhs@mcmail.com; *Internet*: http://www.qfhs.mcmail.com. Est. in 1993. Publishes journal *Quaker Connections* three times a year. Also a directory of members interests, 1995; postal bookshop service; extensive library.

[727] **ROMANY AND TRAVELLER FAMILY HISTORY SOCIETY**. *Secretary*: Mrs Janet Keet-Black, 6 St James' Walk, South Chailey, East Sussex BN8 4BU, *Tel*: (01273) 400699. Publications include a journal *Romany Routes*, and a *Register of Traveller Research*, supplement No 1, 1997.

* GARDENS AND PARKS *

The [728a] **GARDEN HISTORY SOCIETY** is at 77 Cowcross St, London EC1M 6BP, *Tel*: (020) 7608 2409; *Fax*: (020) 7490 2974; *Email*: 10635.3372@compuserve.com. It was est. in 1965 and is now an influential body for historic parks, gardens and designed landscapes. It has a journal and newsletter; with the Victorian Society it published *Public prospects: historic urban parks under threat*; and with the Landscape Design Trust *Historic parks and gardens in the planning system*.

The [728b] **ASSOCIATION OF GARDEN TRUSTS** is at 70 Cowcross St, London EC1, *Tel*: (020) 7251 2610.

[729] **LONDON HISTORIC PARKS AND GARDENS TRUST**. Duck Island Cottage, St James's Park, London SW1A 2BJ, *Tel*: (020) 7839 3969; *Chair*: Pamela Paterson; *Secretary*: Elizabeth Fry. Aims 'to promote education about historic parks and gardens in London and to seek to conserve and enhance these gardens for the education and enjoyment of the public'. Information, research and recording are important activities, and there is an annual journal *The London Gardener*, as well as a newsletter. Proceedings of the last three annual conferences cover: London squares; funding London's heritage landscapes; and London's cemeteries and churchyards: a dying legacy? Lectures are held at the Linnean Society, Burlington House. The Trust also organises the *London Squares Day*.

[730] **MUSEUM OF GARDEN HISTORY**. The Tradescant Trust, Lambeth Palace Rd, London SE1 7LB, *Tel*: (020) 7261 1891. *Hours*: Mon-Fri. 10.30-4; Sun 10.30-5. Part of the churchyard is designed as a 17th century garden.

[731] **THE ROYAL PARKS AGENCY**. *Chief executive*: David Welch, The Old Police House, Hyde Park, London W2 2UH, *Tel*: (020) 7298 2000; *Fax*: (020) 7298 2005. Representatives of the Friends organisations (see under sections for Camden, Greenwich, Kensington, Richmond, Westminster) come together within the ROYAL PARKS FORUM, *Current chair*: Alan Bailey (Chair of Friends of Greenwich Park).

Interesting, illustrated books are available from the Royal Parks office: *London's royal parks: an appreciation*, by Richard Church; *Buildings and monuments in the royal parks*; *Trees of the royal parks: a guide to common and rare species*. There are also guides to the individual parks: St James' Park and Green Park; Greenwich Park; Richmond Park; Bushey Park; Hyde Park and Kensington Gardens; and Regents Park.

Some other recent publications include: *The parks and woodlands of London*, by Andrew Crowe, Fourth Estate, 1987; *The royal parks of London*, by Guy Williams, published by Constable in 1978; *A walk round London's parks*, by Hunter Davies, Hamish Hamilton, 1983; and *Walking London's parks and gardens*, by Geoffrey Young, from New Holland Publishers, 1998.

* HOSPITALS *

Friends organisations are attached to some 100 London hospitals, including all of the large central ones. They are affiliated to the: [732] **NATIONAL ASSOCIATION OF HOSPITAL AND COMMUNITY FRIENDS**, 2nd Floor, Fairfax House, Causton Rd, Colchester, Essex CO1 1RJ, *Tel*: (01206) 761227; *Fax*: (01206) 560244. *Development manager*: Mike Cable.

For hospital records: see entry 800.

* LIBRARIES *

All local studies libraries hold material which extends beyond their boundaries. The following non-council London-wide collections should also be noted.

[733] **BISHOPSGATE INSTITUTE REFERENCE LIBRARY**. 230 Bishopsgate, London EC2M 4QH, *Tel*: (020) 7247 6198. *Librarian*: Alice McKay. Assistant librarian (until October 1998): Anne Oatley. A 22-page centenary history was published in 1991.
The London collection now contains some one million volumes, with parallel collections of maps and illustrations covering the whole of the Inner London area; long, important runs of directories; Howell collection on the Labour movement, early trade unionism, political and economic history 1830-1914; Holyoake collection on the co-operative and secular movements 1820-1900; library of the National Secular Society (with important archive of manuscript material on Charles Bradlaugh), archives of the London Co-operative Society, library of the Freedom Press (East End anarchist organisation), and the Derrick Collection on modern co-operative and distributive movements; most recently the Samuel Raphael papers/archives have been deposited.

[734] **MUSEUM OF LONDON LIBRARY**. 150 London Wall, London EC2Y 5HN, *Tel*: (020) 7814 5588; *Email*: sbrooks@museumoflondon.org.uk. *Library officer*: Sally Brooks. The collection is open only to researchers, by appointment. There are some 4,000 items on London history, topography, archaeology and general arts. Special collections include the Bell collection on the plague and fire, the Warwick Wroth scrapbooks on pleasure gardens and the Tangye collection of Cromwelliana.
Other departments in the museum cover: paintings, prints and drawings; photographs; archaeological archive; printed ephemera (including suffragette collection), all with their curators.

[735] **UNIVERSITY COLLEGE LONDON LIBRARY**. London History Collection, Gower St, London WC1E 6BT, *Tel*: (020) 7504 2827. *Librarian* (subject librarian for history): Michael Jahn. The collection originates from a bequest from Captain Henry Ward in about 1870 and has extensive holdings for the whole of Greater London and consists of some 6,000 volumes, 500 maps and a large pamphlet collection. Most books published after 1914 are on open access, older material and all pamphlets and maps are in store.

Librarians (as opposed to archivists) concerned with local studies in Greater London may be members of the London and Home Counties branch of the Library Association's [736] **LOCAL STUDIES GROUP**. *Chairman*: Mick Scott, Senior librarian, London Metropolitan Archives, 40 Northampton Rd, London EC1R 0HB, *Tel*: (020) 7332 3823.

* SOME NATIONAL LOCAL HISTORY ORGANISATIONS *

[737] **ASSOCIATION OF LOCAL HISTORY TUTORS**. *Secretary*: Mrs Joan Dils, 47 Ramsbury Drive, Earley, Reading, Berks RG6 7RT, *Tel*: (0118) 926 4729. Has some 100 members. Publishes a bulletin.

[738] **BRITISH ASSOCIATION FOR LOCAL HISTORY**. *Contact*: Michael Cowan, PO Box 1576, Salisbury SP2 8SY, *Tel*: (01722) 332158; *Fax*: (01722) 413242. *Current chairman*: David Dymond (an ex-editor of The Local Historian journal

and author of *Writing local history: a practical guide*, BALH, 1988). There is an important publishing programme: the quarterly journal *The Local Historian* contains research articles and reviews and listings of new books received (articles editor: Dr Margaret Bonney, 7 Carisbrooke Park, Knighton, Leicester LE2 3PQ; reviews editor: Peter Christie, 30 Lime Grove, Bideford, North Devon EX39 3JL). *Local History News* is especially useful for its news items on societies, education, archives, libraries and museums (contact address: Michael Cowan, as above). The association publishes practical booklets such as *Recording the present*, by Valerie Norrington, 1989; *Running a local history society*, by Mary Paget, 1988; and *Running a local history fair*, by Vic Gray and Bill Liddell, 1988; also research guides and surveys for specialist areas such as: *From Chantry to Oxfam: a sort history of charities and charity legislation*, by Norman Alvey, 1996; *The late Victorian town*, by Frank Grace, 1991; and *The union workhouse*, by Andy Reid, 1994. The association also sells a selection of books from other publishers.

[739] **HISTORICAL ASSOCIATION**. 59a Kennington Park Rd, London SE11 4JH, *Tel*: (020) 7735 3901. Membership is open to anyone interested in the study or teaching of history. A wide range of pamphlets is published as well as the journal *History*, and *Teaching History*, a newsletter *The Historian*, and the *Annual Bulletin of Historical Literature*. There is a local history committee, chairman: John Hare.

There are a number of London branches, all of which have their own programmes of lectures and events (often, but not exclusively relating to London):

Beckenham & Bromley branch. *Secretary*: Mr P. Ellis, 63 Groveland Rd, Beckenham BR3 3PX, *Tel*: (020) 8650 2826.

Central London branch. *Secretary*: Mrs J. Lewis, 3 Sunnydale Gardens, Mill Hill, London NW7 3PD, *Tel*: (020) 8959 6162.

Ealing branch. *Secretary*: Peter Hounsell, 17 Downing Drive, Greenford, Middx UB6 8BD, *Tel*: (020) 8678 0217.

Hampstead and N.W. London branch. *Secretary*: Mr Hugh Hamilton, 2 Wild Hatch, London NW11 7LD, *Tel*: (020) 8455 8318. *Chairman*: Harry Cobb.

North London branch. *Secretary*: Mr R. Blades, 32 Ashfield Rd, London N14 7JY, *Tel*: (020) 8368 5328. Will probably merge with the Central London branch shortly.

Richmond and Twickenham branch. *Secretary*: Miss C.M. Bartlett, 12 Arnold Crescent, Isleworth, Middx TW7 7NT, *Tel*: (020) 8898 5016.

[740] **OPEN UNIVERSITY HISTORY SOCIETY**. *Membership secretary*: Mr D. Vincent, 53 Studley Rd, Redditch, Worcs B98 7HE. Est. in 1983, currently with some 200 members. Publishes the quarterly newsletter *Open History*.

* MILLENNIUM PROJECTS/EVENTS *

A regional list (including UK-wide projects) is available from the MILLENNIUM COMMISSION, Portland House, Stag Place, London SW1E 2EZ, *Tel*: (020) 7880 2001; *Fax*: (020) 7880 2000; *Internet*: http://www.millennium.gov.uk.

See also: GREENWICH chapter.

Some Central London projects:

[741] **BRITISH AIRWAYS LONDON EYE** (previously the 'Millennium Wheel'). Planned for 2000 the structure will ruse to 135m (450 feet) and offer dramatic and unprecedented views of the river and the city. It has been designed by architects David Marks and Julia Barfield, 50 Bromells Rd, London SW4 0BG, *Tel*: (020) 7738 8080.

[742] **HUNGERFORD BRIDGE**. For publicity, contact Julia Corkey, Westminster City Council, *Tel*: (020) 7641 2354. The project architect is Charles Borthwick, of Lifschutz Davidson.

[743] **MILLENNIUM BRIDGE**. *Project manager*: Chris Wise, Ove Arup & Partners, consultant engineers, 13 Fitzroy St, London W1, *Tel*: (020) 7636 1531.

Also: Tate Gallery of Modern Art, Bankside; British Museum Great Court; Mile End Park; Thames 2000 (piers); Southwark Cathedral; London Zoo Conservation Education Centre; Croydon skyline; Memorial Gates, Constitution Hill; Renue - Millennium initiative, Wandsworth; St Barnabas Church Hall, Ealing; Millennium Centre, Eastbrookend Country Park (Dagenham).

[744] **STRING OF PEARLS MILLENNIUM FESTIVAL**. *Director*: Dylan Hammond; *Administrator*: Penelope Sydenham, 1 Hobhouse Court, Suffolk St, London SW1Y 4HH, *Tel*: (020) 7665 1540/1598. *Fax*: (020) 7665 1537. The publicity pack for this major event states its aims eloquently: 'Many of the great 'building blocks' of society - such as democracy, justice, faith, freedom of speech, education, culture, commerce, technology, medicine and defence - are embodied in buildings and organisations which line the River Thames like a 'string of pearls'. During the year 2000 these organisations will open

themselves up to the public, both physically and intellectually. Some will open their doors for the first time ever. Others will create access to parts of their buildings not previously visited. Many will mount special exhibitions and events which explain what they do and why. Some will collaborate with artists, or one another, to provide a new perspective on their role and meaning. All will be inviting people through their doors to see new things, explore, question and find out'.

[745] Some small enterprises and organisations will be featured alongside the big institutions: The **COUPER COLLECTION**, Riverside Walk, Hester Rd, Battersea, London SW11 4AN, *Tel*: (020) 8871 7572 features the artwork of Max Couper, Thames-based/inspired artist and mariner.

[746] The **SOUTHWARK MYSTERIES**, a new 'Southwark cycle' of mystery plays commissioned especially for the millennium from playwright John Constable: 22 Trinity Church Square, London SE1 4HY, *Email*: mysteries@southwark.org.uk; *Website*: www.southwark.org.uk/mysteries. This is an epic community drama acted out in Southwark Cathedral, the Globe and on the streets of Bankside - presenting a vision of the sacred revealed in the profane history of London's 'outlaw' borough. There will also be street theatre and site-specific drama celebrating the spirit of Southwark, at Bankside; and a performance at the Southwark Playhouse.
The Parish of Waterloo, St John's Church, *Tel*: (020) 7633 9819; (020) 7928 2003; (020) 7928 4470 (vicarage); address for correspondence: 1 Secker St, London SE1 8UF), has plans for a community festival, exhibitions, and access to buildings in Waterloo. The Millennium Green, on the corner of Bayliss and Waterloo Roads, has been masterminded by the [747] **WATERLOO COMMUNITY DEVELOPMENT GROUP**, 14 Bayliss Rd, London SE1, *Tel*: (020) 7633 9291, and will incorporate a new youth centre.

* MUSEUMS *

[748] **LONDON MUSEUMS SERVICE**. *Contacts*: Fiona Talbott, Rowena Ferneley, Frazer Swift, Sara Coker. Ferroners House, Barbican, London EC2Y 8AA, *Tel*: (020) 7600 0219. Est. in 1983 as a division of the South Eastern Museum Service. It provides subscribing members with current information, through newsletters, bulletins and information sheets, grant-aid for museum projects, advice on conservation, registration and guidance for HLF bids, training and support to local authorities with information on museums and heritage policies. The *London Museums Guide* is now in its 6th edition and covers many little known places. There are also thematised leaflet guides: to crime and punishment, gardens, homes of the famous, museums of health and medicine, ships and seafarers. A report *New visions for London's museums* was published in 1996. It contains case studies on the Royal Arsenal, Croydon Museum, The Grange Museum, Neasden, the London Museums of Health and Medicine Group, and the Central London Museums Group 'Victorians' education pack.

Museums in Greater London are divided into groups, for: Central London, North and East London, South London and West London.
Collectively they are represented by the *London Museums Consultative Committee* and the *London Federation of Museums and Galleries*. There are also a *London Curatorial Advisors Network*; a *London Museums and Galleries Marketing Officers Association*, and a group for journalists *London Museums and Attractions Press*.
There are also London groups within specialist groups: the Group for Education in Museums, and the Museums and Galleries Disability Association.
There are also groups for different fields of activity: Costume Curators Group, London Museums of Health and Medicine Group, Military Museums Group, Pathology Museums Group, etc.

* SPECIALIST LONDON-WIDE MUSEUMS *

[749] **THE JEWISH MUSEUM**. At Camden Town: Raymond Burton House, 129-131 Albert St, London NW1 7NB, *Tel*: (020) 7284 1997; *Fax*: (020) 7267 9008. *Hours*: Sun-Thurs 10-4.
At Finchley: 80 East End Rd, London N3 2SY, *Tel*: (020) 8349 1143; *Fax*: (020) 8343 2162.. *Hours*: Mon-Thurs 10.30-5. *Internet*: http://www.ort.org/jewmusm/.
Staff: *Director*: Rickie Burman; *at Camden Town: Curator*: Jennifer Marin; *Registrar*: Alisa Jaffa; *Administrator*: Norma Yantin.
At Finchley: Curator: Carol Seigel; *Assistant curator*: Sarah Jillings; *Education officer*: Ruth-Anne Lenga.
Founded in 1932, the museum has one of the world's finest collections of Jewish ceremonial art. In 1995 it relocated to new premises in Camden (from Upper Woburn Place). It has now amalgamated with the former London Museum of Jewish Life on a two site basis. The museum in Finchley has social history displays, tracing Jewish immigration and settlement in London, including a reconstruction of an East End tailoring workshop. There is also a Holocaust Education Gallery. The Oral History Archive has some 400 tape-recorded memories, and there is a large photographic archive. There are 20 loan exhibitions on topics such as Jewish roots, refugees from Nazism, weddings and the clothing trade.

Publications currently available: *Boris: the studio photographer*, 1986 (on Boris Bennett); *Child's play: Jewish children's books and games from the past*, 1997; *Immigrant furniture workers in London 1881-1939* and the Jewish contribution to the furniture trade, by William I. Massil, 1997; *The Jews of Aden*, 1991; *The last goodbye: the rescue of children from Nazi Europe*, 1996; *Leon Greenman: Auschwitz survivor 98299*, published 1996; *Living up West: Jewish life in London's West End*, by Gerry Black, 1994; *Map of the Jewish East End* (reproduced from 'The Jew in London', 1901); *150 years of progressive Judaism in Britain 1840-1900*, published 1988; *The Portuguese Jewish community in London (1656-1830)*, by Edgar Samuel, 1992; *What about the children? 200 years of Norwood child care 1795-1995*, published in 1995; *Yiddish theatre in London 1880-1987*, by David Mazower, 1987.

There are also three research papers published in association with the Department of History, University of Leicester (series editors: Professor Aubrey Newman, and Dr David Cesarani): No 1: *Trade unionism amongst the Jewish tailoring workers of London 1872-1915*, by Anne J. Kershen, 1988; No 2: *Hopeful travellers: Jewish migrants and settlers in nineteenth century Britain*, by Harold Pollins, 1989; and No 3: *The Heymishe front: Jews in war-time Britain*, by Tony Kushner, 1992.

There is a Friends organisation with a newsletter, and complementing it the newly formed Society of the Jewish Museum. The museum's annual report gives much useful information on current activities.

Family history workshops run in association with the JGS of GB are held at the Finchley museum.

[750] **LONDON CANAL MUSEUM**. 12-13 New Wharf Rd, London N1 9RT, *Tel*: (020) 7713 0836. *Internet*: http://www.charitynet.org/~LCanalMus. *Chair of trustees*: Alex Nunes; *Secretary*: Martin Sach. *Hours*: Tues-Sun, 10-4.30. The museum was opened in 1992 and is housed in an ice warehouse built in the 1850's for Carlo Gatti, the famous ice cream maker. It covers the development of London's canals, including trade, vessels and way of life of the canal people. There is a programme of exhibitions, lectures and events; there is an educational service, a shop, and Friends organisation.

[751] **LONDON FIRE BRIGADE MUSEUM**. Winchester House, 94a Southwark Bridge Rd, London SE1 0EG, *Tel*: (020) 7587 2894; *Fax*: (020) 7587 2878. Tours take place at 10.30 (sometimes at 11.30) and 1.30. The museum has major collections of firefighting equipment and memorabilia.

[752] **LONDON TRANSPORT MUSEUM**. Covent Garden, London WC2E 7BB, *Tel*: (020) 7379 6344; *Fax*: (020) 7565 7250; *Email*: contact@ltmuseum.co.uk; *Internet*: http://www.ltmuseum.co.uk. *Hours*: daily 10-6 (Fri 11-6). Parts of the LT's collection has been displayed on and off for many years, but it was not until 1980 that the present museum came into being - utilising the vacant great cast-ironed framed hall built by the Duke of Bedford in 1870 to extend Covent Garden market. A major lottery-funded programme will open up total access to the entire collection; a new museum store at Acton Town, an advanced multimedia database and learning centre, and a programme of restoration and conservation.

A guide book: the *New London Transport Museum and its collections* is available. A list of transport societies and associations can be obtained from the reference library. There is a well developed shop and a Friends organisation, with a newsletter. Secretary at: 15 Springbank, Eversley Park Rd, Winchmore Hill, London N21 1JH.

[753] **MUSEUM IN DOCKLANDS LIBRARY AND ARCHIVES**. Unit C14, Poplar Business Park, 10 Prestons Rd, London E14 9RL, *Tel*: (020) 7515 1162; *Fax*: (020) 7538 0209. *Hours*: Closed to researchers until further notice, but telephone calls accepted and help given if possible. *Contacts*: Bob Aspinall, Librarian (also secretary of the Docklands History Group); Andy Topping, Interpretation officer.

Bob Aspinall has contributed the following article:

'This is the Docklands wing of the Museum of London at the Barbican, and has been located in Docklands since 1984. Under normal circumstances, the library offers a research and information service, open to the general public strictly by prior appointment with the librarian. However, this service has been suspended for the foreseeable future while staff plan and design the new Museum in Docklands, which is due to open opposite Canary Wharf in the year 2000. Major collections include the unique historical records of the private dock companies 1799-1909 and the Port of London Authority from 1909; Corporation of London river records 1770-1857; Thames Conservancy records 1857-1909; British Ports Association archives 1911-1907; London Wharfingers Association archive; and London Port Employers Association archive. There is a photographic collection (c. 20,000 images) including dock and riverside cargo-handling activities and aerial views, mostly b/w, colour, 1865-1970, and prints can be supplied within a few working days. Three historic films of cargo-handling in the Port of London are available in a variety of formats for viewing and extracts. Growing collection of material on the regeneration of Docklands 1981 onwards, drawn from a wide spectrum of sources. Provision of free educational services based on the National Curriculum to schools in the Docklands boroughs, including material for loan to schools - details from the Interpretation Officer on request'.

[754] **MUSEUM OF LONDON**. London Wall, London EC2Y 5HN, *Tel*: (020) 7600 3699. *Hours*: Tues-Sat 10-5.50; Sun 12-5.50. *Director*: Dr Simon Thurley.

Exhibitions:

The museum presents a rich and varied programme of temporary exhibitions each year. The annual reports 1994/5, 1996/7, and 1997/8 record the following:

10 May - 11 September 1994: *Artists and craftspeople in education.*

13 June - 17 October 1994: *Carry on collecting: the people's show.*

7 June - 17 July 1994: *A woman's place.*

20 September - 10 December 1994: *Witnesses and dreamers: painters of the inner city.*

26 September 1994 - 15 January 1995: *From Ridley Road to Radlett* (Jewish food shops from Ridley Rd in Dalston to Radlett in Hertfordshire, photographs by Ian Lillicrap, with oral historian Alan Dein).

26 February - 9 July: *The prophetic eve: the life and work of George Peabody (1795-1869).*

19 March - 27 October 1996: *London on film.*

30 April - 7 July 1996: *Soccer City: the photographs of David Trainer.*

30 July 1996 - 26 January 1997: *Whitefriars glass: the art of James Powell & Sons of London.*

18 November - 16 December 1996: *Pieces from the past*: finds from the excavations for the Jubilee Line extension project.

26 November - 31 December 1996: *Streets in the sky: the paintings of David Hepher.*

21 January - 9 March 1997: *Sixties London: photographs by Dorothy Bohm.*

4 March - 1 June 1997: *Walking about old Moscow*: prints and water-colours from the Moscow City History Museum.

11 March - 27 April 1997: *Finding London*: student photography exhibition.

20 May - 23 November 1997: *In Royal fashion*: the clothes of Princess Charlotte of Wales and Queen Victoria.

2 October 1997 - 15 March 1998: *Bedlam: custody, care and cure, 1247-1997.*

25 November 1997 - 4 January 1998: *Turned on: campaign for better Christmas lights.*

20 January - 15 February 1998: *Saxons at the opera: archaeological excavations at the Royal Opera House.*

28 January - 26 July 1998: *The life and times of N.M. Rothschild, 1777-1836.*

19 February - 29 March 1998: *Sole city: London shoes from the 1st to the 21st century.*

3 February - 1 March 1998: *The whirlwind continues: users' views on Britain's mental healthcare system.*

18 March - 26 April, 1998: *London's found riverscape* (two sequences of photographs of the riverside panoramas, London Bridge to Greenwich: 1937, commissioned by the PLA from Avery Illustrations, and 1997 from Charles Craig, Graham Diprose, and Mike Seaborne, commissioned by LDDC.

25 March - 19 April 1998: *Playthings from the past* (over 600 items from the unique 'Pilson' collection of toys unearthed in the City over the last twenty years, acquired with a Heritage Lottery fund grant).

2 April - 10 May 1998: *London's lost map.* (third section of copper-plate map found).

28 April - 31 May 1998: *The laundry project* (photographs of launderettes).

14 May - 28 June 1998: *Windrush: sea change.*

30 June - 12 July 1998: *Pride photographs* (of the Gay Pride March).

2 July - 16 August 1998: *London's rivers: turning the tide* (archaeology and ecology on the Thames foreshore).

21 August - 4 October 1998: *The Artists' Room at Pagani's* (London celebrities 1871-1939).

3 September - 27 September 1998: *Carnival costumes 98.*

9 October 1998 - 17 January 1999: *Cathedrals of industry: paintings by Mark Cazalet.*

15 October - 24 November 1998: *Objects of beauty* (photographs of objects of self-beautification).

27 October 1998 - 21 February 1999: *Lodon bodies*: changing shapes from prehistoric times to the present day.

1 December 1998 - 3 January 1999: *Toy stories*:

8 January - 28 February 1999: *Cromwell: warts and all.*

22January - 28 February 1999: *Conflicts of interests* (photographs, paintings of riots, etc).

5 March - 25 April 1999: *Drugs: what should London do?*

17 March - 1 August 1999: *The eye that never sleeps*: Terence Donovan London photographs.

30 April - 4 July 1999: *Tower blocks: love them or loathe them?*

2 July - 22 August 1999: *Pride and prejudice* (gay issues).

10 July - 30 August 1999: *The Art Bronze Foundry.*

27 August - 19 September 1999: *Power dressing: the fashion of politics.*

1 September - 30 October 1999: *The art of the Jubilee Line* (paintings by Robert Soden).

8 September 1999 - 9 January 2000: *Alfred the Great 849-899*: London's forgotten king.

22 October 1999 - 27 February 2000: *London eats out with Simply Food.co.uk.* (eating out over the last 500 years).

Publications:

Mol publications cover historical, artistic, and exhibition related subjects: archaeological works include: a three volume archaeological gazetteer series summarising excavations over the 20th century: *Archaeology in Greater London 1972-90; Archaeology in the City of London 1908-91; Post-war archaeology in the City of London 1946-68*: a guide records of excavations by Professor W.F. Grimes.

There is a study of *The Rose Theatre: an archaeological discovery*, by Julian Bowsher, 1998; and the pioneering *London before history: prehistory in the middle and Lower Thames Valley*, by Jonathan Cotton, John Lewis and Nick Merriman, 1999. *The Cheapside hoard*: Jacobean jewellery from London (selection of essays on a jewellery find in 1912) is a future publication.

The holdings of the museum are covered in a comprehensive guide *The Museum of London: a guide to the collections*, by Valerie Cumming, Nick Merriman and Catherine Ross (winner of the Museum Trading and Publishing Group ' best value guide' 1997). The background to the development of the museum (formed in 1976 through the amalgamation of the Guildhall Museum and the London Museum) is told in *The treasury of London's past*, by Francis Sheppard. A major reference source to a little-known part of the museum (held in store) is *London in paint: oil paintings in the collection at the Museum of London*, by Mireille Galinou and John Hayes, foreword by Peter Ackroyd.

Photography is covered by the important collection (from many public and private sources) *Photographer's London 1839-1901*, by Mike Seaborne. There are also collections by individual photographers: *Deptford Creek*, by Jim Rice; and *Eels, pie and mash*, by Chris Clunn. Another important survey is *London on film*: 100 years of film-making in London, by Colin Sorenson.

Other publications based on museum collection and the subjects of exhibitions are:
The purple, white and green: suffragettes in London 1906-14, by Diane Atkinson; also by Diane Atkinson: *The suffragettes in pictures*.
Whitefriars glass: James Powell & Sons in London, by Wendy Evans, Catherine Ross and Alex Werner.
The literary response to London is the subject of the three volume work *London 1066-1914*: literary sources and documents, edited by Xavier Baron.
An important fashion publication (subject of exhibition) is *In Royal fashion: the clothes of Princess Charlotte of Wales and Queen Victoria, 1796-1901*, by Kay Staniland.

Lastly, there are important academic studies, collections of essays:
London: world city 1800-1840, edited by Celina Fox; *The peopling of London*: 15,000 years of settlement from overseas, edited by Nick Merriman; and *Women in industry and technology*: from prehistory to the present day, edited by Amanda Devonshire (30 papers given at the 10th anniversary conference of Women, Heritage and Museums in 1994; concerned also with museum and curatorial practice, and contemporary collecting and oral history).

Two important out of print exhibition-related books are *The image of London*: views by travellers and émigrés, 1550-1920, introduction and catalogue by Malcolm Warner (with contributions by Brian Allen, John House, Robin Spencer and Samuel F. Clapp) from Trefoil Publications, in association with the Barbican Art Gallery, 1987; and *Londoners*, by Celina Fox, 1987 (Mol exhibition), ten chapters on: the crowd, society, merchants, craftsmen, servants, markets, street traders, labourers, the poor, law and criminals, education and the young, sickness and old age; with a select bibliography).

* NATURAL ENVIRONMENT *

The national organisation for conservation voluntary activity is the [755] **BRITISH TRUST FOR CONSERVATION VOLUNTEERS**. 36 St Mary's St, Wallingford, Oxon OX10 0EU, *Tel*: (01491) 839766. The main London office is at: 80 York Way, London N1 9AG, *Tel*: (020) 7278 4294; *Fax*: (020) 7278 5095; *Email*: BTCV-London@dial.pipex.com. Affiliated local groups including nature and wildlife gardens can be accessed through the website at www.btcv.org.uk. There is a quarterly newsletter *The London Conserver*, and a projects newsletter *Greenwork*.
Croydon BTCV office: Shaun Waddell, c/o Parks and Amenities, Taberner House, Park Lane, Croydon CR9 3RN, *Tel*: (020) 8760 5405; *Fax*: (020) 8760 5622.
BTCV Lambeth office: Del Redvers, c/o Metropolitan Housing Trust, Former Hillmeads Infant School, Eaton Drive, Brixton, London SW9 8NA, *Tel*: (020) 7274 4994; *Fax*: (020) 7738 5368.
BTCV Lea Valley office: Liz Roberts, 1a Connaught Close, off Lea Bridge Rd, Leyton, London E10 7QS, *Tel*: (020) 8986 7173/8173.
Richmond BTCV office: Lisa Martin, c/o L.B. Richmond Leisure Services Dept, Langholm Lodge, 146 Petersham Rd, Richmond upon Thames TW10 6UX, *Tel*: (020) 8332 1995; *Fax*: (020) 8940 7568.
BTCV Thames Chase office: Andrew Williams, The Forest Centre, Broadlands Farm, Pike Lane, Cranham, Epminster, Essex RM14 3NS, *Tel*: (01708) 641880; *Fax*: (01708) 640581.

[756] **CAMPAIGN FOR THE PROTECTION OF RURAL ENGLAND**, London branch. 5 Cowcross St, London EC1M 6DR, *Tel*: (020) 7253 0300; *Fax*: (020) 7490 3001. Campaigns for a coherent, unified planning for issues affecting the whole

of London, a sustainable development, reduction of car use, protection of parks, provision of more open spaces, to reuse derelict land and empty buildings, etc.

[757] **FLORA - for - FAUNA** (postcode plants database) (fff). c/o The Linnean Society, Burlington House, Piccadilly, London W1V 0CQ. *Internet*: http://fff.nhm.ac.uk/fff. This new database locates the names of flowers, trees, butterflies and birds for each home address in Scotland, Wales and England; by typing in the first four characters of their postcode, householders and others can obtain tailor-made lists of local plants and fauna which are both hospitable and garden-worthy.

[758] **FRIENDS OF THE EARTH**. 26-28 Underwood St, London N1 7JQ, *Tel*: (020) 7490 1555; *Fax*: (020) 7490 0881; *Email*: info@foe.co.uk. 'A registered charity committed to the conservation and protection of the environment through research, information and education'. It is the largest international environmental network in the world with 57 groups across five continents and one of the UK's most influential national pressure groups with some 250 local campaigning groups. HQ office advised compiler to insert the above address only as local contacts change frequently. The local groups hotline is: (0990) 224488. The website is: www.foe.co.uk.

A leading UK environmental 'partnership organisation' is [759] **GROUNDWORK**, national office at: 85-87 Cornwall St, Birmingham B3 3BY, *Tel*: (0121) 236 8565; *Fax*: (0121) 236 7357; *Email*: info@groundwork.org. uk. Its full colour newsletter is *Groundwork Today*. The London and South East regional office is at: 1 Kennington Rd, London SE1 7QP, *Tel*: (020) 7922 1230. A newsletter *Groundwork focus: update in London and the South East* is issued.
Greater London borough branches are as follows:
Groundwork Camden, Crowndale Centre, 218 Eversholt St, London NW1 1DE, *Tel*: (020) 7388 1500.
Groundwork Hackney, 6-8 Lower Clapton Rd, London E5 0PD, *Tel*: (020) 8985 1755.
Groundwork Merton, Marlborough Hall, Compton Rd, London SW19 7QA, *Tel*: (020) 8947 5750.
Groundwork Southwark: The Old Library, 39 Wells Way, London SE5 0PX, *Tel*: (020) 7252 7666.
Groundwork West London, 214 Goldhawk Rd, London W12 9NX, *Tel*: (020) 8743 3040.

[760] **LEARNING THROUGH LANDSCAPES** (in London). London project office: c/o Environmental Curriculum Service, 77 Bexley Rd, London SE9 2PE, *Tel*: (020) 8850 3112; *Fax*: (020) 8859 2180. Head of research and training: Mrs Wendy Titman, PO Box 283, Elton, Peterborough PE8 6SZ, *Tel*: (01832) 280659. Est. in 1996 (with funding from London Electricity and the Bridge House Estates Trust Fund), the organisation 'works with schools, local authorities and voluntary organisations to transform the grounds of London's schools into safe, stimulating and enjoyable environments for young people'. Over one third of the capital's schools have benefited from advice and information, and two schools grounds co-ordinator posts have been established in partnership with the boroughs of Greenwich and Hackney. Publications (from Southgate Publishers) include *Fundraising for school grounds* and *Trees in the UK*: a directory of resources for school and youth groups.

[761] **LEE VALLEY REGIONAL PARK AUTHORITY**. Myddleton House, Bulls Cross, Enfield, Middx EN2 9HG, *Tel*: (01992) 717711; *Fax*: (01992) 650714. *Information centre* at: Abbey Gardens, Waltham Abbey, Essex EN9 1XQ, *Tel*: (01992) 02200. The authority aims 'to regenerate, develop, conserve and manage the Lee Valley as a unique leisure resource for the whole community in a way that protects and enhances its environment and sustains it for future generations'. Leaflets are issued on topics such as *Discover Lee Valley Park's past, Visit historic Waltham Abbey*. There is an events listing guide; booklets include: *Walthamstow Marsh: a guide to its history; Middlesex filter beds nature reserve* (Hackney site, one of the earliest waterworks in the country); and *Stratford's hidden heritage*.

[762] The **LIVING LONDON FESTIVAL**. The first ever big open air event highlighting sustainability issues in London was held over the weekend of 4-6 June 1999 in Battersea Park. Campaigning organisations, pressure groups, local authorities, businesses and individuals will demonstrate ways to improve the environmental future of London. *Contact*: Global Partnership, PO Box 1001, London SE24 9NL, *Tel*: (020) 7738 7512; *Email*: globalpartnership@yahoo.com.

[763] **LONDON ECOLOGY UNIT**. *Administration office*: Ian Yarham, 125 Camden High St, Camden Town, London NW1 7JR, *Tel*: (020) 7267 7944; 7485 1485. *Director*: Professor David Goode. Works 'to create a greener and pleasanter urban environment, advising planners, parks managers and local people'. It maintains a database of London's wildlife habitats, with information on what is to be found in each place. In addition to London-wide handbooks it publishes an important series of borough handbooks, with colour photographs, maps and detailed accounts of the borough's history. Handbooks have appeared on: Barking and Dagenham, Barnet, Camden, Croydon, Ealing, Greenwich, Hammersmith and Fulham, Harrow, Hillingdon, Hounslow, Islington, Kingston upon Thames, Lambeth, Merton, Newham, Richmond, Southwark, Sutton, Tower Hamlets and Waltham Forest.
Nominated councillors represent 26 London boroughs on the unit's main committee. In 1999/2000 it will become part of the GLA.

[764] **LONDON GREEN BELT COUNCIL.** *Secretary*: G. Holt, 13 Oakleigh Park Avenue, Chislehurst, Kent BR7 5PB, *Tel*: (020) 8467 5346. Formed over 30 years ago to keep under review London's Green Belt as a whole - from Maidenhead to Southend, from Epping to Reigate. The membership consists of amenity groups, village societies, parish councils, as well as county and national organisations. Regular bulletins are issued; several meetings annually in London.

[765] **LONDON IN BLOOM COMPETITION** (run by the Tidy Britain Group). London office at: 3rd Floor, Premier House, 12-13 Hatton Gardens, London EC1N 2NH, *Tel*: (020) 7831 2543. *Chairman*: Jim Buttress, *Tel*: (020) 8316 7669.

[766] **LONDON NATURAL HISTORY SOCIETY.** *Secretary*: Tony Barrett, 21 Green Way, Frinton-on-Sea, Essex CO13 9AL, *Tel*: (01255) 674678. *Membership secretary*: P.C. Holland, Flat 9, Pinewood Court, 23 Clarence Avenue, Clapham, London SW4 8LB. Est. in 1858, and today one of the largest of its kind in the world. Publishes the *London Naturalist* and the *London Bird Report* annually.

[767] **LONDON WILDLIFE TRUST.** Central office at: Harling House, 47-51 Great Suffolk St, London SE1 0BS, *Tel*: (020) 7261 0447; *Fax*: (020) 7261 0538; *Email*: londonwt@cix.co.uk. Membership enquiries: (01732) 520040. Est. in 1981, the organisation cares for over 50 wildlife sites throughout Greater London, ranging from a small natural park at King's Cross to a remnant of ancient woodland at Sydenham and 120 acres of open land at Dagenham. In addition, it is concerned with community involvement, organising over 600 free events a year, and offering free advice to individuals and groups; providing information through leaflets and packs and maintaining close links with the 32 London authorities, and with education, working with all ages. Wildlife Watch is an environmental club for the junior members of the trust. There is a newsletter *Wild London* and an events listing *Going Wild in London. Natural World* is the national magazine published by *The Wildlife Trust UK*, The Green Witham Park, Waterside South, Lincoln LN5 7JR, *Tel*: (01522) 544400.

[768] **METROPOLITAN PUBLIC GARDENS ASSOCIATION.** *Secretary*: Mrs Joyce Bellamy, 3 Mayfield Rd, Thornton Heath, Croydon CR7 6DN, *Tel*: (020) 8689 4197.

[769] **OPEN SPACES SOCIETY.** 25a Bell St, Henley-on-Thames, Oxon RG9 2BA, *Tel*: (01491) 573535.

[770] **SUSTAINABLE LONDON TRUST.** 7 Chamberlain St, London NW1 8XB, *Tel*: (020) 7722 3710; *Fax*: (020) 7722 3959; *Email*: slt@gn.apc.org; *Website*: http://www.greenchannel.com/slt/index.htm. Est. in 1985, the trust aims 'to promote the protection and improvement of the natural environment by increasing public knowledge and understanding in the area of Greater London of human behaviour which is not harmful to man and other living species and to planetary ecology'. *Creating a sustainable London* report was issued recently, and a network London 21 (the London region of UK21, a country-wide network) has been launched. A key resource of the network is a directory of organisations and individuals.

[771] **SOUTH LONDON BOTANICAL INSTITUTE.** 323 Norwood Rd, London SE24 9AQ, *Tel*: (020) 8674 5787; *Email*: slbi@minerva.dircon.co.uk. Est. in 1910 by Allan Octavian Hume to promote the study of plants. It was intended as a local alternative to the British Museum or Kew and was aimed at ordinary people. Members include amateur and professional botanists, gardeners, artists, photographers, etc. There is a botanic garden, a reference library, herbarium, lecture room and photographic darkroom; there are lectures, workshops, field meetings, garden open days, botanical art classes and occasional courses. There is a journal the *SLBI Gazette*.

[772] **TRUST FOR URBAN ECOLOGY.** Unit 13, Dock Offices, Surrey Quays Rd, London SE16 2XU, *Tel*: (020) 7237 9165; *Fax*: (020) 7237 5070; *Email*: TRUE@dial.pipex.com. Est. in 1977 as the Ecological Parks Trust by environmentalist Max Nicholson to run Britain's first urban natural park, the William Curtis Ecological Park at Tower Bridge. It provides much technical advice and training, has published the influential *Promoting nature in cities and towns*, and manages its own three sites in Southwark: *Lavender Pond*, Lavender Rd, Rotherhithe SE16, *Tel*: (020) 7232 0498; *Stave Hill*, Timber Pond Rd, Rotherhithe SE16, *Tel*: (020) 7237 9175; and *Dulwich Upper Wood*, Farquhar Rd, Crystal Palace SE19 1SS, *Tel*: (020) 8761 6230. There are information leaflets for these sites.

Trees:
[773] **TREES FOR LONDON.** First Floor, 25 Foubert's Place, London W1V 1HE, *Tel*: (020) 7287 5407; *Fax*: (020) 7434 3243; *Email*: a2629877@infotrade.co.uk. An independent charity working to improve the environment in London by involving local people in tree planting and landscaping projects. It aims to target the poorest parts of the capital with projects in schools, housing estates, streets and other public spaces across Greater London. There is an illustrated booklet: *Trees matter! the benefits of trees and woods in towns*.
Tree officers within the boroughs are brought together within the [774] **LONDON TREE OFFICERS ASSOCIATION,** current chairman: Jim Smith, 227-229 Essex Rd, London N1 3PW (London Borough of Islington), *Tel*: (020) 7828 9928.

There is also the [775] **LONDON TREE FORUM**, secretariat at office of South East Region of the Countryside Commission, 71 Kingsway, London WC2, *Tel*: (020) 7831 3510; or PO Box 15146, London WC2B 6SJ, *Tel*: (020) 7831 3510. Has a Great Trees of London scheme (website: http://www.forestry.gov.uk). The national [776] **TREE COUNCIL**, 51 Catherine Place, London SW1E 6DY, *Tel*:(020) 7828 9928; *Fax*: (020) 7828 906, has within its membership national organisations such as the: International Tree Foundation, the National Small Woods Association, the Tree Advice Trust, Tree Aid, and the Woodland Trust.

The Trust founded and co-ordinates the National Grid Tree Warden Scheme (for local volunteers) and in the Greater London area there are networks in Barnet, Bromley, Camden, Croydon, Hackney, Haringey, Islington, Kensington and Chelsea, Lambeth, Merton, Waltham Forest and Wandsworth.

* ORAL HISTORY *

See also: [514] **ETHNIC COMMUNITIES ORAL HISTORY PROJECT**

[777] **THE CENTURY SPEAKS**. This is a nation-wide oral history project on local radio. For Greater London, contact: Oral History Project, BBC GLR, 35 Marylebone High St, London W1A 4LG, *Tel*: (020) 7208 9289 (contact: David Barrett). 16 half-hour programmes will be transmitted every Sunday from September 1999.

[778] **THE NATIONAL LIFE STORY COLLECTION**. At: The British Library National Sound Archive, 96 Euston Rd, London NW1 2DB, *Tel*: (020) 7412 7404; *Fax*: (020) 7412 7441. *Director*: Dr Robert Perks; *Administrator*: Jennifer Verlini. The NLSC is an independent charitable trust and has provided funding and voluntary support for a series of special ongoing projects: City lives (the experiences of City of London professionals); The Living Memory of the Jewish Community; Lives in Steel; Forgotten Feminism; Artists Lives (in conjunction with the Tate Gallery); Retail Lives (shopkeeping), for example. Two new projects are on: food - from source to salespoint, on the changing food industry; and book trade lives.

Deposited collections at the National Sound Archive include: the Methodist Sound Archive, Television History Workshop recordings, the Hall-Carpenter gay-lesbian oral history archive, interviews with music hall performers and with members of the RSC, and entries for the National Life Story awards (Britain's first oral history competition). Other collections cover aspects of health and medicine and Jewish history.

The Oral History section of the National Sound Archive is a national centre and provides advice and training in oral history methods, and maintains close contact with oral history groups in Britain and abroad.

Dr Robert Perks is the secretary and the London and South East regional contact for the ORAL HISTORY SOCIETY, and a member of the editorial team of the society's journal *Oral History*.

* PHOTOGRAPHS *

Some useful sources of information on photographs/photographers:
The *Directory of London photographers 1841-1908*, by Michael Pritchard (38 Sutton Rd, Watford, Herts WD1 2QF) was published in a second edition in 1994. Michael Pritchard specialises in old cameras at Christies. The book is distributed by his father Alan Pritchard (ALLM Systems and Marketing, geographical/post code information service, 21 Beechcroft Rd, Bushey, Herts WD2 2JU, *Tel*: (01923) 230150).

An important directory of photographic collections by Hilary and Mary Evans is published by the Mary Evans Picture Library, 59 Tranquil Vale, London SE3, *Tel*: (020) 8318 0034; *Picture Researchers Handbook*: an international guide to picture sources and how to use them (7th edition, 1999/2000, in preparation).

The Secretary of the Historical Group of the [779] **ROYAL PHOTOGRAPHIC SOCIETY** is John Warr, 6 Mansion Drive, Tring, Herts HP23 5BD, *Tel*: (01442) 822108. *Photo historian*: the group's journal, is edited by Colin Osman (of Creative Camera magazine), 14 Fairgreen, Cockfosters, Barnet EN4 0QS, *Tel*: (020) 8449 8883. Supplements list old photographic businesses nationally. Photographic fair, organised by the RPS have been held for many years at the Bonnington Hotel (92 Southampton Row, London WC1).

Some 'elusive' collections might include:

[780] **FRANCIS FRITH COLLECTION**. *Contact*: Tina Bradshaw, The Frith Barn, The Street, Teffont, Salisbury SP3 5QP, *Tel*: (01722) 716376. Archive founded in 1860 by eminent Victorian photographer Francis Frith; by 1970 the business had accumulated over 330,000 monochrome photographs for over 5,000 English towns and villages. There is a series of albums *Photographic Memories of...* published for Selectabook Ltd, distributors, and now out of print. *Photographic memories around London: a century of change*, was published in 1996. A new series Pictorial Memories, to include volumes on central London,

East London and outer London is to be issued by Frith Publishing, Waterton Industrial Estate, Bridgend, Mid Glamorgan, *Tel*: (01656) 668836. Frith's Photographic Directory Vol One and CD-ROM provides access to some 3,500 images. The business was purchased by managing director John Buck in 1977.

[781] **LONDON AERIAL PHOTO LIBRARY**. PO Box 35, Ashwellthorpe, Norwich NR16 1HL, *Tel*: (01508) 488320; *Email*: aerialphotos@btinternet.com. Covers all kinds of buildings and sites in London and the Home Counties, with extensive coverage of most parts of the UK.

[782] **HULTON-GETTY PICTURE COLLECTION**. 21-31 Woodfield Rd, London W9, *Tel*: (020) 7266 2662. Owned by Mark Getty; holdings include pictures from *Picture Post* magazine.

Postcards:
[783] **NORTH LONDON POSTCARD CLUB**. *Secretary*: Rachel McDonald, 13a Palmerston Rd, Bower Park, London N22 8QH, *Tel*: (020) 8889 7388.

[784] **WEST LONDON POSTCARD CLUB**. *Secretary*: Keith Cruttenden, 55 Clyde Rd, Staines, Middx TW19 7RG, *Tel*: (0784) 256894.

[785] **CROYDON POSTCARD CLUB**. *Secretary*: Bill Tonkin, 23 Bramley Way, West Wickham, Kent BR4 9NT, *Tel*: (020) 8777 8861.

* PLANNING AND RESEARCH *

[786] **ASSOCIATION OF LONDON BOROUGH PLANNING OFFICERS**. *Contact* (1999): Stuart MacMillan, Civic Centre, Stockwell Close, Bromley BR1 3UH, *Tel*: (020) 8313 4444; *Fax*: (020) 8313 0095. Jointly with Planning Aid for London has published *Planning in London: councillor's guide* with contacts such as the current chief planning officers.

[787] **ASSOCIATION OF LONDON GOVERNMENT**. 36 Old Queen St, London SW1H 9JF, *Tel*: (020) 7222 7799; *Fax*: (020) 7799 2339. Est. in 1995, replacing the Association of London Authorities, and the London Boroughs Association, to represent the interests of all 33 London councils and the London Fire and Civil Defence Authority. It has a full programme of conferences, seminars and publications. There is a *London Bulletin* published ten times a year and the important *ALG London Government Directory*, with listings of principal council officers, councillors and their wards, specialist committees, and statistical information: national and London-wide organisations are also listed. The European-funded *London Study* report was published in 1998 and provides a vision of a sustainable urban economy, including an action plan for the new GLA.

[788] **LONDONOMICS LTD**. *Contacts*: Dr Amer Hirmis, Darshan Patel, 14-16 Cowcross St, London EC1M 6DG, *Tel*: (020) 7251 4102; *Fax*: (020) 7253 3259. An independent research consultancy. The *London Economy report* published in August 1998 contains forecasts for London over the period 1998-2000.

[789] **LONDON PLANNING ADVISORY COMMITTEE**. Artillery House, Artillery Row, London SW1P 1RT, *Tel*: (020) 7222 2244; *Fax*: (020) 7222 2656; *Email*: lpac@lpac.gov.uk; *Website*: http://www.lpac.gov.uk/. Set up in 1986 as the borough's statutory planning committee for London, advising government and boroughs on strategic planning matters and representing London in the regional planning of the South East; advising government on parking policy. There is a wide ranging publications list. There is a quarterly newsletter *Update on Planning for Greater London*.
The work of LPAC will be taken over by the new Greater London Authority (GLA) in 1999/2000.

[790] **LONDON RESEARCH CENTRE**. 81 Black Prince Rd, London SE1 7SZ, *Tel*: (020) 7787 5500; *Fax*: (020) 7787 5605. Est. in 1986, following the abolition of the GLC in 1986, to provide information and research for all those working to improve the quality of urban life at home and abroad.
There are five departments: *Demographic and statistical studies*, director: Rob Lewis, *Tel*: (020) 7787 5652; *Environment and transport studies*, director: Aleyne Friesner, *Tel*: (020) 7787 5682; *housing and social research*, director Julia Atkins, *Tel*: (020) 7787 5634; *Research library*, director: Annabel Davies, *Tel*: (020) 7787 5661.
Some reports include: *Cosmopolitan London: past, present and future*, 1997; *London at work*, 1995; *Unemployment in London*, 1995; *London and the tourism policy of the European Union*, 1995; *The capital divided: mapping poverty and social exclusion in London*, 1996. *London local government in the information society*, 1997 (includes details of borough networks, and use of the Internet and World Wide Web).
The research library publishes the monthly *Urban Abstracts*, and bulletins on: arts and leisure, daily information bulletin on urban affairs, education, environment, housing, labour market, European local government, local management and finance,

planing and transport, social services. *Public and Social Policy* is a quarterly journal published jointly with the British Library, with details of research and report literature.

[791] **PLANNING AID FOR LONDON**. Calvert House, 5 Calvert Avenue, London E2 7JP, *Tel*: (020) 7613 4435. Provides free and independent town planning advice to those who cannot afford to pay consultancy fees. It especially targets minority groups within the community; it has its own team of experts and a London-wide network of experienced volunteers in planning, architecture and law. There is a quarterly newsletter *Planning Aid Reports*; publications include *Conservation planning* (legal procedures on listed buildings and conservation areas), by Ruth Richards, 1998.

[792] **VISION FOR LONDON**. 1 Queen Anne's Gate, London SW1H 9BT, *Tel*: (020) 7222 6400; *Fax*: (020) 7222 4440; *Email*: visionforlondon@compuserve.com. Est. in 1990 following widespread concern that the capital was losing out to continental cities in the fields of planning, transport and urban design. The organisation is a membership body, open free to all, providing a focal point, through its events and publications, for information and constructive debate about London's future. Its network links London's community, local and central government, business, arts, education and research, architecture, planning, urban design and transport. There are two regular publications: the monthly *Diary*, and the quarterly journal *Network News*. Report publications include: *King's Cross: past, present and future; Abercrombie's Plan for London: 50 years on; Employment effects of the Millennium; The rise and fall of London's town centres*; and *Revitalising London's town centres*.

* PUBS *

[793] **BREWERY HISTORY SOCIETY**. Contact address: Brewery History Society Bookshop, Long High Top, Heptonstall, Hebden Bridge, West Yorkshire HX7 7PF. Norman Barber is the author of their *A century of British brewers 1890-1990*.

[794] **INN SIGN SOCIETY**. *Chairman*: Ray Gattrell, 20 Rivington Rd, Hale, Altrincham WA15 9PH. Newsletter issued.

Two contacts (English Heritage officers) for the [795] **LONDON PUBS GROUP** are Eric Martin and Geoff Brandwood, c/o CAMRA Headquarters, 230 Hatfield Rd, St Albans, Herts AL1 4LW, *Tel*: (01727) 867201; *Fax*: (01727) 867670. *Action line*: (0845) 60 30 20 8. *Email*: camra@camra.org.uk. A national inventory of historic pubs is maintained. *Heritage pubs of Great Britain*, by James Belsey and Mark Bolton was published by CAMRA Books in 1998. A newspaper *What's brewing* is published quarterly. Regional CAMRA guides have been published for North London, South East London and South West London.

Research literature on pubs is relatively small; Mark Girouard's *Victorian pubs*, published by Yale University Press, 1984 is profusely illustrated, with much material on London pubs. There is also Robert Elwall's *Bricks and beer: English pub architecture 1830-1939*, published 1983 to accompany an exhibition at the RIBA Heinz Gallery. Guides to pubs in London boroughs appear from time to time (see chapters on Barking, Barnet, Sutton).

The pubs of North Lambeth: a guide to the pubs and street corners of Waterloo, Kennington and Vauxhall today and yesterday, by Peter Walker (208 Turnpike Link, Croydon CR0 5NZ, *Tel*: (020) 8680 3815) was published in 1989 and stands out as an especially thorough piece of research with its historical listings and illustrated surveys of contemporary establishments. A comparable guide to South Lambeth may be published.

* THE RECORD OFFICES *

[796] **FAMILY RECORDS CENTRE**. 1 Myddleton St, London EC1R 1UW. General enquiries: *Tel*: (020) 8392 5300; *Fax*: (020) 8392 5307; *Internet*: http://www.open.gov.uk/pro/prohome.htm. Certificate enquiries: *Tel*: (020) 8392 5300. *Website*: http://www.ons.gov.uk. *Hours*: Mon 9-5; Tues 10-7; Wed 9-5; Thurs 9-7; Fri 9-5; Sat 9.30-5.

The Centre provides a new home for the research facilities previously provided at St Catherine's House and the Census Reading Rooms in Chancery Lane. It is especially well known as central archive of indexes of births, marriages and deaths in England and Wales since 1837. Services include a bookshop and information point, and a family history reference area. *Never been here before?* by Jane Cox and Stella Colwell is an introductory guide to records at the centre.

[797] **LONDON METROPOLITAN ARCHIVES**. 40 Northampton Rd, London EC1R 0HB, *Tel*: (020) 7332 3820; *Fax*: (020) 7833 9136; *Email*: lma@ms.corpoflondon.gov.uk. *Head archivist*: Dr Deborah Jenkins. *Hours*: Mon, We, Fri 9.30-4.45; Tues, Thurs 9.30-7.30. A recent publication is: *We think you ought to go: the evacuation of London's children*. The following information leaflets are available free from the London Metropolitan Archives:

Family history in London; International Genealogy Index; Licensed victuallers records; Convicts from Middlesex; The City of London and Tower Hamlets Cemetery; Wills in the London Metropolitan Archives and elsewhere; The Middlesex Deeds Registry 1709-1938; School attendance medals; History of nursing: major sources; The evacuation of children from the county of London during the Second world War 1939-45; Records of gardening and horticulture among the London Metropolitan

Archives holdings; Vehicle registration and drivers' licence records; Hospital records; An outline of sources for the history of the Anglo-Jewish community; The German community in London; Non-Anglican register transcripts; The Great Dock Strike 1889; The Metropolitan Board of Works; Electoral registers at London Metropolitan Archives; George Godwin and the 'Builder'; Directories of London and the Home Counties; Publications of the Huguenot Society.

Some art reproductions are also sold: of Hogarth's *Morning, Noon, Evening and Night,* 1738; of *London as it was,* 1842, by Thomas Shotter Boys; and *London from the Thames,* 1842, by William Parrot.

[798] **NATIONAL REGISTER OF ARCHIVES** (Royal Commission on Historical Manuscripts), Quality House, Quality Court, London WC2, *Tel*: (020) 7242 7198.

[799] **PUBLIC RECORD OFFICE.** Kew, Surrey TW9 4DU, *Main switchboard tel*: (020) 8876 3444. Sales and marketing: (020) 8392 5271; *Fax*: (020) 8392 5266; *Email*: bookshop@pro.gov.uk. The PRO publications programme covers many readers guides, works on 'popular history'; guides to military records, and handbooks for family history (e.g.: *Tracing your ancestors in the Public Record Office*, edited by Amanda Bevan, and *New to Kew?* by Jane Cox). The comprehensive *Guide to the Public Record Office* (January 1999) is only available on microfiche.

Record repositories in Great Britain (10th edition, December 1977) is co-published with the Royal Commission on Historical Manuscripts.

A major source for medical history is [800] **WELLCOME INSTITUTE LIBRARY**, 183 Euston Rd, London NW1 2BE, *Tel*: (020) 7611 8582; *Email*: library@wellcome.ac.uk. Three recent projects are: the *Medical Archives and Manuscripts Survey* (non-hospital records of London area libraries, health authorities, doctors, etc); the Business Archive Council's *British Pharmaceutical Records Database* (more than 5,000 companies 1750-1968); and the *Hospital Records Database*, a joint project with the Public Record Office.

RECORD OFFICES FOR THE ADJACENT SOUTH EAST COUNTIES:

[801] **ESSEX RECORD OFFICE.** County Hall, Chelmsford CM1 1LX, *Tel*: (01245) 492211. Some 100 publications are in print (available from the Bookshop, *tel*: (01245) 430066) on many topics, photographers, architects, town histories; studies in Essex history in conjunction with the Local History Centre of the University of Essex, picture booklets, an Essex wills series (to cover more than 12,000 Elizabethan wills), historical documents, etc. Records relating to the London boroughs of Barking, Havering, Newham, Redbridge and Waltham Forest are described in *Essex in London* (2nd edition: 1996).

[802] **HERTFORDSHIRE COUNTY RECORD OFFICE.** County Hall, Hertford SG13 8DE, *Tel*: (01992) 555105.

[803] **CENTRE FOR KENTISH STUDIES.** Sessions House, County Hall, Maidstone, Kent ME14 1XO, *Tel*: (01622) 694363; *Fax*: (01622) 694379.

[804] **SURREY HISTORY CENTRE.** 130 Goldsworth Rd, Woking, Surrey GU21 1ND, *Tel*: (01483) 594594.

---

* REMINISCENCE *

See also: ORAL HISTORY

[805] **AGE EXCHANGE.** The Reminiscence Centre, 11 Blackheath Village, London SE3 9LA, *Tel*: (020) 8318 9105; *Fax*: (020) 8318 0060; *Email*: age-exchange@lewisham.gov.uk. *Artistic director*: Pam Schweitzer. *Administrator-Manager*: Andrew Green. *Education co-ordinator*: David Savill. An important centre for reminiscence work, both locally, nationally and internationally, aiming to improve the quality of life for older people through pioneering artistic, educational and welfare activities involving reminiscence: exhibitions, books, theatre, museum, education work in schools. Also important programme of short courses. Age Exchange co-ordinates the European Reminiscence Network, and publishes its magazine *Reminiscence* (magazine published previously by Help the Aged). Practical guides include: *Many happy retirements*; and *A practical guide to reminiscence*. Age exchange also has an important reminiscence publishing programme, and the following titles are currently available:

Across the Irish Sea, 1988 (memories of London Irish pensioners); *A day at the fair*, 1990 (memories of fairs on Bank Holidays in the 1920's and 1930's); *All our Christmases*, 1983 (Christmas past); *Can we afford the doctor?*, 1985 (health and social welfare in the early part of the 20th century); *Fifty years ago*, 1983 (life in the 1930's as recalled by South East London people); *Good morning children*, 1988 (school days in the 1920's and 1930's); *Goodnight children everywhere*, 1990 (memories of evacuation in the Second World War); *Health remedies and healthy recipes*, 1990 (Caribbean reflections on health and diet in Jamaica and in Britain); *Just like this country*, 1991 (story of families who moved from inner city tenement blocks to the new cottage estates of outer London in the inter-war period); *Living through the Blitz*, 1991; *My first job*, 1984 (memories of pensioners who started work between 1912 and 1940); *On the river*, 1989 (184 pages, recollections of Londoners who have lived by and worked on the River Thames); *Our lovely hops*, 1991 (memories of hop-picking in Kent, 112 pages); *The time of our lives*, 1986 (memories of leisure time in the 1920's and 1930's); *What did you do in the war Mum?*, 1985 (women's work and lives during the two world wars); *When the lights go on again*, 1994 (London at the end of the war); *When we were young*, 1990 (memories of growing up in five villages in South Somerset).

Some organisations for the elderly:

[806] **AGE CONCERN LONDON**. 54 Knatchbull Rd, London SE5, *Tel*: (020) 7737 3456.

[807] **GREATER LONDON FORUM FOR THE ELDERLY**. 47 Charlton St, London NW1, *Tel*: (020) 7383 4008; *Fax*: (020) 7387 3222.

---

* RIVERS AND CANALS *

Books on the Thames are described in *The Thames, 1580-1981: a general bibliography* written and published by Ben Cohen, 1985 (716 Endsleigh Court, Upper Woburn Place, London WC1H 0HW). He has also compiled a bibliography on the River Clyde, 1998.

[808] **LONDON RIVERS ASSOCIATION**. 24-31 Greenwich Market, London SE10 9HZ, *Tel*: (020) 8293 9275/9276; *Fax*: (020) 8293 9277. Est. in 1987 the association 'acts as a co-ordinating body to spotlight the contribution the Thames and its tributaries make to the life and economy of London'. The objective is 'to ensure that the Thames is recognised as a resource for transport, economic activity and civic amenity and that the integrity of the river's natural environment and character is protected and enhanced'. The association engages in monitoring and advice, holds bi-monthly meetings, has conferences and seminars, and runs a library and information resource. In the late 1980's and early 1990's studies were published on the riverside at Barking, Greenwich, Brentford, Tilbury Dock and riverside, Lambeth, Hammersmith and Fulham.
Other publications include: *Survey of boatyards and ancillary facilities*, 1989; *Getting residential moorings right*, 1990; *River transport in London: the case for action*, 1991; *Thames-side safety study: a guide to good practice*, 1992; *The working Thames: an agenda for action*, 1992; *Land use policy and land use change on Thames-side, 1967-1991*, 1992; *Audit of the Greenwich waterfront*, 1993; *A tale of two rivers* (comparative analysis between the Port of London, and the ports on the River Seine in Paris), 1994; *Towards a modern working waterfront: a study of river-dependent industry in Greenwich and Lewisham*, 1995; *Rivers of meaning: getting in touch with the Thames*, 1996; *Passenger services on the Thames: the constraints and opportunities*, 1998.

[809] **POOL OF LONDON PARTNERSHIP**. 6 Tooley St, London SE1 2SY. *Tel*: (020) 7407 4701; *Fax*: (020) 7407 4702. Covers the riverside area in Southwark and the City and Tower Hamlets bounded in the south by Borough High St and Mill St, and to the north by King William St and Thomas More St (core area), aiming to create improvements, economic regeneration and community involvement. Small grants are made to voluntary organisations working in the fields of education, history and tourism; festival events; environment. An impressive pictorial folding map/guide is issued. Responsible for the recent erection of plaques, signs and information in panels on the riverside.

[810] **RIVER AND ROWING MUSEUM**. Mill Meadows, Henley-on-Thames, Oxon RG9 1BF, *Tel*: (01491) 410909.

[811] **RIVER THAMES BOAT PROJECT**. 66 Hill St, Richmond, Surrey TW9 1TW, *Tel*: (020) 8940 3509; *Mobile*: (0589) 272985. Aims 'to give schools and community groups from Greater London the chance to discover the Thames by providing environmental education and outdoor pursuits facilities on board the specially adapted barge 'Richmond Venturer'. There is a Friends organisation.

[812] **THE RIVER THAMES SOCIETY**. *Administrator*: Mrs Valerie Andrews-Jones, Fair Lawn, 51 Kewferry Road, Northwood, Middx HA6 2PE, *Tel/Fax*: (01923) 823199; *Membership secretary*: Mrs Alix Horne, Side House, Middle Assendon, Henley-on-Thames, Oxon RG9 6AP, *Tel*: (01491) 571476. There are seven branches:
Thames Head: *Chairman*: Mr K. Burgin, The Pike Lock House, Eastington, Stonehouse, Glos GL10 3RT, *Tel*: (01453) 827414; *Membership secretary*: Mr A.R. Burton, Highclere, Watledge, Nailsworth, Stroud GL6 0AY, *Tel*: (01453) 832228.
Upper Thames: *Chairman*: Mrs Colin Reynolds, Rose Island, Heyford Hill Lane, Littlemore, Oxford OX4 4YH, *Tel*: (01865) 779241; *Secretary*: Mrs Louisa Astrop, 17a Thompson Terrace, Littlemore, Oxford OX4 50D, *Tel*: (01865) 778399.
Middle Thames: *Chairman*: Mr John Skuse, Moorlands, Pinkneys Green, Maidenhead, Berks SL6 6QE, *Tel*: (01628) 24025.
Secretary: Mr Owen Bryant, 67 Bath Road, Taplow, Maidenhead, Berks SL6 0NZ, *Tel*: (01628) 605702.

Teddington to Old Windsor: *Chairman*: Mr Patrick Protts, 128 Ruden Way, Epsom Downs, Surrey KT17 3LP, *Tel*: (01737) 352028; *Secretary*: Mrs Margery Day, 15 Cherry Orchard Gardens, West Molesey, Surrey KT8 1QY, *Tel*: (020) 8224 1643.
Upper Tideway: *Chairman*: Mr D. Craddock, The Arches, Richmond Bridge, Richmond Road, Twickenham, Middx TW1 2EF, *Tel*: (020) 8891 1485. *Secretary*: Mrs Janice Robertson, 42 Alder Lodge, Stevenage Road, London SW6 6NP. *Tel*: (020) 7386 9914.
Central Tideway: *Contact*: Mr W. Barber, 10 Ruvigny Gardens, London SW15 1JR, *Tel*: (020) 8788 0655.
Lower Tideway: *Chairman*: Mr B. Hardwick, 31 Addington Road, West Wickham, Kent BR4 9BW, *Tel*: (020) 8462 9439; *Secretary*: Miss Freda Leipe, 40 The Winter Gardens, Macklin Street, Drury Lane, London WC2B 5NB, *Tel*: (020) 7242 8576. The society is concerned with the preservation of the Thames from source to sea. Its members include walkers, fishermen, boat owners, as well as those interested in the river's history, traditions, architecture and wildlife. It is involved with educational work, in monitoring all planning and development applications, and runs a volunteer River Warden Scheme. There is an annual RTS trophy for the best project or scheme and a cup for the best contribution from an individual. There is an annual conference. *The Thames Guardian* journal is published quarterly, *Editor*: Dieter Jebens, 60 Middle Bourne Lane, Farnham, Surrey GU1 3NJ, *Tel/Fax*: (012527) 715230.

[813] **THAMES EXPLORER TRUST**. The Pier House, Corney Reach Way, Chiswick, London W4 2UG, *Tel/Fax*: (020) 8742 0057; *Email*: tet@mbreliance.demon.co.uk. Est. in 1989 to provide a range of educational support and activities. Programmes on many aspects of geography, history and science are run at the Chiswick Centre, at St Peter's Church, Vauxhall, at the Millennium Bridge (in partnership with the Millennium Bridge Trust and the Thames Archaeological Survey) at the Golden Hinde and the Tower of London.

[814] **THE THAMES FESTIVAL**. *Director*: Adrian Evans, Oxo Tower Wharf, Barge House Street, London SE1, *Tel*: (020) 7928 8998; *Fax*: (020) 7928 2927; W*ebsite*: www.thamesfestival.co. 1999 Festival on 19th September.

[815] **THAMES LANDSCAPE STRATEGY**. (Hampton to Kew). *Co-ordinator*: Donna Clack, c/o The Royal Parks, Holly Lodge, Richmond Park, Richmond TW10 5HS, *Tel*: (020) 8940 0654; *Fax*: (020) 8332 2730; *Email*: tls@richmond.gov.uk. Est. in 1994 to achieve 'integrated environmental planning and management'. The partners in the strategy are Richmond, Kingston, Elmbridge and Hounslow borough councils, the Environment Agency, English Heritage, the Countryside Commission, English Nature and the Royal Parks Agency. Some 50 out of a planned 180 projects have been completed; they include: Garrick's Temple and Lawn, Hampton (Richmond Council, Temple Trust, Hampton Riverside Trust); Brentford Waterside - publication of a report *A brighter waterside for Brentford* (Hounslow Council, Groundwork Thames Valley, Brentford Waterside Forum and other local community groups). A leaflet *Thames gardens* aims to encourage riverside gardeners to help wildlife; and there is a newsletter *Watermark.*

[816] **THE THAMES PATH**. New Countryside Commission National Trail following its source in Gloucestershire to the Thames Barrier. Official guide from Countryside Commission Postal Sales, PO Box 124, Walgrave, Northampton NN6 9TL, *Tel*: (01604) 781848.

[817]**THAMES 21**, c/o Corporation of London, Walbrook Wharf, Upper Thames Street, London EC4R 3TD. *Project manager*: Mark Lloyd, *Tel*: (020) 7236 1281; *Project officer*: Lynsey Butterfield, *Tel*: (020) 7248 2916. *Email*: thames21.tbg@virgin.net; *Internet*: www.thames21.org.uk; *Fax*: (020) 7236 1281. A joint venture between the Tidy Britain Group, the Port of London Authority, the Environment Agency, Thames Water and the Corporation of London, aiming to improve and enhance London's rivers, through litter prevention and clearance, as well as through the sustainable development of river environments by working with local communities and businesses. The organisation aims to continue the work of the Thames Clean project set up in 1994. A CD-ROM *London's Thames: the living, working river* is available (price: £19.50; it was distributed free of charge to 7,500 schools in June 1997). There is also a newsletter *Thames 21 Network News.*

Waterways and Canals:
The London Region Secretary of the [818] **INLAND WATERWAYS ASSOCIATION**, and editor of its magazine *Excalibur* is Dr Mike Stevens, 333 Lyham Road, London SW2 5NS, *Tel*: (020) 8647 9387; *Email*: michael.stevens@which.net; *Internet*: http://homepages.which.net/~michael.stevens/. He is also chairman of the IWA Towpath Walks Society. It runs the towpath walks of the original London Walks organisation.

[819] **BRITISH WATERWAYS**. London Regional office: The Toll House, Delamere Terrace, Little Venice, London W2 6ND, *Tel*: (020) 7286 6101. A booklet *Explore London's canals* is published. British Waterways is now the responsible body for managing the waterways previously the control of the LDDC. Its office is at: West India Dock Pierhead, 420 Manchester Road, London E14 9ST, *Tel*: (020) 7515 1046; *Fax*: (020) 7538 5537. A folding leaflet is issued.

* SPORTS AND RECREATIONS *

The national organisation is the [820] **BRITISH SOCIETY FOR SPORTS HISTORY**, *Chairman and secretary*: Dr Richard Cox, University of Manchester Institute of Science and Technology, Registrars department, PO Box 88, Manchester M60 1QD, *Tel*: (0161) 200 4013. The society publishes the *Sports Historian* twice a year. The May issue has an annual bibliography; the society is due to publish the second edition of Dr Cox's comprehensive bibliography *Sport in Britain* (1st edition: 1991, Manchester University Press).

[821] **SPORTS COUNCIL** (London Region). PO Box 480, Crystal Palace National Sports Centre, Ledrington Road, London SE19 2BQ, *Tel*: (020) 8778 8600; *Fax*: (020) 8676 9812; *Email*: peters@english.sport.gov.uk; *Website*: www.english.sport.gov.uk.

[822] **LONDON SPORT**, c/o ALG, 36 Old Queen Street, London SW1H 9JE, *Contact*: Karen Ramsay, *Tel*: (020) 7447 6225. *Fax*: (020) 7799 2339.

[823] **SPORTSLINE INFORMATION SERVICE** (for Londoners' participating opportunities) 33 Bedford Street, London WC2, *Tel*: (020) 7222 8000.

Running:
Details of some 100 London runs, with map, itinerary, and other information can be found on the website [824] www.runlondon.co.uk. A booklet *Run London* was published recently by the Guardian and Observer Development Department.

Walking:
[825] **LONDON WALKING FORUM**. *Contacts*: Jim Walker, Susannah Peckham, Room 19-21, 2nd Floor, Albert Buildings, 49 Queen Victoria Street, London EC4N 4XP, *Tel*: (020) 7213 9714; *Fax*: (020) 7248 2583; *Email*: info@londonwalking.com. A partnership between 80 organisations including the London boroughs and the Corporation of London, the Countryside Commission, Lee Valley Regional Park Authority, LPAC, Ramblers Association and voluntary organisations, aiming to promote and support walking initiatives throughout London and to make London a better place to walk.

[826] **The London LOOP orbital route** is a 150 mile walking route in the outer London boroughs; so far 8 of the 24 sections are open to the public and have leaflets: *Section 3*: Jubilee Country Park, Bromley to West Wickham Common, Bromley (9 miles); *Section 4*: West Wickham Common, Bromley to Hamsey Green, Croydon (9 miles); *Section 5*: Hamsey green to Coulsdon South Station, Croydon (6 miles); *Section 6*: Coulsdon South Station, Croydon to Banstead Downs (4.5 miles); *Section 8*: Bourne Hall Park, Ewell to Kingston-upon-Thames 7.25 miles); *Section 16*: Elstree to Cockfosters, Barnet (10.5 miles); *Section 17*: Cockfosters, Barnet to Enfield Lock (8.25 miles); *Section 18*: Enfield Lock to Chingford, Waltham (6.5 miles).

[827] **The Capital Ring** will have a total of 15 stages, covering 72 miles. Section 11 (Hendon to Highgate, 5.3 miles) will be the first to open.

[828] **The South East London Green Chain Walk** covers the London boroughs of Bexley, Bromley, Greenwich and Lewisham and dates back to 1977. Four attractive guides have been produced, replaced more recently by 10 route cards. The Green Chain project officer is Stephen Cowell at: first floor, Peggy Middleton House, 50 Woolwich New Road, Woolwich, London SE18 6HQ, *Tel*: (020) 8854 8888, ext. 5876.

Other London walks completed cover: Banstead countryside walk; Beverley Brook walk; Brent River Walk; Down and circular walk; Havering riverside path; Hillingdon trail; Lea Valley walk; Pymmes Brook trail; River Crane walk; Sutton countryside walk; Woldinham countryside walk.

[829] The **Downlands Countryside Management Project** is at: Highway House, 21 Chessington Road, West Ewell, Surrey KT17 1TT, *Tel*: (020) 8541 7282. A newsletter is issued.

[830] **RAMBLERS ASSOCIATION**. 1-5 Wandsworth Road, London SW8 2XX, *Tel*: (020) 7339 8500; *Fax*: (020) 7339 8501; *Email*: ramblers@london.ramblers.org.uk: *Website*: www.ramblers.org.uk. Aims 'to facilitate, for the benefit of everyone, the enjoyment and discovery on foot of Britain's countryside; and to promote respect for the life of the countryside'.

There is an annual Rambler's Yearbook and accommodation guide. The following regional contacts for London are listed in the 1999 guide:

Essex: *Havering and East London*: Mrs S. Green, 5 Salcombe Drive, Chadwell Heath, Romford, Essex RM6 6DU, *Tel*: (020) 8599 4719. *Redbridge*: Mr B. Speller, 15 Gloucester Road, Wanstead, London E11 2ED.

Hertfordshire & North Middlesex: *Finchley and Hornsey*: Ms C. Cahn, 153 North View Road, London N8 7ND, *Tel*: (020) 8347 9561. *North London and South Herts*: Mrs Ann Scrimshaw, Friars Oak, 1 Oak Way, London N14 5NP, *Tel*: (020) 8361 8138.

Inner London: Area Secretary: Mr D. Purcell, 8 Dryburgh Mansions, London SW15 1AJ, *Tel*: (020) 8788 1373. *Blackheath*: Mr D. Bollen, 119a, Culverley Road, Catford, London SE6 2JZ, *Tel*: (020) 8244 0557. *Hammersmith and Wandsworth*: Miss K.G.M. Plowman, 109 Altenbury Gardens, London SW11 1JQ. *Hampstead*: Mr K.D. Jones, Flat 4, 144 Agar Grove, Camden, London NW1 9TY, *Tel*: (020) 7485 2348. *Kensington and Westminster*: Ms J.M. Mack, 8 Grove End House, Grove End Road, London NW8 9HN. *North East London*: Mr P. Weaire, 25 Cromer Road, Leyton, London E10 6JA, *Tel*: (020) 8556 3884. *South Bank*: Mr M.R. Jackson, Flat 7, 57 Crystal Palace Road, East Dulwich, London SE22 9EX.

Kent: *Bromley*: Mr R.M. Howells, 1 Pine Avenue, Gravesend, Kent DA12 1QY.

Surrey: *Area secretary*: Mr G. Butler, 109 Selsdon Park Road, South Croydon CR2 8JJ.

Croydon: Mrs L. Serafino, 48 Priory Crescent, Beulah Hill, London SE19 3EF. *Kingston*: Mr M. Lake, 87 Porchester Road, Kingston-upon-Thames, Surrey KT1 3PW. *Richmond*: Miss G.M. Taylor, 58 Richmond Road, London SW20 0PQ, *Tel*: (020) 8748 2604. *Sutton/Wandle Valley*: Mr J.C. Parkin. 59 Beechwood Court, West Street Lane, Carshalton, Surrey SM5 2QA, *Tel*: (020) 8773 0048.

* TOURISM *

Tourist offices and tourism officers are listed in many of the London borough chapters. There are associations for guides in the City, Greenwich, Clerkenwell and Deptford.

[831] **ASSOCIATION OF LEADING VISITOR ATTRACTIONS**. 4, Westminster Palace Gardens, Artillery Row, London SW1P 1RL, *Tel*: (020) 7222 1728; *Fax*: (020) 7222 1729. Est. in 1990 to represent and bring together big tourist attractions: museums and galleries, heritage groups (e.g. National Trust, Historic Royal Palaces, cathedrals, gardens (Regents Park, Kew, etc.), and leisure attractions.

[832] **GUILD OF REGISTERED TOURIST GUIDES**. The Guild House, Borough High Street, London SE1, *Tel*: (020) 7403 1115. Publishes an annual list of members.

[833] **LONDON TOURIST BOARD AND CONVENTION BUREAU**. Glen House, Stag Place, Victoria, London SW1E 5LT, *Tel*; (020) 7932 2000; *Fax*: (020) 7932 0022; *Email*: www.LondonTown.com. The Board's annual report should be consulted for current achievements and concerns. The website contains much information on events, attractions and accommodation. A new consumer magazine *The Spirit of London*, in English and French has been launched recently for international distribution. In addition to its consumer and trade guides, the development department publishes a number of research reports on tourism in Greater London *Business Confidence Monitor*, issued quarterly; *London tourism statistics*, 1997; *Survey among overseas visitors to London*, Summer 1998; *The tourism strategy for London action plan 1997-2000*.

[834] **TOUR EAST LONDON**. c/o Docklands Railway Management Ltd. Castor Lane, London E14 0DS, *Tel*: (020) 7531 1996; *Fax*: (020) 7531 1997. *Contacts*: Charlotte Stirrup, James Marshall. A partnership of public and private organisations 'committed to marketing and developing the East of London as a tourism destination'. The focus of the organisation is the major part of the boroughs of Hackney, Tower Hamlets and Newham, together with North Southwark, North Greenwich (waterfront area), including the whole of London Docklands area. A *Travel trade guide* and various visitors' leaflets are produced. A range of hotels now exists in the region.

* TRANSPORT *

Research and campaigning organisations:
[835] **CAPITAL TRANSPORT CAMPAIGN**. 3rd Floor, Walkden House, 10 Melton Street, London NW1 2EJ, *Tel*: (020) 7388 2489/6902; *Fax*: (020) 7388 7632. Est. in 1983 to work for better, safer, cheaper accessible public transport for London. There is a bi-monthly *Capital Transport Bulletin*.

Also at the above address is [836] **TRANSPORT 2000**, the national environmental transport campaign. *Tel*: (020) 7388 8386; *Fax*: (020) 7388 2481; *Email*: transport2000transport2000.demon.co.uk. It is affiliated to the *European Federation for Transport and Environment and Transport 2000 International*. Quarterly magazine *Transport Report* and wide range of reports. A wide range of national organisations are affiliated to the UK office, environmental, transport, trade unions, etc.; e.g. Community Transport Association, Environmental Transport Association Trust, National Federation of Bus Users, Pedestrian's Association, Railway Development Society, Socialist Environment and Resource Association.

[837] **CENTRE FOR INDEPENDENT TRANSPORT RESEARCH IN LONDON**. 3rd Floor, Universal House, 88-94 Wentworth Street, London E1 7SA, *Tel*: (020) 7247 1302; *Fax*: (020) 7247 4725; *Email*: cilt@dial.pipex.com. A research and resource unit which 'explores ways of making public transport accessible, efficient and safe for all those who want to use it'. A journal *Transition* is published quarterly, and there is a range of reports from the mid 1980's and early 1990's.

LONDON TRANSPORT MUSEUM, *see*: Museums chapter.

[838] **PEDESTRIANS ASSOCIATION**. Third Floor, 31-33 Broadway, London SW8 1SJ, *Tel*: (020) 7820 1010.

[839]**RAILWAY AND CANAL HISTORICAL SOCIETY**. Contact for the London group is: Mr N.A. Howell, 21 Terminus Street, Brighton, East Sussex BN1 3PE. There are also groups for tramroads, road transport, docks and shipping, air transport and railway chronology. The society maintains a research index (on cards) of canal and railway material held in libraries and record offices; and there are collections of photographs; a register of members' special interests is issued and there is a *R & CHS Journal*, and bulletin. Specialist books are published with Atlantic Publishers (Penryn, Cornwall).

Ballooning:
[840] **THE LONDON BALLOON**. 4 Auckland Street, London SE11, *Tel*: (020) 7587 1111; *Fax*: (020) 7587 1113. Based at site of old Vauxhall Pleasure Garden; goes up every day for some 15 minutes in area.

[841] **ADVENTURE BALLOONS LTD**. 3 Queens Terrace, Boston Road, London W7, *Tel*: (020) 8840 0108. Goes up for about an hour from Tower Hill and Vauxhall Bridge on Tuesday, Wednesday and Thursday mornings.

Buses:
[842] **LONDON OMNIBUS TRACTION SOCIETY**. Office address is: Unit 8, Battersea Business Centre, 103-109 Lavender Hill, London SW11 5QF, *Tel*: (020) 7924 5701. Est. in 1964 to provide accurate and detailed information on all aspects of bus operation in the area bounded by London Transport central and county bus departments as formed in 1933. There are monthly meetings and two major sales events annually at the Old Horticultural Hall, Westminster. There is a monthly newsletter *The London Bus*, the quarterly *London Bus Magazine*, and the annual review.

[843] **LONDON TRANSPORT BUSES**. 172 Buckingham Palace Road, London SW1 9TN, *Tel*: (020) 7222 5600.

[844] **OMNIBUS SOCIETY**, London Historical Research Group. Vice-c*hairman*: L.E. Akehurst, 3 Ivy House, Eastbury Road, Watford, Herts WD1 4QH. *Bulletin editor*: G. Seward, 18 Charles Street, Market Harborough, Leics LE16 9AB.

Cycling:
[845] **LONDON CYCLING CAMPAIGN**. 228 Great Guildford Business Square, 30 Great Guildford Street, London SE1 0HS; *Tel*: (020) 7928 7220; *Fax*: (020) 7928 2318; *Website*: http://www.lcc.org.uk/lcc/. Est. in 1978 to promote the needs and rights of all cyclists in Greater London. Publishes a bi-monthly magazine *London Cyclist* and the manual *On your bike* including the Central London Cyclist's Route Map. At national level there is the *Cycle Campaign Network*.

Railways:
A *Directory of Rail Users Groups* is published by the Rail Regulator's office, 1 Waterhouse Square, 138-142 Holborn, London EC1N 2TQ, *Tel*: (020) 7282 2000; *Fax*: (020) 7353 5103.

[846] **LONDON REGIONAL PASSENGERS COMMITTEE**. 14/18 Gresham Street, London EC2V 7PR, *Tel*: (020) 7505 9000; *Fax*: (020) 7505 9003.

[847] **LONDON UNDERGROUND LTD**. 55 Broadway, London SW1H 0BD, *Tel*: (020) 7222 5600; *Fax*: (020) 7918 3447; *Website*: www.londontransport.co.uk.

[848] **LONDON UNDERGROUND RAILWAY SOCIETY**. *Secretary*: Eric Felton, 54 Brinkley Road, Worcester Park KT4 8JF, *Tel*: (020) 8330 1855. Editor of monthly *Underground News*: Brian Hardy, 325 Aylsham Drive, Ickenham, Uxbridge UB10 8UJ. Est. in 1961, now with some 900 members.

[849] **RAILWAY RAMBLERS**. 12 Harefield Gardens, Middleton-on-Sea, Bognor Regis, West Sussex PO22 6ED, *Tel*: (01243) 582242. Promotes the preservation of disused railway lines for walking and cycling.

Trams:
[850] **LONDON TRAMWAYS HISTORY GROUP**. *Contact*: P.J. Davis, 33 Mayplace Road East, Barnehurst, Bexleyheath, Kent DA7 6EA. To date the group has published two definitive works on *L.C.C. tramways*, by the chairman E.R. Oakley: each volume has just under 500 pages with numerous illustrations and diagrams. The third volume *London Transport tramways* taking the history on to the final abandonment of London's tramways in 1952 is to be published in 1999.

* WALKS AND TOURS ORGANISATIONS *

(NB: This is not an exhaustive listing). Guides' organisations for specific boroughs are listed in the borough chapters.

[851] **ANGEL WALKS**. Peter Powell, 26b Canonbury Square, London N1 2AL, *Tel*: (020) 7226 8333. Peter Powell has lived in Islington for 27 years: for many years he worked as a professional actor and singer. He has three walks: An Islington Village walk, Charles Dickens and Islington, and George Orwell's Islington. Also Hampstead, Highgate, Joe Orton walk, arts theatres and pubs of Islington, Clerkenwell, Canonbury and the Alwynes.

[852] **BANKSIDE WALKS**. *Contact*: Neil Spillane, 40 Stowe Road, Orpington, Kent BR6 9HQ, *Tel*: (01689) 838410; *Fax*: (01689) 875513. Associated with guides at the Globe Theatre. Groups only.

[853] **CAPITAL WALKS**. Alex Gifford, 16 Ridgdale Street, London E3, *Tel*: (020) 8980 5565.

[854] **CITYGUIDE WALKS**. *Contact*: Graeme Matthews, 269 Eascote Road, Ruislip, Middx HA4 8BN, *Tel*: (01895) 675389. Subjects cover: Crime and punishment, gardens, Broadgate, Mail coach to modem, old London in the shadow of St Paul's.

[855] **CULTURAL HERITAGE RESOURCES**. Kevin Flude, 213 Brooke Road, London E5 8AB, *Tel*: (020) 8806 3742; *Fax*: (020) 8806 4325. *Email*: kpflude@aol.com. A former MoL archaeologist, consultant and director of the Old Operating Theatre Museum since 1992. Organises walks and tours for groups and organisations.

[856] **DOCKLAND TOURS**. (Customised itineraries). 3, Goldcrest Close, London E16, *Tel*: (020) 7474 0171.

[857] **HIDDEN CITY**. John Garrod, 26 Gables Avenue, Ashford, Middx TW15 2TA, *Tel*: (01784) 252517; or (020) 7261 9211. Subjects include: the blitzed city, princes and politicians, city stages (theatrical life), secret gardens, ancient alleys and lanes.

[858] **HISTORICAL WALKS OF LONDON**. *Contact*: John Muffty, 3 Florence Road, South Croydon CR2 0PQ, *Tel*: (020) 8668 4019; or (020) 8688 5327; or (0956) 220373; *Fax*: (020) 8668 4019. Team of professional guides/historians provide wide range of thematised walks in Central London, the City and East End.

[859] **LONDON STREET MARKET TOURS**. Sandra Shevey, 66E, Blomfield Road, London W9 2PA, *Tel*: (020) 7286 5647. Bell and Church Street; Petticoat and Brick Lanes, Spitalfields; Southall Horse Market; Whitechapel, etc.

[860] **MILLENNIUM MILE WALK**. (from Westminster Bridge to the Millennium Bridge). John Walker, (Freeman of City of London, qualified City of London guide). 63 River Court, Upper Ground, London SE1 9PB, *Tel*: (020) 7261 9211. Every Tuesday.

[861] **THE ORIGINAL LONDON WALKS**. *Contacts*: David and Mary Tucker (established organisation some 35 years ago), PO Box 1708, London NW6 4LW, *Tel*: (020) 7624 3978: *Fax*: (020) 7625 1932; *Email*: london.walks@mail.bogo.co.uk; *Internet*: http://london.walks.com.
Very wide range of guides (specialists, qualified guides, actors and actresses, journalists), provide some fifteen walks throughout Central London every day of the week.

[862] **PETER LAWRENCE**. 349 Chigwell Road, Woodford Green, Essex IG8 8PE, *Tel*: (020) 8491 6837. Talks and walks on wide range of Essex, East and Central London topics, often quite specialist, e.g.: The hidden historical treasures of Whitehall, The rise and fall of Wanstead House (more talks than walks).

[863] **RIPPING YARNS**. A. Strafford, 12 The Casemates, Tower of London E1, *Tel*: (020) 7702 9987.

[864] **SOUTHWARK WALKS/DISCOVER SOUTHWARK**. *Contact*: Val Burton, 3 Urlwin Street, London SE5 0NF, *Tel*: (020) 7703 3393; or (0976) 389 285. Walks on the riverside areas.

[865] **STEPPING OUT**. *Contact*: Diane Burstein, 32 Elvendon Road, London N13 4SJ, *Tel*: (020) 8881 2933, *Fax*: (020) 7405 6036; *Internet* http://www.walklon.ndirect.co.uk. A co-operative of ten guides offering a wide range of walks in Central London and the City.

[866] **WALKS ALL OVER LONDON**. Peter Byfield, 30 Frearson, Weston Rise, London WC1X 9EB, *Tel*: (020) 7837 2841.

[867] **YE OLDE WALKS OF LONDON**. Daphne Walpole, 6 Abbey Drive, Tooting, London SW17, *Tel*: (020) 8672 5894. Themes: Samuel Pepys and the Great Fire of London, Bankside and the Globe Theatre, Wesley's London, Business City walk, Tower to Monument, In the footsteps of the Lord Mayor, Tower Bridge.

PUBLISHERS AND SMALL PRESSES

AFTER THE BATTLE *Proprietor*: Winston Ramsey, Church House, Church Street, London E15 3JA, *Tel*: (020) 8534 8833; *Fax*: (020) 8555 7567. Essentially a World War I & II specialist publisher, but some local titles include: *The East End then and now*, by Winston G. Ramsey (528pp, over 1800 illus); *Epping Forest then and now*, by Winston G. Ramsey and Reginald L. Fowkes; *Old Plaistow*, by John Spencer Curwen (reprint of 4th, 1905 edition); *Woodford then and now*, by Reginald L. Fowkes.

IAN ALLAN PUBLISHING. Terminal House, Station Approach, Shepperton, Surrey TW17 8AS, *Tel*: (01932) 255500. Extensive list includes titles on London transport (rail, bus) subjects.

ALPHA PRESS/SUSSEX ACADEMIC PRESS. PO Box 2950, Brighton, East Sussex BN2 5SP, *Tel*: (01273) 699533; *Fax*: (01273) 621262. London titles include: *From palace to power: an illustrated history of Whitehall*, by Susan Foreman; *Huguenots of London*, by Robin Gwynn.

BARN ELMS PUBLISHING. Jane Crawley, 93 Castelnau, Barnes, London SW13 9EL, *Tel*: (020) 8748 6875; *Fax*: (020) 8846 9550; Jessica Smith, 11 Chartfield Avenue, Putney, London SW15 6DT, *Tel/Fax*: (020) 8789 7677. Small list includes: *Knot gardens and parterres*, by Robin Whalley and Anne Jennings (garden director for the Tradescant Trust and the Museum of Garden History in Lambeth); *The flowers of William Morris*, by Derek Baker, and *The story of the privy garden at Hampton Court*, by Mavis Batey (President of the Garden History Society), and Jan Woudstra.

BARON BOOKS. (Barracula Collection). Clive Birch, King's Cote, Valley Road, Finmere, Buckingham MK18, *Tel*: (01280) 848847.

BREEDON BOOKS PUBLISHING CO LTD. 44 Friar Gate, Derby DE1 1DA, *Tel*: (01332) 384235; *Fax*: (01332) 292755. Football and local interest books. 'Images of...' series in collaboration with newspaper photographic archives, includes: *Images of Croydon*; also *London moments in time*, by Rupert Matthews; and *London's parish churches*, by John Leonard, 1997 (a retired physician, and author of other church books).

BREWIN BOOKS. Doric House, Church Street, Studley, Church Street, Studley, Warwickshire B80 7LG, *Tel*: (01527) 854228; *Fax*: (01527) 852746. Essentially a Midlands interest publisher, (especially Birmingham), but list includes some genealogy and family history including *Recording the past: a photographer's handbook*, and *Register Offices of births, deaths, marriages in England, Scotland, Wales & Ireland*; also: *Exploring the New River*, and *Exploring the Regent's Canal*, both by Michael Essex-Lopresti.

CAPITAL TRANSPORT. 38 Long Elmes, Harrow Weald, Middx HA3 5JL. *Tel*: (020) 8863 8996. Specialist list includes titles on London buses and trams and the underground (including *Underground architecture*, by David Lawrence); also *Docklands Light Rail*, the official handbook.

CHENER BOOKS. *Proprietor*: John Kennedy, 14 Lordship Lane, London SE22 8HN, *Tel*: (020) 7299 0771. An East Dulwich bookshop. Has published *The Architecture of Peckham*, by Tim Charlesworth, 1988; and *Who was Who in Peckham*, 1985. A book on Peckham/Camberwell police in planned.

CONNOR & BUTLER. 69 Guildford Road, Colchester, Essex C01 2RZ, *Tel*: (01206) 867874/860949. Small list of histories of London Railway lines, mostly by J.E. Connor; also a quarterly magazine *The London Railway Record.*

CONSTABLE & CO LTD. 3 The Lanchesters, 162 Fulham Palace Rd, London W6 9ER, *Tel*: (020) 8741 3663; *Fax*: (020) 8748 7562. Wide ranging, general interest list includes: *Crime and scandal: the black plaque guide to London*, by Felix Barker and Denise Silvester-Carr; *Guide to London's churches*, by Melvyn Blatch; *London's statues*: a guide to London's outdoor statues and sculpture, by Arthur Bryon.

COUNTRYSIDE BOOKS. *Contacts*: Nicholas and Suzanne Battle, 2 Highfield Avenue, Newbury, Berkshire RG14 5DS, *Tel*: (01635) 43816.

T & P DOUGLAS. Tentallon, Drumberg Loan, Killearn, Stirlingshire G63 9LG, *Tel*: (0141) 946 6600. Publishers of *Entirely by the way,* by Robert Shiers, on Central London street names and their origins.

DEPTFORD FORUM PUBLISHING LTD. 441 New Cross Road, London SE14 6TA, *Tel*: (020) 8692 7115; *Fax*: (020) 8694 1327; *Email*: deptnet7@dircon.co.uk. *Directors*: Jess Steele, Mike Steele, Christine Shearer, Juliet Desailly. This flourishing community publishing project is the initiative of Jess Steele, an anthropologist/historian, trained at LSE who discovered there the Booth Notebooks. She plans to issue a series of 6 transcripts of them. Volume I, South East London appeared in 1977, and Volume 2, East London is in preparation. *Longest journey: a history of black Lewisham*, by Joan Anim-Addo was published in 1995.

Jess is the author of *Turning the tide: the history of everyday Deptford*, 1993; and edited the forthcoming study: *Deptford Creek: surviving regeneration,* articles on history, wildlife, regeneration drawn from some 20 surveys. She also publishes autobiography and reminiscence: *Abraham's daughter: the life and times of Rose Hacker* (N. London GLC 1960's councillor); *Memories of Brockley*, by Harry Monk; *Rations and rubble: remembering Woolworths*, by Deptford History Group (the New Cross V2 disaster); *A working class war: tales from two families* (in Stratford and Deptford), in collaboration with Stratford Challenge Community History Project. There is also a series of booklets written and illustrated by local schools: *Deptford Park Live!* was written by Deptford Park and Francis Drake primary schools and Deepway Residential Home, 1996. She also undertakes editorial and publishing work for other organisations: *A century of the OBC*, by Mark Say for the Oxford & Bermondsey Club; *A trip around Lewisham*, for Lewisham Shopping Centre for example. Her course 'Local history in action' (S.E. London history and techniques for recording it) starts at Goldsmith's College in September 1999.

DUCKWORTHS. Frith Street, Soho, London W1V 5TA, *Tel*: (020) 7434 4242. Publishers of Bill Fishman's East London books: *East End and Docklands*; *East End Jewish radicals*; *Streets of East London.*

EDWARDS, John. 26 Rhondda Grove, London E3 5AP, *Tel*: (020) 8981 5812. Publishers of *London zoo from old photographs, 1852-1914.* John Edwards is a professional solicitor, and amateur zoologist.

GRANTA EDITIONS. An imprint of Book Production Consultants PLC, 25-27 High Street, Chesterton, Cambridge CB4 1ND, *Tel*: (01223) 352790.
Publishing services company working with a range of organisations, e.g.: South Eastern Museums Service (*The London Museums Guide*); Guys Hospital Nurses' League (*Nursing at Guy's 1727-1996*); city financial institutions (their histories), such as the Prudential, General Accident, London Futures.

HAGGERSTON PRESS. Roger Hudson, Joe Whitlock Blundell, 38 Kensington Place, London W8 7PR, *Tel*: (020) 7229 3080. Three titles to date in the 'London Guides' series cover: Covent Garden, Trafalgar Square and the Strand; Bloomsbury, Fitzrovia and Soho; and Fleet Street, Holborn and the Inns of Court. Roger Hudson is an editor and prolific author, and writes many of the Folio Society 'presentation' volumes.

ROBERT HALE, Publishers. Clerkenwell House, 45-47 Clerkenwell Green, London EC1R 0HT, *Tel*: (020) 7251 2661; *Fax*: (020) 7490 4958. Recent City of London publications have included: *The City Companion*, 1994, by Martin Mason and Malcolm Sanders; and two studies on stockbroking firms: *From diamond sculls to golden handcuffs: a history of Rowe and Pitman*, by Andrew Lycett; and *Phillips & Drew: professionals in the city*, by W.J. Reader (in 1978 he helped to set up the Business History Unit at the LSE), and David Kynaston (author of histories of the FT, 1988; Cazenove & Co, 1991; LIFFE,

1997; and two volumes, 1994 and 1995 on the City of London). Robert Hale are also the publishers of books by E.J. Burford: *The Bishop's brothels*; *London: the synfalle citie*; *Private vices, public virtues*; *Wits, wenches and wantons*.

HAMBLEDON PRESS. *Proprietor*: Martin Sheppard, 102 Gloucester Avenue, London NW1 8HX, *Tel*: (020) 7586 0817. *Fax*: (020) 7586 9970; *Email*: ms@hambledon.co.uk. Extensive list of academic studies on English history. London subjects include: *The city churches of Sir Christopher Wren*, by Paul Jeffrey, 1996; *London and the English economy 1500-1700*, by F.J. Fisher, 1990; *Medieval London widows 1300-1500*, by Caroline Barron, 1994; *Medieval Southwark*, by Martha Carlin, 1996; *Politics and the people of London*, by Andrew Saint, 1989; *The University of London and the world of learning 1836-1986*, by F.M.L. Thompson, 1990.

HANDBOOK PUBLISHING. 14 Anhalt Road, London SW11 4NX, *Tel*: (020) 7223 2452. General interest thematised guides, such as: *Rock and pop London*, *Gardens and wildlife in London*, *Film and TV location London*, *The River Thames*, *Villages of London*.

HENDON PUBLISHING CO LTD. *Proprietor*: Henry Nelson, Hendon Mill, Nelson, Lancs BB9 8AD, *Tel*: (01282) 613129. Collections of old photographs for West London localities; books on the Tower of London by retired beefeater G. Abbott. Also: series on Wolverhampton, Lincoln, Scarborough, etc.

IAN HENRY PUBLICATIONS LTD. 20 Park Drive, Romford, Essex RM1 4LH, *Tel/Fax*: (01708) 749119. Publishers of Essex interest books; London and East Anglian. Greater London interest titles currently in print include: *The Bank of England: its origins and development*, by Maberley Phillips (a 1920 lecture by one of its older employees); *Country rambles around Romford, Hornchurch and Upminster*, by George E. Tasker (first published in 1911); *Grandfather's Romford*, by H.J. Crossley; *Growing up in North Ockendon and Upminster*, by Margaret Crabtree; *An Ilford boyhood*, by Peter Ford; *John Wilton's music hall*, by David Occomore; *Over here and over there: Ilford aerodromes and airmen of the Great War*, by John Barfoot; *Rogues river*, by Frank Martin; *Treasures of Havering: listed and historic buildings of Havering*, by John Drury.

HISTORICAL PUBLICATIONS. *Contact*: John Richardson, 32 Ellington Street, London N7, *Tel*: (020) 7607 1628. Historical, profusely illustrated, accounts of London localities in the '...Past' series; many localities have now been covered and books are distributed by Phillimore (HPL in catalogue). John Richardson's books cover: Camden Town and Primrose Hill; Covent Garden, Highgate, Islington, Kentish Town. He is currently working on a chronicle of London's history for Weidenfeld and a social history for Random House.

JAMES & JAMES. *Proprietor*: Hamish Macgibbon, Gordon House Business Centre, 6 Lissenden Gardens, London NW5 1LX, *Tel*: (020) 7482 4596. Publishers of specially commissioned school histories, including: Charterhouse, City of London, Kings College, Highgate, Latymer Upper School, St Paul's, Westminster. Also some general interest titles including a historical guide to Westminster Abbey: *Kingdom, power and glory*, by john Field. In 1996 the firm published Thomas Hinde's *An illustrated history of the University of Greenwich*.

K T PUBLISHING. One title only: *London: the German connection*, by Kay Mann c/o 15 Barton Rise, Chilton Polden, Bridgwater, Somerset TA7 9EB.

LILBURNE PRESS. Nicholas Reed, 1 Dover House, Maple Road, London SE20 8EN, *Tel*: (020) 8659 5776. Booklets, often by Nicholas Reed, on Pissaro: *Camille Pissarro at Crystal Palace*, 1995; *Pissarro in Essex*, 1992; *Pissarro in West London*, 1997; also: *Sisley and the Thames*, 1992; *Richmond and Kew Green*, 1992; *Edith Nesbit in S.E. London and Kent*, 1997. Author of *Crystal Palace and the Norwoods* from Tempus (archive photographs series).

LOCAL HISTORY PUBLICATIONS. *Proprietor*: John W. Brown, 316 Green Lane, Streatham, London SW16 3AS, *Tel*: (020) 8677 9562. Specialises mainly in reprints of extracts from antiquarian local history works: Manning & Bray, Lysons, Brayley, Walford's. Also a bookseller of local history books in print.

MACMILLAN PUBLISHERS LTD. 25 Eccleston Place, London SW1, *Tel*: (020) 7881 8000; *Fax*; (020) 7881 8001. The publishers of *The London Encyclopaedia*, edited by Ben Weinreb and Christopher Hibbert, 2nd edition, 1993. Customer services/orders: Houndmills Estate, Brunel Road, Basingstoke, Hants RG12 6XS, *Tel*: (01256) 329242. Other recent London titles include *London and the civil war*, 8 essays, edited by Stephen Porter.

MAINSTREAM PUBLISHING COMPANY LTD. 7 Albany Street, Edinburgh EH1 3UG, *Tel*: (0131) 557 2959; *Fax*: (0131) 556 8720; *Email*: 101464.537@compuserve.com. Large general interest publishers, with strong Scottish dimension, but a few London titles: *The best kid's guide to London and the home counties...ever*, by Judith Milling, 1998; *Country walks* *around London* by Geoff Garvey and Leigh Hatts, 1998, (in association with London Transport); *Dockland life* (historical photographs), by Chris Ellmers and Alex Werner; *London, England: a day-trippers travelogue from the coolest city in the world*, by Derek Hammond, 1998; and *London lines: the capital by underground*, by Michael Kelly.

MATCHING PRESS. 1 Waterman's End, Matching, Harlow, Essex CM17 0RQ, *Tel*: (01279) 731 308. Books written and published by Patrick Streeter, a former liberal councillor in Tower Hamlets, including: *Streeter of Bond Street*, a Victorian jeweller; and *For whom the bells toll: Lloyds of London.*

MERRELL HOLBERTON PUBLISHERS LTD. Willcox House, 42 Southwark Street, London SE1 1UN, *Tel*: (020) 7403 2047; *Fax*: (020) 7407 1333; *Email*: merrholb@dircon.co.uk. Specialist art publishers; a new departure for the publishers and an important study is *London suburbs*, edited by Andrew Saint, published in association with English Heritage.

METRO PUBLICATIONS. *Proprietor/author*: Andrew Kershman, PO Box 6336, London N1 6PY, *Tel*: (020) 8533 7777. Publishers of illustrated guides: *Bargain hunters London*; *Gay London*; *London Market Guide*; *Museums and Galleries*; *Veggie London.*

MIDDLETON PRESS. Easebourne Lane, Midhurst, West Sussex GU29 9AZ, *Tel*: (01730) 813169; *Fax*: (01730) 812601. Extensive list includes a series on London suburban railways (written almost exclusively by V. Mitchell and K. Smith), and a tramways series (mainly London), many titles written by Robert J. Harley.

MUDLARK PRESS. *Proprietor*: James Page-Roberts, PO Box 13729, London W6 9GN, *Tel*: (020) 8748 6866. Books on docklands subjects written by James Page-Roberts including: *Guide to a Dockland of change*: a present day, historical, anecdotal and (1949-1969) photographic guide to the riverside docks and wharves between The Tower of London and Limehouse, 1997; and *Docklands buildings old and new*, 1998.

JOHN MURRAY, publishers. 50 Albemarle Street, London W1X 4BD, *Tel*: (020) 7493 4361; *Fax*: (020) 7499 1792; *Email*: johnmurray@dial.pipex.com. Distinguished general interest publisher with a few London titles: *Betjeman's London*, edited by Penny Denton; *London: a literary companion*, by Peter Vansittart; *London as it might have been*, by Felix Barker and Ralph Hyde; and *London under London: a subterranean guide* by Richard Trench and Ellis Hillman.

Dr S.K. AL NAIB. Head of Department of Civil Engineering, University of East London, Longbridge Road, Dagenham, Essex RM8 2AS, *Tel*: (020) 8590 7722. Books on docklands, e.g.: *London docklands past, present and future*; *Discover London Docklands A-Z*; *European Docklands, past, present and future*. Imprint is now Research Books (PO Box 82, Romford, Essex).

NEW HOLLAND PUBLISHERS LTD. 24 Nutford Place, London W1H 6DQ, *Tel*: (020) 7724 7773; *Fax*: (020) 7724 6184. *Email*: postmaster@nhpub.co.uk. Large, trade publisher with extensive lists on home interiors, DIY, crafts, cookery, diving and climbing guides, natural history and travel, and a few London titles: *Walking London*, *Secret London*, *Village London*, all by Andrew Duncan; *Walking haunted London*, by Richard Jones; and *Walking London's parks and gardens*, by Geoffrey Young.

OLD HOUSE BOOKS. *Proprietor*: Edward Allhusen, The Old Police Station, Pound Street, Moretonhampstead, Nr Newton Abbot, Devon TQ13 8PA, *Tel/Fax*: (01647) 440707. Publishers of reprints of *Dickens' Dictionary of London*, 1888; and *Dickens' Dictionary of the Thames*, 1887; also: *A street map of London, 1843* published by the Society for the Diffusion of Useful Knowledge; and a detailed coloured map The British Empire throughout the world, 1905. The business concentrates nowadays on the publishing of calendars. Hamlet Distribution (West Country books) is also based here.

PENGUIN BOOKS LTD. 27 Wrights Lane, London W8, *Tel*: (020) 7416 3000; *Fax*: (020) 7416 3099. The publishers of Pevsner's *Buildings of England* series. New editions of the London Volumes have been issued recently:
Vol. 1: The City of London, by Simon Bradley and Nikolaus Pevsner; *Vol 2: South*, by Bridget Cherry and Nikolaus Pevsner; *Vol 3: North West*, by Bridget Cherry and Nikolaus Pevsner; *Vol 4: North*, same authors. New titles are: *London: the city churches*, by Simon Bradley and Nikolaus Pevsner; and *London Docklands: an architectural guide*, by Elizabeth Williamson and Nikolaus Pevsner. Other recent London titles include Roy Porter's *London: a social history*, 1996.

PENTLAND PRESS. Hutton Close, South Church, Bishop Auckland, Co Durham DL14 6XB, *Tel*: (01388) 776555. Publishing services to authors, for example: *Mill Hill: a history of Mill Hill and its environment*, by Bernard H Oak, 1994; and *Woolwich remembered*, by John Peters, 1994; *A giant among giants* (the author's grandfather, a rabbi) by Samuel C. Melnick (on 19 Princelet Street, Spitalfields, occupants, and the history of the synagogue there).

PHILLIMORE & CO LTD. Shopwyke Manor Barn, Chichester, West Sussex P020 6BG, *Tel*: (01243) 787636; *Fax*: (01243) 787639. England's most famous, and longest established publisher of local history with extensive lists for all regions, as well as many titles on family history generally, and family histories. For each region there are pictorial histories as well as more academic and specialist titles. The London list includes those distributed for Historical Publications (John Richardson's London 'Past' series.)
Many of the London titles are quoted in the sections for the different London boroughs. An account of the firm '100 years of Phillimore & Co' was published in the Local History Magazine, No 64, Nov/Dec. 1997.

PITKIN UNICHROME LTD. (formerly Pitkin Pictorial), Healey House, Dene Road, Andover, Hants SP10 2AA, *Tel*: (01264) 334303; *Fax*: (01264) 334110. Well known series of over 200 titles, colour guides with informative text to major tourist sites and historical subjects, initiated over 50 years ago with Mr Pitkin's pictorial souvenir of the Queen's wedding in 1947.
London titles include: *Buckingham Palace*; *City of London churches* (by John Betjeman); *The Crown jewels*; *The Cutty Sark*; *The guards*; *Haunted London*; *Houses of Parliament*; *Illustrated walks in London*; *Prisoners in the tower*; *Royal Mews*; *Royal Palaces*; *St Paul's*; *Tower of London*; *Wesley's chapel*; *Westminster Abbey*.

SAVOY PRESS. *Contact*: David J.N. Nabarro, Little Benville House, Benville, Nr Dorchester, Dorset DT2 0NN; *Office tel*: (020) 7710 7400. Publisher of one book only: *London's immortals*, by John Blackwood, a detailed, photographic account of London statues. Second edition may be published next century.

S.B. PUBLICATIONS. c/o 19 Grove Road, Seaford, East Sussex BN25 1TP, *Tel*: (01323) 893498. Regional, general interest publishers - a large Sussex list and a few London titles: two collections of old picture postcards *From Highgate to Hornsey* by Ken Gay, and *Wimbledon Then and Now*, by R. Milward; and *Walks in haunted London* by John Wittich.

SHIRE PUBLICATIONS LTD. Cromwell House, Church Street, Princes Risborough, Bucks HP27 9AA, *Tel*: (01844) 344301; *Fax*: (01844) 347080; *Email*: shire@shirebooks.co.uk; *Website*: http://www.shirebooks.co.uk. An extraordinary list of countless small books (mainly under £5) on diverse British historical, heritage, natural historical, arts and crafts, subjects, written by specialists for the layman. London titles include: *Discovering country walks in North London*, by Merry Lundow; *Discovering London curiosities*, by John Wittich; *Discovering London's guilds and liveries*, by John Kennedy Melling; *Discovering London's inns and taverns*, by John Wittich; *Discovering London street names*, by John Wittich; *Discovering off beat walks in London*, by John Wittich and Ron Phillips; *London signs*, by Dominic Rotheroe; *London statues and monuments*, by Margaret Baker; *London villages*, by John Wittich.

DARRELL SPURGEON. 72 Kidbrooke Grove, Blackheath, London SE3 0LG, *Tel*: (020) 8858 5831. Author/publisher of a series of architectural/topographical guide books to S.E. London localities: Woolwich, Plumstead, etc.; Greenwich, Charlton; Eltham, etc.; Bexley, etc.; Crayford, Thamesmead, etc.; Sydenham, etc. Enthusiastic, exploratory guides, free of the architectural jargon and weighty erudition which characterises the more professional architectural writers.

SUNRISE PRESS. *Contact*: James Dowsing, 34 Churton Street, London SW2V 2LP, *Tel*: (020) 7821 9899. Author and publisher of mainly booklets on a variety of localities and subjects: *An Australian's Britain*; *Belgravia* (112pp); *Byways of Westminster*; *Forgotten Tudor palaces*; *Guide to Bayswater*; *Guide to Pimlico*; *Haunts of Charles II*; *Hidden world of Regent's Park*; *Little Venice*; *The London cat*; *Places of the pilgrim fathers*; *Showbiz London*; *TV London: the studios, stars, landmarks* (108pp).

SUTTON PUBLISHING LTD. Phoenix Mill, Thrupp, Stroud, Glos GL5 2BU, *Tel*: (01453) 731114; *Fax*: (01453) 731117. *Email*: sales@sutton-publishing.co.uk. Major publisher on English history; also art and architecture, biography, transport and military. Especially well known for its never-ending Britain in Old Photographs series. The London list has some 70 titles, including a few thematic collections, for example: *Black Londoners 1880-1990*; *Irish Londoners*; *Theatrical London*; and *Along the Thames*. Collections for the specific localities are often listed in the chapters on the different London boroughs in this handbook.

TEMPUS PUBLISHING (previously Chalford Publishing Co). The Mill, Brimscombe Port, Stroud, Glos GL5 2QG, *Tel*: (01453) 883300; *Fax*: (01453) 883233. Archive photograph series (England and Wales) and a series on aircraft and railways. Some thirty titles in the Greater London and Middlesex list. Also archaeology series.

TYMSDER PUBLISHING. Gerry Black, PO Box 16039, London NW3 6WL, *Tel/Fax*: (020) 7372 9015. Books written and published by Dr Gerry Black (President of the Jewish Historical Society and a trustee of the Jewish Museum): *J.F.S: the history of the Jews' Free School since 1732*; and a forthcoming history of the London Jewish Hospital, Stepney. He is also the author of a biography of Samuel Lewis, *Lender to the Lords, giver to the Poor*, 1992, Valentine Mitchell, and *Living up West*, 1994, Jewish Museum.

UNICORN PRESS. *Contact*: Hugh Tempest-Radford, 21 Afghan Road, London SW11 2QD, *Tel*: (020) 7223 5126; *Fax*: (020) 7738 9428; *Email*: unicorn@tradford.demon.co.uk. Titles include: *Ceremonial barges on the River Thames*, by Kenneth N. Palmer.

WICKED LONDON. *Proprietor*: Steve Jones, 222 Highbury Road, Bulwell, Nottingham NG6 9FF, *Tel*: (0115) 975 6828. Titles such as: *London through the keyhole*; *London: the sinister side*, etc.

WINDRUSH PRESS. Little Window, High Street, Moreton-in-Marsh, Glos GL56 0LL, *Tel*: (01608) 652012/652025; *Fax*: (01608) 652125. History, travel, local interest. The Travellers History series includes: *A travellers' history of London*, Richard Tames; and more specifically there is *The square mile: the city of London in historic postcards* by Warren Grynberg.

YALE UNIVERSITY PRESS. 23 Pond Street, London NW3 2PN, *Tel*: (020) 7431 4422; *Fax*: (020) 7431 3755; *Email*: sales@yaleup.co.uk. Colossal academic publisher; its art and architecture includes some London studies: *Imperial London: civil government building in London 1851-1915*, by M.H. Port, 1995; *Medieval London houses*, by John Schofield, 1995; *London: world city, 1800-1840*, edited by Celina Fox, 1992; *Westminster Abbey and the Plantagenets*, by Paul Binski; *Town planning in London: the eighteenth and nineteenth centuries* by Donald J. Olsen. Mark Girouard's books are of special interest to all students of cities: titles such s *The English town*, 1990; *Sweetness and light: the Queen Anne Movement 1860-1900*, 1983; *Victorian pubs*, 1975.

PERIODICALS (Selective Listing)

Family and Community History: journal of the Family and Community Historical Research Society; published by W.S. Maney Publishing, PO Box YR7, Leeds LS9 7UU, *Tel*: (0113) 2497481.

Family History Monthly: published by The Diamond Publishing Group, 45 St Mary's Road, Ealing, London W5 5RQ, *Tel*: (020) 8579 1082.

Family Tree Magazine: published monthly by Armstrong, Boon and Marriott, 61 Great Whyte, Ramsey, Huntingon, Cambridgeshire PE17 1HL, *Tel*: (01487) 814050; *Fax*: (01487) 711361.

The Local Historian; *Local History News*. Both are published quarterly by the British Association for Local History, *Secretary*: Mr Gowan, 24 Lower Street, Harnham, Salisbury SP2 8EY, *Tel*: (01722) 320115. *Membership/subscriptions*: BALH, PO Box 1576, Salisbury SP2 8SY. *The Local Historian* (1952-) has articles of national and local interest, reviews and listings. *Editor*: Dr Margaret Bonney, 7 Carisbrooke Park, Knighton, Leicester LE2 3PQ; *Reviews editor*: Peter Christie, 30 Line Grove, Bideford, North Devon EX39 3JL. *Local History News* has reports of current activities of societies, record offices, libraries, museums, etc.

Local Studies Librarian: The newsletter/journal of the Local Studies group of the library Association. *Current editor*: Ian Jamieson, 12 Glenville Drive, Newcastle upon Tyne NE3 5PA.

The Local History Link. *Contact*: David Brown, 2 West Street Farm Cottages, Maynards Green, Heathfield, Sussex TN21 0DG, *Tel*: (01435) 812506. A new twice-yearly listings magazine for local history authors principally in the Home Counties; local history lecture courses, events, etc.

Local History Magazine: edited and published bi-monthly by Susan and Robert Howard. The Local History Press, 3 Devonshire Promenade, Lenton, Nottingham NG7 2DS, *Tel*: (0115) 9706473; *Fax*: (0115) 9424857; *Email*: editor@local-history.co.uk.
Robert Howard surveys his own achievement in an article 'Fifty not out', in issue No 50, July/August 1995. Another survey article in No 52, Nov/Dec 1995 was 'Communicate and educate': the role of society journals and newsletters.

The London Archaeologist. *Secretary/Treasurer*: Sheila Broomfield, 8 Woodview Crescent, Hildenborough, Tonbridge, Kent TN11 9HD. *Editor*: Clive Orton, Institute of Archaeology, University of London. *Promotions and Advertising*: Roy

Stephenson, 65 Shawley Crescent, Epsom, Surrey KT18 5PQ, *Work tel*: (020) 7490 8447, ext. 248. Quarterly magazine est. in 1968. Specialist reports and articles, and listings.

The London Journal: a review of metropolitan society past and present. *Business Manager*: Reg Free, 3 Foster Drive, Hitchin, Herts SG4 9EH, *Tel*: (01462) 4359 10. The current chief editor is: David R. Green, lecturer in geography at Kings College, London. It is published by the London Journal Trust, c/o Centre for Metropolitan History. Each issue has academic articles, and substantial book reviews. An index to volumes 1-20, 1975-1995 was published in the second issue of 1995. The same issue has bibliographical survey articles (books and articles) for the same period: Roman London, by Michael Fulford; Early Middle Ages, 600-1300, by Derek Keene; Later Middle Ages 1300-1550, by Caroline Barron; Early modern London 1550-1700, by Vanessa Harding; 1700-1850, by Leonard Schwarz; Modern London 1850-1939, by John Davis; London recent and present, by Michael Hebbert.
A register of research in progress on the history of London was published in Vol 3, no 1, 1987/8, with supplements, in Vol 17, No1, 1992, Vol 18, No 2, 1993, and Vol 22, No 1, 1997. Vol 21, No 1, 1996 was a special issue on industry in London 1750-1945; Vol 22, No. 2, 1997 on Health in London.

Rising East, journal of East London Studies; a new publication from Lawrence and Wishart, 99a Wallis Road, London E9 5LN, *Tel*: (020) 8533 2506; edited by Tim Butler, Department of Sociology, University of East London, Longbridge Road, Dagenham, Essex RM8 2AS, *Tel*: (020) 8590 7000. Winter 1998/9 issue was on the impact of LDDC.

LONDON LISTINGS MAGAZINES

London in one, Metropolist Magazines, W13, Westminster Business Square, Durham Street, London SE11 5JA, *Tel*: (020) 7771 6465; *Fax*: (020) 7820 0330; *Email*: metromags@btinternet.com.

Time Out. Universal House, Tottenham Court Road, London W1, *Tel*: (020) 7813 3000.
Welcome to London. Published bi-monthly by Pareto Communications, 33 Princes Court, Greenhead Passage, London SE16 1TD, *Tel*: (020) 7231 6772; *Fax*: (020) 7231 7957.

What's on in London. 180 Pentonville Road, London N1, *Tel*: (020) 7278 4393/7551; *Fax*: (020) 7837 5838.

SOME OTHER RELATED DIRECTORIES

National:
The Genealogical Services Directory, compiled and published annually by Geoff Heslop and Robert Blatchford (GR Specialist Information Services, 33 Nursery Road, Nether Poppleton, York YO26 6NN, *Tel*: (01937) 833716).

Historical, archaeological and kindred societies in Great Britain, (compiled by Malcolm Pinhorn); current edition: 1996 (Pinhorns, c/o Carisbrooke Cottage, 94 Carisbrooke High Street, Newport, Isle of Wight P030 1NU).
There is also a listing of local studies libraries available from the same author/publisher.

UK Visitor attraction directory; compiled by the Oxford Centre for Tourism and Leisure studies at Oxford Brookes University; published by Cassell (first edition: 1994).

London-wide:
The London government directory: a guide to local government in London. (current edition: September 1998), published by the Association of London Government, 36 Old Queen Street, London SW1H 9JF, *Tel*; (020) 7222 7799. Useful for its listings of councillors, MP's, senior executives; also listings of 'other useful addresses'.

Voluntary action across London. Published by the London Voluntary Service Council, 356 Holloway Road, London N7 6PA, *Tel*: (020) 7700 8107.

INDEX OF ORGANISATIONS

This index is arranged letter by letter; it excludes the organisations listed in the sections 'non-council sources of information'. Friends organisations (of parks, churches, etc) are indexed under the name of the amenity; Friends organisations attached to historic properties and museums are not indexed.

ADVERTISEMENTS

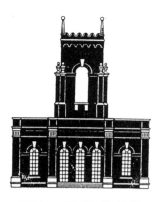